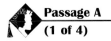
Passage A: Roller Coasters

Have you ever wondered why it feels so strange to ride a roller coaster? The hills, turns, and loops all affect your body in various ways, causing the range of physical feelings people experience when riding a roller coaster. The forces that make the roller coaster work cause these physical effects.

Most roller coasters start out by pulling you up a large hill using a ch[...] point, you are not moving very quickly, and you tend to be moving a[...] speed. The only force you feel is gravity, which means you do not fe[...] different than you would if you were standing on the ground. As soo[...] start down the other side of the hill, however, the feeling changes.

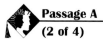
Roller coasters are basically powered by gravity. Once you start down the first hill, gravity causes the car to accelerate, or speed up. Meanwhile, your body continues to move at the same speed and in the same direction that it was going before you started down the hill. This is called inertia. When the roller coaster speeds up, the back of the seat pushes you forward, but inertia makes you feel like you are being pushed backward. At the same time, gravity is pulling you down toward the ground. When the roller coaster reaches a certain speed, these two forces balance each other out. As a result, you feel weightless for a brief period.

When a roller coaster is moving at a constant speed, your body cannot actually feel it. You can tell you are moving quickly as a result of visual cues, such as seeing how fast you are moving past trees or the roller coaster's supports. Because of this, coaster designers work in many sharp turns and other cues to

A

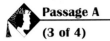

show you how fast you are moving.

Roller coaster designers also use the effects of gravity and acceleration to make the rides more interesting. They know how these two forces interact; therefore, they are constantly changing both throughout the ride. They change the effect of gravity on the coaster car by changing its distance from the ground, and they change acceleration by having the car go up and down many hills of different sizes. By doing these things, roller coaster designers can make you go from feeling heavier than normal to lighter than air in a matter of seconds.

Another trick designers use to make roller coasters feel more interesting is the loop-the-loop. When you travel around a loop, you go from feeling heavy to feeling very light to feeling heavy again. This is because of the way gravity, inertia, and acceleration work with one another as you go around the loop.

A

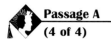
Sometimes they pull you in the same direction, which is what makes you feel heavy, and sometimes they pull you in opposite directions, which is what causes the feeling of weightlessness. In fact, the way these forces act together would probably keep you in your seat even without a safety bar holding you in.

The variety of exciting feelings you get when you ride a roller coaster is what attracts millions of people to roller coasters every year. Some people enjoy the unique combination of feelings so much that they will travel hundreds of miles to ride the most exciting roller coasters they can find. This desire for excitement encourages roller coaster designers to cooperate with one another. They share their knowledge and stretch their imaginations to create the most interesting rides they can think of. With inventions such as hanging cars and new ways to launch you up that first hill, don't expect the demand for roller coasters to die down anytime soon.

A

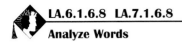
1. Read this sentence from "Roller Coasters."

    This desire for excitement encourages roller coaster designers to cooperate with one another.

    a. What is a prefix?

    b. Identify the prefix in the word *cooperate*.

    c. What does the word *cooperate* mean?

A1

Analysis

a. A prefix is a word part that comes before the root.

b. The word "cooperate" contains the prefix "co-."

c o	operate
prefix	root
The prefix "co-" means "together" or "with."	The root "operate" means "to work."
c. The word "cooperate" means "to work together" or "to work with."	

Common Prefixes

Prefix	Meaning	Example
de–	away from reverse	derail defrost
dis–	fail opposite	dissatisfy dishonest
en–	to make into	enable encase
pro–	forward in favor of	project prolabor
re–	back again	return reclaim

A1

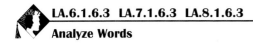

2. Read this sentence from "Roller Coasters."

    As a result, you feel weightless for a brief period.

    a. What is a suffix?

    b. Which word contains a suffix? What is the suffix?

    c. What does the word mean?

A2

Analysis

a. A suffix is a word part that comes after the root.

b. The word "weightless" contains the suffix "-less."

weight	less
root	suffix
The root "weight" means "an amount of heaviness."	The suffix "-less" means "without."
c. The word "weightless" means "without weight."	

Common Suffixes

Suffix	Meaning	Example
–ize	make	emphasize
–ish	origin resembles	Irish clownish
–like	characteristic of	doglike
–ment	act of state of	impressment contentment
–y	tend to	faulty

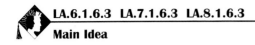
Short-Response Question

3. What is the main idea of the sixth paragraph from the article, "Roller Coasters"?

A3

Short-Response Analysis

When you are asked to give the main idea, you are asked to tell the message of the article or the paragraph in your own words. Main idea examples for the sixth paragraph of "Roller Coasters" are given below.

Sixth Grade	Seventh Grade	Eighth Grade
The sixth paragraph is about why roller coaster designers use a tool called the loop-the-loop, which makes riders feel very light at points and very heavy at other points.	The sixth paragraph discusses the loop-the-loop, a tool used by roller coaster designers that combines the forces of gravity and acceleration to create feelings of weightlessness and heaviness for the rider.	The sixth paragraph discusses the loop-the-loop, a tool used by roller coaster designers that combines the forces of gravity and acceleration to create feelings of weightlessness and heaviness for riders, which may make them feel as though they are being pulled in opposite directions.

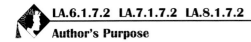
Short-Response Question

4. What is most likely the author's purpose for writing the
    article, "Roller Coasters"?

Short-Response Analysis

The author wrote "Roller Coasters" to give the reader information. The author's purpose was to inform.

Tip!

A short-response question asks you to use your own words to answer the question being asked.

The author's purpose is the reason an author writes an article. Here are some common author purposes.

to give information or to inform
to tell a story
to give an opinion
to persuade
to convey a mood

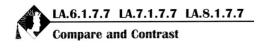

LA.6.1.7.7 LA.7.1.7.7 LA.8.1.7.7   Show What You Know® Florida!

Compare and Contrast   Reading Flash Cards for Grades 6–8

5.   How is what the body feels on a roller coaster starting up
     the first hill **similar** to how the body feels when the roller
     coaster moves over and down the hill?

     How is what the body feels when a roller coaster starts up
     the hill **different** from how the body feels when the roller
     coaster moves over and down the hill?

Compare		Contrast	
"how things are alike"		**"how things are different"**	
starts up hill	over and down hill	starts up hill	over and down hill
There is movement, which the rider notices because of cues.	There is movement, which the rider notices because of cues.	Movement is steady. Gravity pulls you down; it feels like you're standing on the ground.	Movement accelerates. Accelerations makes the body feel as if it is being pulled out of the seat, but then gravity pulls it down; when the forces balance, the body feels weightless.

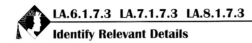

Short-Response Question

6. Why do roller coaster designers include sharp turns in
    order to create visual cues for roller coaster riders?

Short-Response Analysis

When a roller coaster is moving at a constant speed, the riders cannot feel their bodies moving. The visual cues created by sharp turns help the riders notice how fast they are moving. This is why designers include sharp turns and other cues, which help riders see how fast they are traveling.

Tip!

Remember to use complete sentences when answering a short-response question.

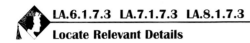
Extended-Response Question

7. How do roller coaster designers use the forces of gravity
    and acceleration to create desired effects on the body?

Extended-Response Analysis

In order to create different effects on the rider's body, designers constantly change the forces of gravity and acceleration throughout the ride. To increase or to decrease the effect of gravity, the designers change how far the roller coaster is from the ground. That's why there are hills and valleys. To vary the acceleration, the heights of the hills differ. This way, riders go up and down different-sized hills at different speeds. All these design elements make the riders feel heavier than normal at one point and lighter than air at another.

Tip!

An extended-response item asks you to use your own words to answer the question being asked. You should use several sentences to answer an extended-response question. Remember to use complete sentences and proper capitalization and punctuation.

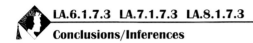
Extended-Response Question

8. Read the sentence from the article.

> **If roller coaster designs did not include visual cues, the rider's body would never feel as though it were in motion.**

Is the sentence true or false? Use details and information from the article to support your answer.

Extended-Response Analysis

The sentence is false. When a roller coaster is moving at a constant speed, the body does not feel the movement; thus, movement is noticed when the rider can use visual clues to tell that the body is moving. According to the article, designers make hills of different sizes so that the acceleration changes. If the acceleration changes, then the roller coaster's speed is not constant. If the coaster's speed changes, the body will feel it. Therefore, visual cues are not the only things that cause riders to know that their bodies are in motion.

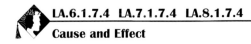
9. Read this sentence from the article, "Roller Coasters."

> **Some people enjoy the unique combination of feelings so much that they will travel hundreds of miles to ride the most exciting roller coasters they can find.**

a. What is a **cause** in this sentence?

b. What is an **effect** in this sentence?

Either answer given below is correct.

a. Cause	b. Effect
"the reason something happens"	"what happens"
Some people enjoy the unique combination of feelings so much	they will travel hundreds of miles to ride the most exciting roller coasters they can find.
to ride the most exciting roller coasters they can find.	they will travel hundreds of miles

A9

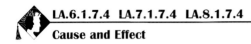

LA.6.1.7.4 LA.7.1.7.4 LA.8.1.7.4   Show What You Know® Florida!

Cause and Effect   Reading Flash Cards for Grades 6–8

10. According to the last paragraph of "Roller Coasters,"
    which of the following is a NOT a reason why people are
    attracted to roller coasters?

    A. to experience exciting feelings

    B. to experience a unique combination of feelings

    C. to fulfill their desire to travel hundreds of miles

    D. to fulfill their desire for excitement

Analysis

A. People want to ride roller coasters because they want to experience exciting feelings. Choice A is incorrect. The question asks which answer choice is NOT a reason people are attracted to roller coasters.

B. People want to ride roller coasters because they want to feel a combination of unique feelings. Choice B is incorrect.

C. People are not attracted to roller coasters because they want to travel hundreds of miles to ride these rides. The question asks you which answer choice is not a reason why people are attracted to roller coasters; therefore, Choice C is correct.

D. People want to ride roller coasters because they want to fulfill their desire for excitement. Choice D is incorrect.

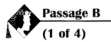
Passage B: Wind Energy

Think about turning on a fan on a hot day. You plug in the fan, turn it on, and within seconds, you feel the effects of a cool breeze. Basically, you are using electrical energy to create wind. Now imagine the process moving backward. Wind blows into a type of fan and turns the blades. The spinning blades capture the energy of the wind, and a generator can turn this energy into electricity. This is the general idea behind wind energy.

To create wind energy, objects that look like giant fans are used. These are called wind turbines, and they come in two groups: horizontal-axis and vertical-axis. To create electricity for an area, wind turbines are grouped together in what is known as a wind farm. The turbines generate electricity, and the electricity is

B

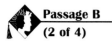
distributed to customers by the same methods as the electricity that comes from power plants.

Although wind energy has been lumped into the category of "new" types of energy by some, it is actually quite old. Our knowledge of people using the wind for power is as old as the oldest recorded history we can find. As long ago as 5000 BC, people used wind energy to send boats along the Nile River. Nearly two thousand years ago, the Chinese pumped water using windmills. Windmills were commonplace in the United States in the late 1800s and were used mostly to pump water in rural areas. Around 1900, the United States developed some small wind systems that could produce electricity, but they were no match for the cheaper types of electricity that later came to these rural areas.

B

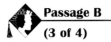
Recently, the idea of using wind for power has become popular again. With concern growing about pollution in the United States, people have started to look at wind energy as a promising, non-polluting energy source. Not only is wind energy clean, it is also renewable and free. No matter how much wind we use for power, there will always be more, which gives it a major advantage over types of energy that rely on limited resources such as coal.

There are, however, obstacles to using wind energy. Even though the wind itself is free, the machines needed to collect the energy from the wind are more expensive than those used for the more common methods of creating electricity. Because the source is free and the operating expenses are not high, the overall cost evens out and becomes cheaper than other methods in the long run. Some

B

Passage B
(4 of 4)

Show What You Know® Florida!
Reading Flash Cards for Grades 6–8

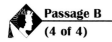

people are also concerned about the noise of the turbines and the appearance of a field full of them. Both of these problems are being addressed, through advances in technology and careful placement of the wind farms.

As of 2002, wind energy made up less than 1% of the electricity supply of the United States. The U.S. Department of Energy set a goal of increasing wind energy to 5% of the total supply by the year 2020, and the American Wind Energy Association has set a goal of 12% for the same year. Although these numbers seem high, energy experts believe that even the 12% goal may be realistic. The price of wind energy has dropped quite a bit since the early 1980s, and it is expected to keep dropping. It may only be a matter of time before the wind that keeps our kites in the air becomes one of our most valuable resources.

B

11. Read this sentence from the article, "Wind Energy."

Although these numbers seem high, energy experts believe that even the 12% goal may be realistic.

Which sentence represents a message communicated by this sentence?

F.   The 12% goal is impossible to reach.

G.   The 12% goal is not real.

H.   The 12% goal can be reached.

I.   The 12% goal cannot be reached.

B11

Analysis

F.   This answer choice incorrectly interprets the sentence to mean the 12% goal cannot be reached. Choice F is incorrect.

G.   This answer choice incorrectly interprets the sentence to mean the 12% goal does not exist. Choice G is incorrect.

H.   There are two parts to this sentence; the answer choices focus on the second half. Think about the message: "energy experts believe that even the 12% goal may be realistic." If something is realistic, it is real, or it is possible. Therefore, if the goal is realistic, it can be reached. Choice H is correct.

I.   This answer choice incorrectly interprets the sentence to mean the 12% goal will never be achieved. Choice I is incorrect.

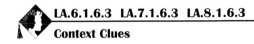
12. Read this sentence from the article, "Wind Energy."

There are, however, obstacles to using wind energy.

What does the word *obstacle* mean in the sentence above?

A. something that promotes

B. something that encourages

C. something that hinders

D. something that observes

B12

Tip!

The fifth paragraph discusses two problems with using wind energy. The first sentence of the paragraph refers to these problems as "obstacles." If something is causing a problem, it is not promoting, encouraging, or observing.

Analysis

A. "Promote" means to move forward. Choice A is incorrect.
B. "Encourage" means to assist something to occcur or increase. Choice B is incorrect.
C. If something hinders, it holds back progress. The obstacles discussed in the fifth paragraph are holding back the use of wind energy. Therefore, an "obstacle" is something that hinders. Choice C is correct.
D. "Observe" means to watch something without taking part. Choice D is incorrect.

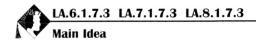
Short-Response Question

13. Write a summary for the first paragraph of "Wind Energy."

<u>Analysis</u>

This question asks for a summary of the first paragraph. Use your own words to describe the most important points. What message does the first paragraph send? Sample responses are given below.

Sixth Grade	**Seventh Grade**	**Eighth Grade**
A fan uses energy to blow air. A backward process is the idea behind wind energy: the wind blows and moves fan blades, thereby generating energy.	A fan uses electrical energy to blow air. A backward process is the idea behind wind energy: the wind blows, moves fan blades, and creates mechanical energy, from which electricity is generated.	A fan uses electrical energy to blow air. A backward process is the idea behind wind energy: the wind blows, moves fan blades, and creates mechanical energy, which is used by a generator to create electricity.

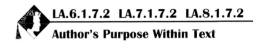

LA.6.1.7.2 LA.7.1.7.2 LA.8.1.7.2   Show What You Know® Florida!

Author's Purpose Within Text   Reading Flash Cards for Grades 6–8

Short-Response Question

14. What is most likely the author's purpose for writing the article, "Wind Energy"? Use details from the article to support your answer.

Short-Response Analysis

Think about why the author wrote "Wind Energy." What details are given by the author? How do these support the purpose? Sample responses are given below.

Sixth Grade	Seventh Grade	Eighth Grade
The author's purpose was to give information about wind energy, including how it's created, its uses, some obstacles, historical information, and its potential future.	The author's purpose was to give information about wind energy, including the principle behind wind energy and how it's created, historical information, its uses in the U.S., some obstacles, and its potential future.	The author's purpose was to give information about wind energy, including the principle behind wind energy and how it's created, historical information, its uses in the U.S., some obstacles, and the potential for increased wind energy use in the future.

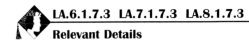

Short-Response Question

15. List the advantages and the disadvantages of using wind
    energy as a power source. Use details and information
    from the article to support your answer.

Advantages	Disadvantages
"favorable reasons"	"unfavorable reasons"
Wind energy is clean.	The machines that collect wind energy are more expensive than more common machines that generate electricity today.
Wind energy is renewable and free.	The machines that collect wind energy are noisy, and the appearance of wind farms bothers some people.

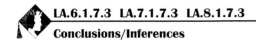
Short-Response Question

16. Read the following statement.

> **Wind energy is an up-and-coming energy source, and its possibilities have been discovered only recently.**

Is this an accurate statement? Use details and information from the article, "Wind Energy" to support your answer.

B16

Tip!

Think about the given statement. Is wind energy "up-and-coming"? Is it really a new energy source? What information from the article either supports or disproves the statement's accuracy?

Short-Response Analysis

The statement given is not accurate. If something is "up-and-coming," it is new. As the passage mentions, wind energy is quite old. It was used in 5000 BC. Back then, people used wind energy to send boats along bodies of water. Since people have been using wind energy for more than 7,000 years, it is not accurate to say wind energy is an "up-and-coming" energy source. Its possibilities have been known for thousands of years.

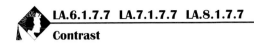

Extended-Response Question

17. How are the early uses of wind energy offered in this article different than the uses of wind energy today? Use details and information from the article to support your answer.

Extended-Response Analysis

Several early uses of wind energy were discussed in the article. Around 5000 BC, people used the wind to move boats along the Nile River. This is the first known use. Many years later, the Chinese pumped water with windmills. Windmills were also common in the United States in the 1800s. Wind energy from small wind systems was used in the United States for generating electricity in the early 1900s.

Today, wind turbines are grouped together in a large wind farm. The turbines generate enough electricity for an entire area.

18. Based on the information in the article, which is the most accurate statement that the use of wind energy in the United States will likely increase?

   F.   "As of 2002, wind energy made up less than 1% of the electricity supply of the United States."

   G. "The price of wind energy has dropped quite a bit since the early 1980s."

   H. "The U.S. Department of Energy set a goal of increasing wind energy to 5% of the total supply by the year 2020."

   I.   "It may only be a matter of time before the wind that keeps our kites in the air becomes one of our most valuable resources."

B18

Analysis

F. This statement describes the use of wind energy in 2002. This does not let readers know what might happen in the future. Choice F is incorrect.

G. The price of wind energy dropped over the past 20 years, but this does not tell readers what might happen to the use of wind energy in the future. Choice G is incorrect.

H. This statement offers a fact: the U.S. Department of Energy has set a goal for increased use of wind energy. This is the best evidence provided because it is rooted in fact. Choice H is correct.

I. While this supports the belief that the use of wind energy will increase, the statement is not backed by research or data. This statement represents the author's opinion. Choice I is incorrect.

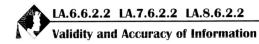

Short-Response Question

17. People who support using wind energy say it's free. They also point out that wind is not a nonrenewable resource such as coal.

   What information could someone who does not favor using wind energy use to dispute these statements? Use details and information from "Wind Energy," as well as your own knowledge about wind, to support your answer.

<u>Short-Response Analysis</u>

There are two statements to dispute. Sample responses are given below.

People who support using wind energy say it's free.
The wind itself may be free, but the machines that are required to collect the wind's power are very expensive.

They also point out that wind is not a nonrenewable resource, such as coal.
Wind may be renewable, but the wind does not always blow. There are times when the air is not moving. If the wind is not blowing, it is hard to produce wind energy.

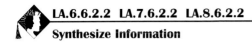

LA.6.6.2.2 LA.7.6.2.2 LA.8.6.2.2   Show What You Know® Florida!

Synthesize Information   Reading Flash Cards for Grades 6–8

Short-Response Question

20. In the United States, in the early 1900s, why did people
    fail to utilize the potential of wind energy?

B20

<u>Short-Response Analysis</u>

In the United States, in the early 1900s, wind energy was more expensive to produce than other forms of energy, so other methods for producing electricity were used. People failed to utilize the potential of wind energy because of the cost.

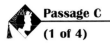
Passage C: Bullies Anonymous

With the exception of the church on one corner, the section of Castleway Street between 7th and 8th Avenues looked no different from any of the other blocks on that street. Recently, however, there had been a major increase in reports of lunch-money stealing, backpack yanking, tripping, and general bullying. As the crime reporter for the *Ivywood Middle School News*, I felt it was my duty to check out the situation.

Since most of the victims reported being bullied between the hours of 3 p.m. and 4 p.m., I decided to head over immediately after school. I needed time to find a spot from which I could see the action without anyone noticing me. A group of large bushes separated the church parking lot from the sidewalk. This would be the perfect place to hide.

C

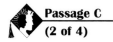
Kneeling in between two bushes, I took out a small notepad and a pen. I wanted to be able to take notes on every bullying incident I saw. Next to me, on the ground, I put a disposable camera, just in case I could get a good picture. I had barely gotten everything set up when I saw a group of kids walking toward the church from the direction of the school. Their path seemed clear; I couldn't spot any evidence of a bully in the area.

The kids had hardly made it to the edge of the church's property when a bully jumped in front of them. "Anyone got any leftover lunch money?" he snarled. I was so shocked I forgot to try to take a picture. I had been watching the street in both directions. Not only that, but by the time I had gotten over my surprise, the group of kids had scattered, and the bully was nowhere to be seen.

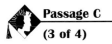

Over the next half hour, the same thing happened again and again. Kids would be walking down Castleway, and there would be no bullies in sight until they reached the church. Right then, every time, a bully would jump out at them. Although I could not see the bullies well enough to write down complete descriptions, I could tell it was not the same one each time. Additionally, none of them seemed to come from either direction down the street. It almost seemed as if they were slipping out of the church.

Another group of kids walked by, and yet another bully jumped in front of them. I stood up in my hiding spot. Even if the bully saw me, I had to figure out what was going on. To my surprise, just as the kids were running away, a small woman in a flowered dress came from the church and took the bully by the arm. "Sam," she said, "if you don't stay in the meetings, we're not going to be able to help you." Sam looked embarrassed as the woman led him into the building.

C

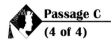

I was too curious not to follow them. The woman took Sam into a room and closed the door. A yellow piece of paper hung over the door's window. I had to step closer to read it: Bullies Anonymous. Slowly, I turned the doorknob and cracked the door open. The woman was standing at the front of the room. "I'm afraid we're not going to be able to leave the side door open for fresh air anymore," she was saying to the group in front of her. "Too many of you have been slipping out and returning to your old habits." I smiled as I pulled the door shut. I jotted down my final notes. Case closed.

C

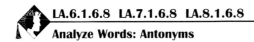
21. Read this sentence from the passage, "Bullies Anonymous."

Not only that, but by the time I had gotten over my surprise, the group of kids had scattered, and the bully was nowhere to be seen.

a. What is an antonym?

b. What are some antonyms for the word *scattered*?

C21

Analysis

a. An antonym is a word that has a meaning opposite to that of another word.

b. The word "scattered" means to spread out or to separate. Some antonyms for the word "scattered" are *assembled*, *gathered*, and *collected*.

Antonym Examples

above	below
open	closed
accept	reject
happy	miserable
fortunate	unlucky

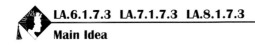

Short-Response Question

22. What is the main idea of the passage, "Bullies Anonymous"? Use details and information from the passage to support your answer.

Short-Response Analysis

When you are asked to give the main idea, you are asked to tell the message in your own words. Main idea examples for "Bullies Anonymous" are given below.

Sixth Grade	Seventh Grade	Eighth Grade
A student crime reporter discovers the truth behind an increase in bullying.	A student crime reporter hides out and discovers the truth behind an increase in bullying.	A student crime reporter hides out and discovers the truth behind an increase in bullying near a local church.

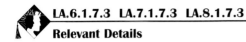

23. Why does the passage, "Bullies Anonymous" end with the words "Case closed"?

A. The narrator no longer cares about bullying.

B. The narrator discovers why the bullies are appearing in the same spot.

C. The narrator joins "Bullies Anonymous" and makes friends with several bullies.

D. The narrator is pressured by the bullies to stop investigating the reports.

C23

Analysis

A. The narrator does care about bullying. Choice A is incorrect.

B. As the passage ends, the narrator has discovered why the bullies keep reappearing in the same location. The "Bullies Anonymous" group is meeting in the church. A few of the bullies slip away and pick on students. Once the narrator, a middle-school reporter, discovers why the bullies keep reappearing, the narrator has an answer as to why there was an increase in the reports of lunch-money stealing and backpack yanking. Because the narrator has discovered the cause of the bullying, the case is closed, meaning it is over. Choice B is correct.

C. The narrator does not join "Bullies Anonymous." Choice C is incorrect.

D. The narrator is not pressured by bullies. Choice D is incorrect.

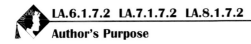

24. What is most likely the author's purpose for writing the passage, "Bullies Anonymous"?

F. to tell the personal story of Sam, a middle school bully

G. to offer readers an entertaining story

H. to entertain readers with a story about stopping bullies

I. to give information on how to investigate bullying

Analysis

Think about why the author wrote this passage.

F. Sam, a bully, is mentioned in the passage, but the entire passage is not about Sam. The author did not write this passage to tell Sam's story. Choice F is incorrect.

G. The author wants to entertain readers with the story of a reporter's investigation and discovery. Choice G is correct.

H. The author does not tell a story about stopping bullies. Rather, the passage details explain the cause of the bullying. Choice H is incorrect.

I. The narrator speaks of investigating the reports of bullying. Overall, however, the author does not describe what readers should do in order to investigate bullying. This passage is not an informational piece. Choice I is incorrect.

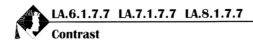
Short-Response Question

25. How was the section of Castleway Street between 7th and 8th Avenues different from other blocks on the street?

   Use two details and information from the passage, "Bullies Anonymous," to support your answer.

C25

<u>Short-Response Analysis</u>

The section of Castleway Street between 7th and 8th Avenues was different from other blocks on the street for two reasons. One, there was a church on one corner. Two, on that section of Castleway Street, there were more reports of bullying crimes than there were on the other parts of the street.

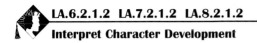
26. Which of the following word pairs best describes the narrator of the passage, "Bullies Anonymous"?

   A. alone; embarrassed

   B. scared; mysterious

   C. quiet; careless

   D. dedicated; curious

Analysis

Think about the narrator and what the narrator does throughout the passage. What words would you use to describe the narrator? Think about each answer choice. Which words offer the best description? Remember, both words should describe the narrator.

A. The narrator is alone in the bushes during the investigation, but there are no instances of embarrassment. Choice A is incorrect.

B. The narrator does not seem scared. The narrator is not mysterious but is trying to solve a mystery. Choice B is incorrect.

C. The narrator tries to be quiet in the bushes so as to not be noticed. However, the narrator is not careless. Choice C is incorrect.

D. The narrator is dedicated to investigating why the bullying reports have increased, and the narrator is curious about the cause. Choice D is correct.

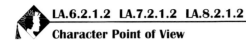

27. If the passage had been told from Sam's point of view, how would the passage have been different?

   F.   Sam might wonder why someone was hiding in the bushes.

   G.   Sam might wonder why there was a "Bullies Anonymous" sign on the door.

   H.   Sam might wonder why the number of bullying reports had increased.

   I.   Sam might wonder why the small woman in the flowered dress shut the door.

Analysis

If the story is told from Sam's point of view, then Sam is aware of events with which the narrator might not be familiar. Think about what Sam knows and what he does not know.

F.   If the story was told from Sam's point of view, Sam would not know why the student reporter was in the bushes. Choice F is correct.

G.   Sam would know the sign was on the door because that's where the meetings he attends are held. Choice G is incorrect.

H.   Sam would know the bullying reports are increasing because the bullies are meeting in the area, and he is doing some of the bullying. Choice H is incorrect.

I.   Sam would know that the woman closed the door because when it was open he and the other bullies kept leaving their meeting to pick on students. Choice I is incorrect.

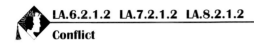
Extended-Response Question

28a. What problem does the narrator in the passage, "Bullies Anonymous" face?

28b. Does the narrator solve the problem? If so, how? Use details and information from the passage to support your answer.

Extended-Response Analysis

You will answer three parts to this question. Make sure you answer all parts. A sample response for each part of the question is given below.

a. What problem does the narrator in the passage, "Bullies Anonymous" face?

The narrator is a reporter with the student newspaper and is trying to find out why there has been an increase in the number of bullying reports in a certain area after school.

b. Does the narrator solve the mystery? Use details and information from the passage to support your answer.

Yes, the narrator solves the mystery. The narrator hides in some bushes and watches for the bullies. The narrator sees where the bullies are coming from: a "Bullies Anonymous" meeting. After seeing this, the narrator knows why there have been so many reports of bullying in the area.

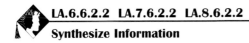

Extended-Response Question

29. What clues does the author give that let readers know the narrator is a crime reporter? Use three details from the passage to support your answer.

Tip!

As a reader, you are given direct information by the author, stating that the narrator is a crime reporter. But, you may also be given clues that support the information. Think about these clues.

Extended-Response Analysis

The passage offers several details which support the narrator's role as a crime reporter. One, the narrator mentions being a crime reporter for the *Ivywood Middle School News*. Two, the narrator hides out in the bushes to investigate the bullying. Three, the narrator takes a small notepad and pen to record what happens. Four, the narrator takes a disposable camera in order to take pictures. Five, the narrator follows the bullies to see what is going on. Six, at the end of the passage, the narrator mentions jotting down the final notes on the investigation.

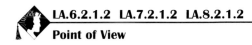
30. Which of the following is an opinion of the narrator?

A. "Most of the victims reported being bullied between the hours of 3 p.m. and 4 p.m."

B. "This would be the perfect place to hide."

C. "Kneeling in between two bushes, I took out a small notepad and a pen."

D. "I had been watching the street in both directions."

C30

Analysis

The question asks for an opinion. An **opinion** is a view or belief that a person has. An opinion is different from a fact. A **fact** is something that can be proven true.

A. The time the victims report the bullying can be proven. This is a fact. Choice A is incorrect.

B. Although the narrator feels the spot is the perfect place to hide, not everyone may agree. Because the statement reflects a personal belief and cannot be proven, it is an opinion. Choice B is correct.

C. The narrator's actions—kneeling and taking out the pad and pen—can be proven. This is a fact. Choice C is incorrect.

D. The narrator's actions—watching the street—can be proven. This is a fact. Choice D is incorrect.

Passage D: Simon the Scientist

My best friend, Simon, is always telling me useless facts. For example, today when we were walking home from school, he started going on about musical notes. "Did you know," he said, "that most Americans' car horns beep in the key of F?" I rolled my eyes. He continued without waiting for any sign of interest from me. "And, at basketball games, when people chant 'air ball,' almost everyone says those words in the same notes." He paused for a breath. "Pretty impressive, since it's almost impossible to get people to sing 'Happy Birthday' in the same key."

I still didn't say anything, and we walked in silence for about a block. "Simon," I said, "do you think you could focus on something useful for a change?" He didn't say anything. Actually, he looked a bit hurt. I rushed on. "I mean, not that

D

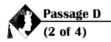 Passage D
(2 of 4)

Show What You Know® Florida!
Reading Flash Cards for Grades 6–8

what you say isn't interesting. But we have that big science report to work on, you know? Maybe we should be thinking about that a little more."

Simon nodded his head slowly. "You're right," he said. "Why don't we both go home and try to come up with some ideas. Then, after dinner, we could meet over at the library to pick one and start doing research." I agreed, and we split in different directions to walk the last couple of blocks home.

When I got to my house, no one was there. Perfect, I thought. I would be able to think about our science report without any interruptions. When I started thinking, though, I found I couldn't think about science. All I could think about was how I had been mean to Simon and had hurt his feelings. I hadn't meant to; I simply thought we should have been focusing on our assignment for school. Now, I

D

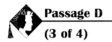

realized that I could have at least pretended to be interested. I could have brought up the science report without saying anything mean to Simon.

I reached for the phone on my desk and dialed Simon's number. He answered the phone, sounding as if he had run a few miles to get there. "Hey Simon," I began, "I'm really sorry about—"

"Julie, sorry, I can't really talk right now." The words came tumbling from Simon's mouth so quickly I could hardly separate them. "I'm in the middle of some great brainstorming for this science report. Meet me at the library at 7:00." There was a click, then a dial tone. Stunned, I sat for a few seconds with the phone still held to my ear. I hung up and tried to come up with some topics of my own, but I couldn't come up with anything that was likely to earn us an 'A' on the report. My ideas sounded like second-grade science projects.

D

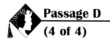
I walked into the library at 7:05 with my pathetic, short list of ideas. Simon nearly tackled me in the doorway as he shoved a piece of paper in my face. I began to read over his topics. I recognized some from his comments this afternoon. Most of them were related to music. Almost all of them were brilliant.

Simon saw that I was about to apologize again and cut me off. "Julie," he said, "I know all my little bits of information can be annoying to listen to sometimes. But the same thing that makes me interested in all this silly information is going to make me a great scientist someday." He threw an arm across my shoulder. "C'mon," he said. "Let's go pick a topic for our 'A+' paper."

D

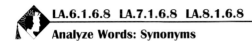
31. Read this sentence from the passage, "Simon the Scientist."

I walked into the library at 7:05 with my pathetic, short list of ideas.

a.　What is a synonym?

b.　What is a synonym for the word *pathetic*?

D31

Tip!

If you're not sure what "pathetic" means, think about how Julie feels about her list. You know she doesn't think highly of her ideas; therefore, "pathetic" must have a similar context.

Analysis

a. A synonym is a word that has the same meaning as another word.

b. A synonym for the word "pathetic" is *pitiful*.

Synonym Examples

joy	bliss
fright	fear
gloat	brag
symptom	sign
donate	give

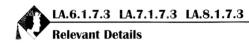
Short-Response Question

32. What does Julie learn about Simon in the passage, "Simon the Scientist"?

Short-Response Analysis

Sample responses are given below.

Sixth Grade	Seventh Grade	Eighth Grade
Julie learns that Simon likes his useless facts even though others think the facts are silly and annoying.	Julie learns that Simon's useless facts will someday help him become a great scientist, even though other people think the facts are silly and annoying.	Julie learns that Simon's useless facts are interesting to him, and that he feels these things will make him a great scientist some day. She learns that Simon knows his facts can get annoying and that others think they're silly.

D32

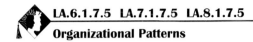
33. Put the following events in chronological order.

    a.   Julie tries to apologize to Simon over the telephone.

    b.   Simon and Julie are silent as they walk home from school.

    c.   Simon tells Julie that people can't sing "Happy Birthday" in the same key.

    d.   Simon and Julie's teacher assigns a science report.

    e.   Julie goes to the library.

    f.   Julie reads Simon's list of ideas for the science report.

    g.   Julie tries to apologize to Simon in person.

    h.   Julie calls Simon.

D33

Tip!

When you are asked to put events in chronological order, you are supposed to
the list the events in the order that they happened. List what happened first,
second, next, last, *etc*.

Analysis

1. d. Simon and Julie's teacher assigns a science report.
2. c. Simon tells Julie that people can't sing "Happy Birthday" in the same key.
3. b. Simon and Julie are silent as they walk home from school.
4. h. Julie calls Simon.
5. a. Julie tries to apologize to Simon over the telephone.
6. e. Julie goes to the library.
7. f. Julie reads Simon's list of ideas for the science report.
8. g. Julie tries to apologize to Simon in person.

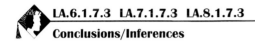
Short-Response Question

34. Read the excerpt from the passage.

I rolled my eyes. He continued without waiting for any sign of interest from me.

What does this tell you about Simon? What does this tell you about Julie? Use details and information from the passage to support your answer.

<u>Short-Response Analysis</u>

There are two parts to this question. Remember to answer both parts.

What does this tell you about Simon?
Even though Julie shows no interest in hearing more facts, Simon continues. He likes giving his useless facts, even if others think the facts are annoying. Simon thinks the information is interesting.

What does this tell you about Julie?
Julie rolls her eyes. This lets readers know Julie is bored with or annoyed by Simon's facts.

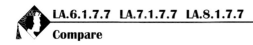
Short-Response Question

35. What is the difference between how Simon feels about going to the library to meet with Julie and how Julie feels about meeting with Simon? Why do the characters feel the way they do?

Use details and information from the passage to support your answer.

<u>Short-Response Analysis</u>

There are several parts to this question. Remember to answer all parts.

How does Simon feel about meeting with Julie at the library to discuss the science report?
Simon is excited about the meeting. He nearly tackles Julie as she arrives.

How does Julie feel about going to the meeting?
Julie is not excited about going to the meeting.

Why do the characters feel the way they do?
Simon is excited because he wants to share his facts with Julie, and he wants her to know that his annoying information will serve a purpose. Julie is not excited about going to the meeting because she feels her list of ideas is pathetic; she says that most of them sound like second-grade science projects.

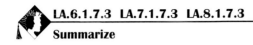

34. Which of the following best summarizes paragraph one of the passage, "Simon the Scientist"?

F. Simon bores his friend, Julie, with useless facts about musical notes.

G. Simon tells his friend, Julie, that most people can't sing "Happy Birthday" in the same key.

H. Simon tells his friend, Julie, why car horns often sound the same.

I. Simon bores his friend, Julie, with useless facts about walking home from school.

Analysis

F. Simon gives Julie, his friend, several facts about musical notes, including information about car horns, fans chanting "air ball," and people singing "Happy Birthday." These facts bore Julie. Choice F is correct.

G. This is only one fact given by Simon in the first paragraph. Therefore, this is not an overall summary. Choice G is incorrect.

H. Simon mentions that car horns are often in the key of F, but this is only one fact he offers in the first paragraph. This is not an overall summary. Choice H is incorrect.

I. Simon bores Julie with useless facts as they walk home from school. These facts are about musical notes; they are not about the walk home from school. Choice I is incorrect.

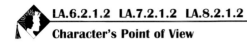

Extended-Response Question

37. How would the passage, "Simon the Scientist," be different if it were told from Simon's point of view? Write a paragraph summarizing the passage as if it had been told from Simon's point of view.

Tip!

If the passage had been told from Simon's point of view, the perspective would be different. As you write your response, think about how Simon would tell this story.

Extended-Response Analysis

On our way home from school, I shared some of my fun facts with Julie. She got annoyed and wanted to focus on the science project. It hurt my feelings, but I know my useless knowledge is a little overwhelming sometimes. I told her she was right, so we agreed to go home, eat dinner, and think about some ideas. When I got home, I started to write down some of my favorite topics. The phone rang; it was Julie. She started to say something, but I cut her off. I wanted to make sure I got all my ideas down on paper. I told her to meet me at the library and hung up the phone. I was really excited to see Julie as she made her way toward the library; I couldn't wait for her to see my list. She must have been impressed by my list, because she started to apologize for her earlier comments. I told her not to worry about it; I know my facts can get annoying. I put my arm around her shoulder, and we went into the library to get started on our A+ paper.

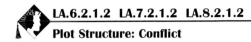
38. Which of the following best describes Julie in paragraph two of the passage, "Simon the Scientist"?

   A. Julie listens well.

   B. Julie is open-minded.

   C. Julie speaks slowly.

   D. Julie is close-minded.

Analysis

A. As the second paragraph starts, Simon and Julie are walking in silence. Therefore, Julie is not listening to anyone speak. Choice A is incorrect.

B. Julie does not want to hear any more facts from Simon. If she were open-minded, she would be more open to hearing what he had to say. Choice B is incorrect.

C. Julie does not speak slowly. According to the second paragraph, Julie rushes on as she speaks to Simon. Choice C is incorrect.

D. Julie does not want to hear any more facts from Simon, and she tells him so. She is close-minded. She is not allowing herself to think of the possibilities Simon's useless knowledge may hold for the science report. Choice D is correct.

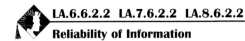
39. Based on the passage, "Simon the Scientist," which sentence best supports Julie's claim that she hadn't meant to hurt Simon when she told him to focus on something useful?

F. "Simon saw that I was about to apologize again and cut me off."

G. "I still didn't say anything, and we walked in silence for about a block."

H. "Actually, he looked a bit hurt."

I. "I could have brought up the science report without saying anything mean to Simon."

D39

Analysis

The question wants you to identify the answer choice that proves Julie felt bad about telling Simon to focus on something useful.

F. This choice reflects Simon's behavior, not Julie's. Choice F is incorrect.

G. This comes before Julie's comment on Simon's facts. Choice G is incorrect.

H. This reflects how Simon feels, not how Julie feels. Choice H is incorrect.

I. When Julie says this, she acknowledges that what she said was hurtful and that she could have said things differently. This is the best support for Julie's claim that she hadn't meant to hurt Simon's feelings. Choice I is correct.

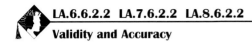
Short-Response Question

40. List some of the topics Simon most likely wrote down as ideas for the science report. Use details from the passage to support your answer.

Short-Response Analysis

List some of the topics Simon most likely wrote down as ideas for the science report. Use details from the passage to support your answer.

- Why Americans' car horns beep in the key of F
- Why basketball fans chant "air ball" in the same notes
- Why people rarely sing "Happy Birthday" in the same key

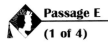
Passage E: A Different Sort of Summer

It was the first day of summer vacation after his seventh-grade year, and Javier was thrilled. He couldn't wait for all the things summer would bring: swimming at the local pool, playing baseball in the park, and the chance to play his new video game all the way through. The warm days stretched in front of him with no end in sight. At breakfast on his first day off, however, his dreams of an endless summer were shattered.

"Javier," his father said, "starting tomorrow, I want you to come and work with me three or four days every week. It's fine for you to play games and hang out with your friends some of the time, but I don't want you killing off all your brain cells splashing around in the pool or sitting in front of the TV. Some relaxation is fine, but I think you should do something useful with your summer as well."

E

Passage E
(2 of 4)

Show What You Know® Florida!
Reading Flash Cards for Grades 6–8

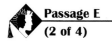

Javier began to protest, but his father declared the matter closed to arguments. His father worked at a retirement center. All Javier could think about was how much he would miss out on while having to spend time with other people's grandparents. He couldn't even begin to imagine what he would have in common with people so much older than him. He thought about it so much that he didn't even enjoy his first day away from school.

At 7:30 sharp the next morning, Javier's alarm began to buzz. With a groan, he rolled over and turned it off. As much as he wanted to go back to sleep, he knew his father would wake him up again in a few minutes anyway. Javier showered, dressed, and went down to join his father.

Throughout the entire ride to the retirement center, Javier didn't speak a single word. The car pulled into the parking lot. Javier's father turned off the car, but

E

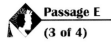
he didn't open his door. "Javier," he said, "I know this isn't what you wanted to be doing with your summer vacation, but please try to keep an open mind. You don't think any of these people have anything to say that is worth your time, but it's really just the opposite. The longer you are alive, the more interesting experiences you have to talk about." Javier nodded. He didn't believe his father, but he didn't want to pick a fight.

When the two entered the building, Javier's father went to his office to take care of what he called his "silly little morning tasks." Javier wandered around the building, trying to decide what would make the day go the fastest. He settled on a room with a giant TV that was playing an old army movie. He had only been watching for a few moments when someone else entered the room. Javier looked up to see a tall man with silver hair and sharp blue eyes.

E

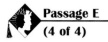
"Hello, son," the man said to Javier. "My name's William. But call me Big Bill—everyone else around here does." Big Bill looked at the TV screen and laughed. "That doesn't look anything like the army I was in. Those TV guys don't have a clue."

Javier could feel his eyes widen. "You were in the army? Wow—I can't even imagine being a soldier. What was it like?" He turned so he could better hear Big Bill's tales of army drills and training camp. The next time Javier looked up at the clock, an hour had passed, and his father was standing in the doorway, watching his son and smiling.

E

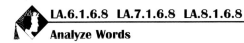

41. Read this sentence from the passage, "A Different Sort of Summer."

At 7:30 sharp the next morning, Javier's alarm began to buzz.

Which of the following has a similar meaning?

A. Javier's alarm went off some time around 7:30 in the evening.
B. Javier's alarm went off at exactly 7:30 a.m.
C. Javier's alarm went off before 7:30 a.m.
D. Javier's alarm never went off.

Analysis

A.   Javier's alarm went off at exactly 7:30 a.m. Choice A is incorrect.

B.   The phrase "at 7:30 sharp" means at exactly 7:30, not one minute before and not one minute after. When the author says that Javier's alarm buzzed, that is the same as saying it went off. You know the alarm buzzed in the morning, so the time is 7:30 a.m. Choice B is correct.

C.   Javier's alarm went off at exactly 7:30 a.m. Choice C is incorrect.

D.   Javier's alarm went off at exactly 7:30 a.m. Choice D is incorrect.

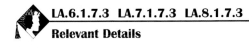

Extended-Response Question

42. Read this sentence from the passage, "A Different Sort of Summer."

   The next time Javier looked up at the clock, an hour had passed, and his father was standing in the doorway, watching his son and smiling.

   What does this tell you about Javier? What does this tell you about Javier's father? Use details and information from the passage to support your answer.

E42

Extended-Response Analysis

There are two parts to this question. Remember to answer both parts.

What does this tell you about Javier?

Even though Javier didn't think he would have anything in common with the people at the retirement center, and he didn't think he would enjoy the experience, Javier is so fascinated by what he is learning from Big Bill that 60 minutes pass by before he looks at the clock again.

What does this tell you about Javier's father?

Javier's father was correct; the people at the retirement center have interesting experiences to share with Javier, and Javier will enjoy learning from them.

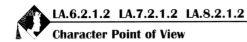
Short-Response Question

43. Read this sentence from the passage, "A Different Sort of Summer."

All Javier could think about was how much he would miss out on while having to spend time with other people's grandparents.

How does this sentence support how Javier initially feels about working at the retirement center? Use details and information from the passage to support your answer.

Tip!

Before you can answer this question, you have to think about how Javier initially feels about working at the retirement center. You know he is not happy.

Short-Response Analysis

Javier does not want to spend his summer at the retirement center because he does not think he will have anything in common with the people there. This sentence lets you know that the people at the retirement center are around the age of his grandparents. Because the people are so much older than Javier, he doesn't think he will enjoy spending time with them.

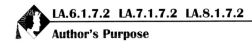
Short-Response Question

44. What is most likely the author's purpose for naming the passage, A Different Sort of Summer"?

Short-Response Analysis

Sample responses are given below.

Sixth Grade	Seventh Grade	Eighth Grade
Javier's summer turns out to be different than what he first expected it would be like.	Javier thinks his summer will be spent with this friends. Then he learns he will also be working at the retirement center. His summer turns out to be different than what he expected.	Javier looks forward to a fun-filled summer but finds out his father expects him to work at the retirement center. Javier expects the worst on his first day on the job, but discovers he just might like the people with whom he will work. Although his summer differs from his original plans, it may still be OK.

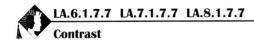

Extended-Response Question

45. How are Javier's feelings about his summer at the
beginning of the passage different than his feelings about
the summer at the end of the passage? Use details and
information from the passage to support your answer.

Tip!

You know this is an extended-response question; therefore, you want to make sure you include as many details as possible in order to give a complete response.

Extended-Response Analysis

At the beginning of the summer, Javier is thrilled. He wants to swim and to play baseball and video games. Then, Javier learns he will have to go to work with his father three or four days a week. Javier is upset and doesn't even enjoy his first day of summer. While at the retirement center with his father, Javier meets Big Bill, a former soldier, who entertains Javier with army tales. Javier wants to learn more about army life; he is no longer upset about being at his summer job.

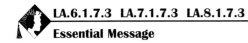
Short-Response Question

46. Describe a lesson learned by Javier in the passage, "A Different Sort of Summer." Use details and information from the passage to support your answer.

Short-Response Analysis

Each of these ideas is a lesson Javier learned.

- Things are not always what they seem.

- You just may find an experience enjoyable, even though the situation doesn't appeal to you at first.

- Look for the positive in every situation; you will be surprised at what you find.

- Be open-minded about new experiences; you never know the potential they may hold.

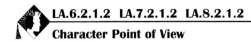

47. Which of the following describes how Javier most likely feels about his father during paragraphs two through five of the passage, "A Different Sort of Summer"?

    F.   Javier feels his father is open-minded.

    G.   Javier feels his father is angry.

    H.   Javier feels his father is unreasonable.

    I.   Javier feels his father is being fair.

Analysis

F. Javier wants to protest his father's decision, but his father declares that the matter is closed to arguments. This shows Javier's father is not open-minded about the subject. Choice F is incorrect.

G. Throughout the passage, there is no mention of Javier feeling as though his father is angry. Choice G is incorrect.

H. Javier is upset that his father wants him to work at the retirement center, and his father won't hear of any reasons why Javier shouldn't have to work. Therefore, readers can assume Javier most likely feels his father is being unreasonable in paragraphs two through five. Choice H is correct.

I. Javier does not feel his father is being fair. Javier doesn't want to work at the retirement center, and his father won't even listen to Javier's arguments. Choice I is incorrect.

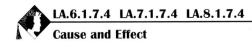
Short-Response Question

48. Why does Javier's father select the retirement center as the place for Javier to work for the summer? Use details and information from the passage to support your answer.

Short-Response Analysis

Javier's father selects the retirement center as the place where Javier will work because that is where he works. Also, he feels it will be good for Javier to do something useful. And, he knows Javier will learn from the people at the center.

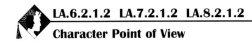

Short-Response Question

49. Why does Javier's father want Javier to work at the retirement center? Use details and information from the passage to support your answer.

Short-Response Analysis

Javier's father wants Javier to work at the retirement center because he feels it will be good for his son to do something useful during the summer. He doesn't want Javier to spend his whole summer killing off brain cells, either at the pool or by sitting in front of the television.

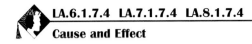
50. What causes Javier's attitude toward working at the retirement center to change?

    A. He learns he will get paid.

    B. He enjoys hearing the stories of Big Bill's life in the army.

    C. He likes to play baseball with people at the center.

    D. He enjoys watching television with Big Bill.

<u>Analysis</u>

A. There is never any mention of whether or not Javier will get paid for working at the retirement center. Choice A is incorrect.

B. Javier doesn't think he will have anything in common with the people at the retirement center. But, he meets Big Bill and is entertained by Big Bill's stories. He wants to hear all about Big Bill's life as a soldier. This experience changes Javier's feelings toward working at the retirement center. Choice B is correct.

C. Javier wants to play baseball in the park with his friends. There is no mention of Javier playing baseball with people at the retirement center. Choice C is incorrect.

D. Javier is watching television when Big Bill enters the room, but the two do not watch television together. Javier spends his time listening to Big Bill's stories. Choice D is incorrect.

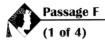
Passage F: The Forgotten Language

Dear Principal Meyer:

I would like to talk to you about the foreign language requirements at our school. Beginning in eighth grade, students are required to start taking a foreign language such as Spanish, French, German, or Latin. After a student chooses a language, he or she will continue to study that language for at least the first two years of high school. The idea is that knowing a foreign language will make us more well-rounded and will enable us to communicate with people different from ourselves.

The reason I am writing is that I think there is a language that has been overlooked: American Sign Language (ASL). Between 100,000 and 500,000 Americans use ASL as a first or second language. There is a good chance that

F

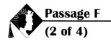
most of us will run into someone who is deaf at some point in our lives. I think having the opportunity to learn how to communicate with a deaf person is just as important as having the opportunity to learn how to speak to someone who speaks Spanish or French.

Although ASL is not a foreign language—it is generally used in the United States and in Canada—learning it would still be as much of a skill as, if not more than, learning any of the other languages offered at this school. It has its own alphabet and grammatical structure, so students of ASL would have to learn the same basic elements they would with any other language that is new to them. In addition, they would learn the skill of speaking with their hands instead of their voices.

Many foreign language programs are not even entirely composed of foreign languages anymore. Some people have the chance to learn a Native American

F

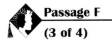

language such as Navajo, which makes me realize that even our "native" English is foreign in origin. So, really, most foreign language programs are more like second-language programs, and ASL certainly qualifies as a second language to most people at this school.

In the past few years, some states have allowed schools to add ASL to their lists of foreign language requirements. If our state has done this, then another issue would be finding a teacher who is qualified to teach ASL. I realize this might be a difficult task, but I have no doubt that you would be willing to undertake it. I believe that you and most of the teachers here truly have the students' best interests at heart, and it would be in the best interest of everyone here to at least have the chance to learn ASL.

If our state has not yet allowed us to add ASL as a class option, then I suggest a letter-writing campaign by the entire student body. We would have the chance

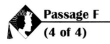

for our voices to be heard. The lawmakers would receive our letters and would know this issue is important to us. This would give us a chance to practice our persuasive writing for an actual cause, instead of the usual class assignment. Plus, it would be good for us to take an active interest in something related to our own education.

Please give the issue of ASL serious consideration. By not offering American Sign Language at this school, you are depriving students of a great learning experience. We are also missing out on the opportunity to learn how to communicate with a large group of people living in our own country. Can you really say it is more important to learn the language of a country you might never visit than to learn how to communicate with someone who may live right around the corner?

Sincerely, Jessie Perkins, 7th Grade

F

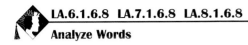LA.6.1.6.8 LA.7.1.6.8 LA.8.1.6.8   Show What You Know® Florida!

Analyze Words   Reading Flash Cards for Grades 6–8

51. Read this sentence from the letter.

If our state has not yet allowed us to add ASL as a class option, then I suggest a letter-writing campaign by the entire student body.

Which of the following best describes a letter-writing campaign?

F. A candidate writes a letter to a voter during the campaign.
G. Students send letters in order to voice their opinions.
H. A lawmaker writes a letter to the student body, asking for votes.
I. Students write letters for an in-class assignment.

Tip!

If you're not sure what a "letter-writing campaign" is, use context clues from the passage. According to the passage, students will be writing letters. This lets you know multiple letters are written during a letter-writing campaign. Lawmakers will receive the students' letters, and the students' voices will be heard.

Analysis

F. Many letters are written during a letter-writing campaign. Choice F is incorrect.

G. This fits with the definition of a letter-writing campaign and the context clues given in the passage. Choice G is correct.

H. Many letters are written during a letter-writing campaign. Choice H is incorrect.

I. During a letter-writing campaign, students' letters are sent to lawmakers. Choice I is incorrect.

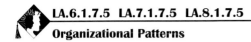

52. How does Jessie Perkins organize her letter?

   A. She offers both facts and opinions to support her argument.

   B. She offers only facts that support her argument.

   C. She offers only opinions that support her argument.

   D. She offers only facts to support the principal's opinion.

<u>Analysis</u>

Before you think about the letter's organization, what is the purpose of the letter? Jessie Perkins is trying to persuade. Knowing Jessie's purpose should help you understand how she organized her letter.

A. Jessie has several arguments as to why an ASL class should be offered at her school. She lists both facts and opinions to support her arguments. Choice A is correct.

B. Jessie also offers opinions, such as how she feels about being able to communicate with people who are deaf and about taking an active interest when discussing the letter-writing campaign. Choice B is incorrect.

C. Jessie also offers facts, such as the number of people using ASL and that some states allow schools to add ASL to their foreign language requirements. Choice C is incorrect.

D. Jessie offers facts and opinions to support her opinion, not the principal's. Choice D is incorrect.

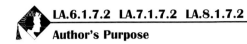

LA.6.1.7.2 LA.7.1.7.2 LA.8.1.7.2   Show What You Know® Florida!

Author's Purpose   Reading Flash Cards for Grades 6–8

Short-Response Question

53. What is most likely the author's purpose for writing this letter? Use details and information from the letter to support your answer.

Short-Response Analysis

Jessie Perkins wrote this letter in order to convince Principal Meyer to add American Sign Language to the list of foreign languages that students at the school can sign up for and take.

Tip!

A short-response question asks you to use your own words to answer the question being asked.

The author's purpose is the reason an author writes. Here are some common author purposes.

to give information or to inform
to tell a story
to give an opinion
to persuade
to convey a mood

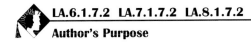
Short-Response Question

54. Why did Jessie Perkins include in her letter information on the number of Americans using American Sign Language?

Short-Response Analysis

Sample responses are given below.

Sixth Grade	Seventh Grade	Eighth Grade
Jessie includes information on the number of people using American Sign Language because she wants the principal to know that students might run into someone who communicates with ASL.	Jessie includes information on the number of people who use American Sign Language because she wants the principal to know that students might run into some people who communicate with ASL, and she thinks students should be able to communicate with them.	Jessie includes the information on the number of people communicating with American Sign Language because the numbers support the fact that students might run into someone who uses ASL. If students will actually have a chance to use ASL, this is a good reason why an ASL class should be offered to them.

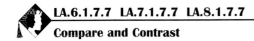
55. How is learning and understanding American Sign Language similar to learning and understanding foreign languages, such as French and Spanish?

How is learning and understanding American Sign Language different than learning and understanding foreign languages, such as French and Spanish?

Use details and information from the letter to support your answer.

Compare		Contrast	
"how things are alike"		"how things are different"	
ASL	foreign languages	ASL	foreign languages
helps people communicate	help people communicate	generally used in the United States and Canada	used all over the world
has an alphabet and its own grammatical structure	have their own alphabets and grammatical structure	hands are used to communicate	voices are used to communicate

F55

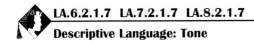

Short-Response Question

56. What tone does Jessie Perkins convey in her letter to
    Principal Meyer? Use details and information from the letter
    to support your answer.

Short-Response Analysis

In the letter to Principal Meyer, Jessie Perkins is serious about her topic. She is trying to persuade her audience and believes in the topic strongly. You know this because she is positive when she discusses it.

Tip!

The author's **tone** reflects how he or she feels about the topic and is the overall feeling the author is trying to convey with his or her words.

Some examples of an author's tone.

serious: the author is straightforward and relays information or details
humorous: the author uses humor and is lighthearted and funny when writing
sarcastic: the author uses sarcasm, wit, and irony when writing
negative: the author doesn't feel good about or does not support the topic
positive: the author feels good about or believes in the topic
angry: the author is unhappy and this is reflected in the writing

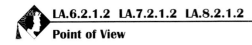

Short-Response Question

57. Is Jessie Perkins the only person who believes an
American Sign Language class is an acceptable addition
to a school's list of foreign language classes? Use details
and information from the letter to support your answer.

Short-Response Analysis

No, Jessie Perkins is not the only person who believes ASL classes are a good addition to the foreign language list of classes. If people in states throughout the United States have allowed ASL classes to be added, then they must believe the classes are a good addition. Therefore, Jessie is not alone in her belief.

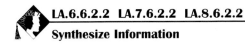
58. Why does Jessie Perkins include the information on the Native American language, "Navajo"?

   F. It supports her argument that the school's foreign language list discriminates against people learning other languages.

   G. It supports her argument that American Sign Language is a foreign language.

   H. It supports her argument that not all languages taught are foreign; there are second languages being taught as well.

   I. It supports her arguments that American Sign Language is not a foreign language and is only used by Native American people.

Analysis

F. Jessie never mentions whether she feels the school's list discriminates against anyone. Choice F is incorrect.

G. Jessie is not trying to convince Principal Meyer that ASL is actually a foreign language. She describes it as a second language. Choice G is incorrect.

H. Jessie points out that some languages are second languages, not necessarily foreign languages. She uses the Navajo example to illustrate her point. Choice H is correct.

I. American Sign Language is not a foreign language, but it is used by many people, not only Native Americans. Choice I is incorrect.

59. Which of the following sections from the letter, "The Forgotten Language," represents Jessie Perkins' opinion?

A. "If our state has done this, then another issue would be finding a teacher who is qualified to teach ASL."

B. "After a student chooses a language, he or she will continue to study that language for at least the first two years of high school."

C. "They would learn the skill of speaking with their hands instead of their voices."

D. "By not offering American Sign Language at this school, you are depriving students of a great learning experience."

F59

Analysis

The question asks you to identify an opinion. An **opinion** is a view or belief that a person has. An opinion is different from a fact. A **fact** is something that can be proven true.

A. If ASL classes are offered at the school, a qualified teacher must be available to teach the students. This is a fact. Choice A is incorrect.

B. It is a fact that students must select a foreign language and take classes for two years. Choice B is incorrect.

C. If students learn ASL, they use their hands to communicate; this is a fact. Choice C is incorrect.

D. Although Jessie Perkins feels deprived by not having ASL offered at her school, this may not be true for everyone. This is an opinion. Choice D is correct.

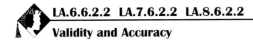
Short-Response Question

60. What facts does Jessie Perkins offer in her letter to
Principal Meyer that support adding American Sign
Language to the list of foreign language classes? Use
two facts and information from the letter to support
your answer.

Short-Response Analysis

Any of the following facts are acceptable. Two facts should be given.

1. Between 100,000 and 500,000 Americans use American Sign Language (ASL) as a first or second language.

2. Learning ASL gives students the opportunity to communicate with deaf people more easily, just as learning French or Spanish helps students communicate with people who use a different language.

3. ASL has its own alphabet and grammatical structure, so students of ASL would have to learn the same basic elements they would with any other language that is new to them.

4. Some states have allowed schools to add ASL to their list of foreign language requirements.

Passage G: Legends of the Isles

Take a good look at any culture, and you will almost certainly find legends somewhere in its history. Usually passed by word of mouth from generation to generation, legends are often thought of as being true stories from the past, but there is rarely proof to back them up. Another trait of legends is that you will often find similar ones in different cultures. As people pass along stories verbally, the stories change and take on details personalized by storytellers. While the details may be different, the overall story is the same.

One such legend exists in a number of versions throughout the British Isles, the islands that make up Great Britain and Ireland. The story involves a person, usually a husband or a wife, who is taken by fairies. The person is later found by a relative, but some mystery remains surrounding what happened.

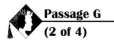
An Irish version of this legend, titled "Twenty Years with the Good People," is narrated by a descendant of the subject of the story. The subject, a recently married man, leaves one day to buy leather and some other items in a nearby town. He doesn't return that night or the next, and his wife begins to worry. On the third morning, she finds his donkey and cart outside their door, but she still cannot find him. She gathers a group of friends, and they go to the town to look for her husband. They search the entire country, and still there is no trace of him.

A number of years later, the woman and her son are eating dinner. A wandering man comes to the door and greets them. The woman invites him in for something to eat, and he accepts. As he reaches out, the woman sees that he has a mole on his wrist in the same spot where her husband had one. The woman asks if he is her husband, and he admits that he is, but he says it will be a long

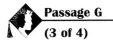

time before he can tell her where he was all those years. He never tells anyone, but the legend claims everyone knew he was with "the good people" (fairies).

In Scotland, there is a version of the tale called "The Stolen Lady." Its main character goes out one night looking for his cattle. While he is out, he runs into a group of fairies, who are carrying something with them. The man knows the fairies have no choice but to exchange their prize if they are offered something else, so he gives his hat to them. In return, he gets their prize, which turns out to be an English lady.

The man takes the lady to his house, where she lives for many years. Later, the king begins to build roads through the area for soldiers to use. Most people in the town dislike having the soldiers pass through, but the man doesn't mind, and

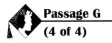

one night he invites a captain and his son to stay in the house. Both captain and son stare at the woman, and the son says she looks a great deal like his mother, who had died. The captain mentions the name of the deceased wife, which causes the woman to recognize the two as her husband and son. The captain and his son thank the man for taking care of her, and the man is happy that he was able to reunite the family.

G

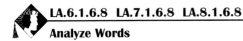
61. Read this sentence from the article, "Legends of the Isles."

Usually passed by word of mouth from generation to generation, legends are often thought of as being true stories from the past, but there is rarely proof to back them up.

What does the phrase *to back them up* mean in the sentence above?

A. to reverse direction
B. to move behind
C. to give support
D. to stand behind physically

G61

Tip!

If you are unsure of a word's meaning or the meaning of a phrase, use context clues. To use context clues, look at the other words and phrases in the sentence or paragraph. These words and phrases should give you some clues about the unknown word or the unknown phrase you are trying to figure out.

Analysis

A. This is not the correct meaning. Choice A is incorrect.

B. This is not the correct meaning. Choice B is incorrect.

C. In this context, "to back them up" means to give support. According to this sentence, there is little proof to support whether the legends and stories told by earlier generations are actually true. Choice C is correct.

D. This is not the correct meaning. Choice D is incorrect.

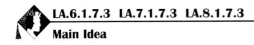

LA.6.1.7.3 LA.7.1.7.3 LA.8.1.7.3   Show What You Know® Florida!

Main Idea   Reading Flash Cards for Grades 6–8

Extended-Response Question

62a. What is the main idea of the article, "Legends of the Isles"?

62b. Where can you find the main idea?

63c. Why did the author put the main idea in that place?

Extended-Response Analysis

There are three parts to this question. Remember to answer all three parts.

a. What is the main idea of the article, "Legends of the Isles"?
The main idea is: legends are passed down through generations and often have similar stories, overall, although different cultures may have differing details.

b. Where can you find the main idea?
You can find the main idea of the passage in the first paragraph.

c. Why did the author put the main idea in that place?
The author put the main idea in the first paragraph because it gives the reader an idea of what the remaining paragraphs will be about: different cultures tell a similar legend with unique details. In this case, Ireland and Scotland have their own versions of a similar story.

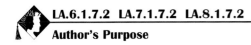
63. Which of the following does NOT represent a reason why the author wrote the article, "Legends of the Isles"?

   F. to give information

   G. to offer a story

   H. to persuade

   I. to entertain

G63

Analysis

F. The author offers information in this article. Choice F is incorrect.

G. The author offers stories in this article. Choice G is incorrect.

H. The author does not try to persuade the reader. Choice H is correct.

I. The author tries to entertain the reader with legends. Choice I is incorrect.

The author's purpose is the reason an author writes an article. Here are some common author purposes.

to give information or to inform
to offer a story
to give an opinion
to persuade
to convey a mood

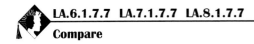
Extended-Response Question

64. How is the legend "Twenty Years with the Good People"
similar to the legend "The Stolen Lady"? Use details from
the passage to support your answer.

Tip!

The question asks how these two things are similar; in other words, "what do these things have in common?" or "how are these things the same?"

Extended-Response Analysis

"Twenty Years with the Good People" and "The Stolen Lady" are both legends from the British Isles. These legends have been passed down through the generations by word of mouth. The legends are based on a similar story, in which a person is taken by fairies; the person is later found, but the events surrounding the disappearance and the return remain a mystery. Also, in both legends, the person who is missing is a spouse (a husband or a wife).

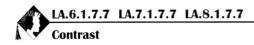
Extended-Response Question

65. How is the legend "Twenty Years with the Good People" different from the legend "The Stolen Lady"? Use details and information from the passage to support your answer.

Extended-Response Analysis

The legends differ in that they are told by different cultures and the lost characters have different ways of finding their families. "Twenty Years with the Good People" is Irish, and "The Stolen Lady" is Scottish. "Twenty Years with the Good People" is about a man who does not return home to his wife one evening. Many years later, the woman takes in a man with a mole on his hand. The mole looks like one her husband had. This is how she knows the man is her husband. "The Stolen Lady" is about a woman who is separated from her family. Many years later, soldiers visit a house in which the woman has been living. After hearing one soldier say her name, the woman recognizes the soldiers as her husband and son.

66. Based on the information given in the article, "Legends of the Isles," which of the following offers the best reason why different cultures have their own versions of a similar legend?

    A. People know the legends are untrue, so they make up details to make the legends more interesting.

    B. Members of one culture want their legend to be different, so they change some of the details.

    C. Legends tell the stories of actual events, but storytellers want to keep some of the details secret.

    D. The legends are passed on by word of mouth through the generations.

Analysis

After reading the article, "Legends of the Isles," you know that different cultures have their own versions of similar stories. Think about how you would explain this. This will help you as you answer this question.

A. According to the first paragraph, "legends are often thought of as being true stories from the past." Choice A is incorrect.

B. There is no mention of changing details purposefully. Choice B is incorrect.

C. The passage never mentions storytellers trying to keep legend details secret. Choice C is incorrect.

D. When legends are passed on by word of mouth, each storyteller tends to add personalized details. This is why different cultures have their own versions of a similar legend. Choice D is correct.

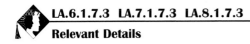
67. People who read the article, "Legends of the Isles," will learn

F. the details of similar legends told in both Ireland and Scotland.

G. how to tell a legend.

H. why legends originated in the British Isles.

I. all the legends told by people who live in the British Isles.

Analysis

F. Two legends are told (an Irish version and a Scottish version), and although some of the details vary, the overall story is the same. Choice F is correct.

G. The passage does not tell readers how to tell a legend. Choice G is incorrect.

H. The passage does not say legends originated in the British Isles. Choice H is incorrect.

I. The passage does not contain all the legends told by people who live in the British Isles. Choice I is incorrect.

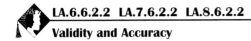

Short-Response Question

68. Based on the information from the article, why is it difficult for storytellers to offer accurate details when passing along legends? Use details and information from the article to support your answer.

G68

Short-Response Analysis

Sample responses are given below.

Sixth Grade	Seventh Grade	Eighth Grade
It is hard to pass along accurate details because the storytellers personalize the legends and because there is no proof to support the stories.	It is difficult for storytellers to pass along accurate details because storytellers may change details in order to personalize stories. Also, because there is rarely proof to support legends, it is hard to know what details are accurate.	It is difficult for storytellers to pass along accurate details because storytellers may change details in order to personalize stories. Once new details are passed on by another storyteller, the accuracy is affected. Also, because there is rarely proof to support legends, it is hard to know what details are accurate.

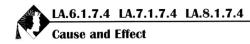
Short-Response Question

69. According to the legend "Twenty Years with the Good People," why was the husband away from his wife for so long? Use details and information from the article to support your answer.

Short-Response Analysis

The man was away from his wife because he was with "the good people," also known as fairies.

Tip!

Remember to use complete sentences when answering a short-response question.

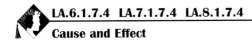
Short-Response Question

70. In the legend "The Stolen Lady," why must the fairies release the woman they are carrying? Use details and information from the article to support your answer.

Short-Response Analysis

A man is looking for his cattle. He sees the fairies carrying something. He offers the fairies his hat. Because he has offered them something, the fairies must exchange what they are carrying. They are carrying a woman.

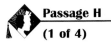
Passage H: Moving

Tara glared at the stack of boxes next to the front door. She wasn't sure why these boxes made her angrier than the boxes in every other room of her house, but for some reason, she felt an extra surge of disgust when she looked at these boxes. Maybe it was because they were there to see her out the door every morning on her way to school, and they were there to greet her every afternoon when she returned home, reminding her that this house would not be home for very much longer.

Every time she thought about moving, Tara wanted to cry. She couldn't imagine what it was going to be like in a new neighborhood and a new school, hundreds of miles away from all her friends. As much as she would miss everything about this house, this neighborhood, and this town, Tara was going to miss her friends

H

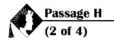

more than anything in the world. Her friends, she was convinced, were the greatest friends there could ever be. She could be the most popular girl at her new school, but it still wouldn't make up for the friends she had to leave behind.

When Tara's mother had explained to Tara and her brother Seth that the family had to move, Tara and Seth took the news in very different ways. Seth was excited to go to a new city, and he couldn't wait to see the new school and the new neighborhood their mom told them about. Tara's reaction was just the opposite. She had shut herself in her room, looking at old yearbooks and thinking about her neighborhood, her school, and especially her friends. All of it would go on without her after she left.

Almost every day, Tara's mom tried to make Tara at least a little bit interested in their new home. "I know you will miss your friends," she said today, "but you

H

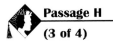
can keep in touch with them. You can call and write them letters, and you can e-mail them every day. Besides," she continued, "there are so many more things to do near our new house, you will be able to make new friends in a heartbeat." Tara shrugged and headed upstairs. She didn't feel like trying to explain to her mom that she didn't really want to make new friends. She wanted to keep her old ones. They were the ones she had known since preschool, the ones who knew all her secrets and who had shared millions of memories with her.

Looking around her bedroom, Tara tried to decide what to begin packing first. By the end of the weekend, she had to have at least half of her room in boxes to add to the pile next to the front door. She stacked some books in a box and threw in some stuffed animals so the box wouldn't be too heavy. Like a robot, she moved around the room, picking things up and deciding automatically whether

H

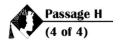
to pack them or throw them away. Although she knew she should pay more attention to what was going where, she didn't want to think about what she was doing. She knew it would make her too sad.

After two hours of packing, Tara came across a heavy shoebox that rustled when she shook it. Opening the lid, she found a mountain of tiny pictures—every school picture that every one of her friends had given her since they had first started school. She dumped them out on her floor and spread them around, looking at a sea of familiar and friendly faces. Maybe somewhere in her new town, she thought, some other girl was doing the same thing. The thought didn't make her feel any better about leaving her old friends, but it did give her a tiny spark of hope that somewhere at her new school, there could be a friend waiting for her.

H

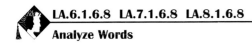
71. Read this sentence from the passage, "Moving."

   Like a robot, she moved around the room, picking things up and deciding automatically whether to pack them or throw them away.

   What do the words *moved like a robot* mean in the sentence above?

   A. Tara moved without thought.

   B. Tara moved without purpose.

   C. Tara moved very stiffly.

   D. Tara moved effortlessly.

Analysis

A. Using the context clues in paragraph 5, you will see that Tara "didn't want to think about what she was doing." This is why the author says Tara "moved like a robot." Choice A is correct.

B. Tara had a purpose. She was packing up her room in order to get ready for the move. Choice B is incorrect.

C. There is no mention of Tara's physical movement and whether it is stiff. Choice C is incorrect.

D. There is no mention of Tara's physical movement and whether it is effortless. Choice D is incorrect.

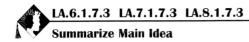
Extended-Response Question

72. Write a summary of the passage, "Moving." Use details and information from the passage to support your answer.

Extended-Response Analysis

Tara and Seth are sister and brother. Their mother tells them the family has to move to a new city. Seth is excited about the move. He can't wait to see the new school and the new neighborhood. Tara has a different reaction. She doesn't want to move. She doesn't want to leave her house, and she doesn't want to leave the only friends she has ever known. She doesn't think anything in the new place will be as good as where she is living. Tara's mom tells her she will make new friends, but Tara is not comforted. Despite her disgust for moving boxes, Tara packs up her room. As she packs, she finds a shoebox filled with school pictures. She spreads her friends' pictures all around her. She thinks about the new school and realizes she just might find a friend there.

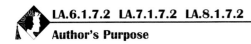
73. Why did the author write the passage, "Moving"?

    F.   to give an opinion

    G.   to tell a story

    H.   to persuade

    I.   to convey a mood

Analysis

F. The author does not give an opinion. Choice F is incorrect.

G. The author tells a story. Choice G is correct.

H. The author does not try to persuade readers. Choice H is incorrect.

I. The author does not attempt to convey a mood. Choice I is incorrect.

The author's purpose is the reason an author writes a passage. Here are some common author purposes.

to give information or to inform
to tell a story
to give an opinion
to persuade
to convey a mood

H73

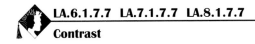

Short-Response Question

74. How are Seth's feelings about moving different than Tara's feelings about moving? Use details and information from the passage to support your answer.

Short-Response Analysis

Sample responses are given below.

Sixth Grade	Seventh Grade	Eighth Grade
Seth is excited about moving, but Tara is not. Seth wants to see new things, but Tara wants to stay with her friends.	Seth is excited about moving to a new city; he can't wait to see the new neighborhood and the new school. Tara, on the other hand, does not want to move. She wants to stay where she is to be with all her friends.	Seth is excited about moving to a new city. He is excited about the new neighborhood and the new school. In contrast, Tara does not want to move. She wants to stay where she is to be with all her friends. She is sad when she thinks about how life will go on without her when she moves.

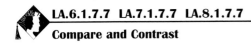

Extended-Response Question

75a. How is Tara's attitude at the end of the passage different
from her attitude at the beginning of the passage?

75b. How is Tara's attitude at the end of the passage the similar
to her attitude at the beginning of the passage?

Extended-Response Analysis

There are two parts to this question. Remember to answer both parts. A sample response for each part of the question is given below.

a. How is Tara's attitude at the end of the passage different from her attitude at the beginning of the passage??

At the beginning of the passage, Tara feels only sadness and disappointment about moving. She sees no good in the situation. At the end of the passage, she thinks she just might meet someone new.

b. How is Tara's attitude at the end of the passage the similar to her attitude at the beginning of the passage?

Both at the beginning of the passage and at the end of the passage, Tara doesn't feel good about leaving her friends.

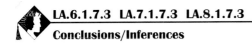

Extended-Response Question

76. The first paragraph of the passage, "Moving," mentions
    Tara's disgust at the sight of so many boxes. Why does
    Tara feel this way? Use details and information from the
    passage to support your answer.

Extended-Response Analysis

Tara does not want to move, and there are only a few days until moving day. The boxes remind her that her house will not be her house for very much longer. Her things and her family's things are being packed up and moved to a new city. In the new city, she will miss her friends, the friends she has known almost all her life, the friends she considers the greatest in the whole world. Tara is disgusted by the boxes because they are a reminder of the changes she will soon face.

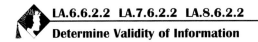
77. Which of the following statements is true?

A. Tara's family has moved into a new house, and the unpacked boxes are cluttering the house.

B. Tara's family is preparing to move, and there are boxes all over the house.

C. Seth's family has moved into a new house, and the unpacked boxes are cluttering the house.

D. Seth's family is helping Tara's family move into a new house.

Analysis

A. Tara and her family have not yet moved into the new house during this passage. They are still in their old house. Choice A is incorrect.

B. Tara and her family are preparing to move, and there are boxes all over the house. Choice B is correct.

C. Seth is Tara's brother. The family has not yet moved into the new house during this passage. They are still in their old house. Choice C is incorrect.

D. Seth is Tara's brother. They are not moving into the new house during this story, they are only packing. Choice D is incorrect.

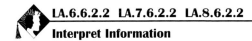
78. People who read the passage, "Moving," will learn

    F. the best way to pack boxes.

    G. why Tara and her family are moving.

    H. how Tara feels about moving.

    I. where Tara's new house is located.

H78

Tip!

Think about what you know after reading the passage, "Moving." Think about each answer choice. Did you learn about any of these as you read the passage?

Analysis

F.   Readers do not learn how to pack boxes. The passage simply mentions that members of the family have packed boxes. Choice F is incorrect.

G.   Readers learn Tara and her family are moving, but the reason why they are moving is not given. Choice G is incorrect.

H.   Readers learn how Tara feels about moving: she is unhappy. Choice H is correct.

I.   Readers never learn specifically where Tara's new house is located. Choice I is incorrect.

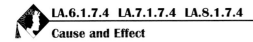
Short-Response Question

79. What sparks Tara's hope at the end of the story?

Short-Response Analysis

Tara looks at all the school pictures she has gathered since she was in preschool. As she spreads the pictures out before her, Tara thinks about a girl from her new school looking at pictures she has collected. If there is another girl like Tara in the new school, then Tara might meet a new friend. This is what sparks Tara's hope.

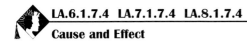
80. Why does Tara's mom think Tara will meet new friends quickly?

A. Tara is the most popular girl in school, and it has always been easy for her to make friends.

B. Tara knows a girl at the new school, and this girl will introduce her to many new friends.

C. Seth is outgoing, and he will introduce his sister to many new friends.

D. There are many things to do near the new house and many ways to meet new friends.

H80

Analysis

A. The passage does not mention that Tara is the most popular girl in school or that Tara makes friends easily. Choice A is incorrect.

B. Tara doesn't know anyone at the new school. Choice B is incorrect.

C. There is no mention of Seth introducing his sister to new friends. Choice C is incorrect.

D. Tara's mom says, "there are so many more things to do near our new house, you will be able to make new friends in a heartbeat." Choice D is correct.

THANK YOU FOR YOUR PURCHASE

ADDITIONAL PRODUCTS

SHOW WHAT YOU KNOW® FLORIDA!
FLASH CARDS FOR
GRADES 3, 4, 5, 6, 7, 8, AND HIGH SCHOOL

FLASH CARDS—with up to 96 question and answer cards per deck, featuring test questions aligned to the Florida Standards and Benchmarks. Use Show What You Know® flash cards for quizzes, team games, assessment, and self-study.

Show What You Know® flash cards review important concepts tested on Florida's state assessment. To help identify which concept is being assessed, the standard is listed in the upper left-hand corner of each question card. Under the standard are keywords that describe the skill being tested.

WATCH AS STUDENTS' CONFIDENCE GROWS!

CONTACT US FOR MORE DETAILS:

1.877.PASSING (727-7464)
www.showwhatyouknowpublishing.com

Item # FL5625

Show What You Know® Florida! Reading Flash Cards for Grades 6-8

This deck of flash cards features important concepts tested by Florida's state assessment in Reading. The deck includes 8 reading passages and 80 questions and answers.

- Students can practice with multiple-choice and open-response items that model Florida's state assessment.
- All questions are perfectly correlated to the Next Generation Sunshine State Standards for Reading.
- Questions are designed to review important reading concepts covered in grades 6–8.
- These flash cards can be used for quizzes, assessment, homework, study groups, and student self-study.

ISBN 978-1-5923-0003-7

© 2010, 2012 Show What You Know® Publishing
Distributed by:
Lorenz Educational Press, a Lorenz company
P.O. Box 802
Dayton, OH 45401-0802

Printed in the U.S.A.

Paul Doherty was born in Middlesbrough. He studied History at Liverpool and Oxford Universities and obtained a doctorate at Oxford for his thesis on Edward II and Queen Isabella. He is now headmaster of a school in north-east London and lives with his wife and family near Epping Forest.

Paul Doherty's previous novels include the Hugh Corbett medieval mysteries, the Sorrowful Mysteries of Brother Athelstan, and the Ancient Egyptian mysteries.

'The book is a pleasure to read and written in an uncompromising prose, the plot developed with intriguing twists and turns ... Superb entertainment'   *Historical Novels Review*

'Medieval London comes vividly to life'
Publishers Weekly

'The maestro of medieval mystery'
Books Magazine

'Historically informative, excellently plotted and, as ever, superbly entertaining'   *CADS*

The Rose Demon
The Soul Slayer
The Haunting

Ancient Egyptian Mysteries
The Mask of Ra
The Horus Killings
The Anubis Slayings
The Slayers of Seth

The Sorrowful Mysteries of Brother Athelstan
The Nightingale Gallery
The House of the Red Slayer
Murder Most Holy
The Anger of God
By Murder's Bright Light
The House of Crows
The Assassin's Riddle
The Devil's Domain
The Field of Blood

Hugh Corbett medieval mysteries
Satan in St Mary's
Crown in Darkness
Spy in Chancery
The Angel of Death
The Prince of Darkness
Murder Wears a Cowl
The Assassin in the Greenwood
The Song of a Dark Angel
Satan's Fire
The Devil's Hunt
The Demon Archer
The Treason of the Ghosts
Corpse Candle

The Canterbury Tales of murder and mystery
An Ancient Evil
Being the Knight's Tale
A Tapestry of Murders
Being the Man of Law's Tale
A Tournament of Murders
Being the Franklin's Tale
Ghostly Murders
Being the Priest's Tale
The Hangman's Hymn
Being the Carpenter's Tale

Domina

Paul Doherty

headline

PRINCIPAL CHARACTERS

EMPERORS OF ROME

Octavian, Augustus:	First Emperor of Rome died AD 14
Tiberius:	AD 14–37 Augustus's successor, his adopted son, the offspring of Augustus's wife Livia and her first husband
Caligula:	AD 37–41 Son of Germanicus, and Agrippina the elder
Claudius:	AD 41–54 Nephew of Tiberius
Nero:	AD 54–68 Son of Agrippina the younger and Domitius Ahenobarbus
Galba, Otho and Vitellius:	Roman generals who seized the purple in the Year of the four Emperors AD 68–69

THE IMPERIAL FAMILY

Gemellus:	Grandson of Tiberius
Germanicus:	Son of Tiberius
Agrippina the elder, his wife Drusus,	children of Germanicus and Agrippina the elder

Caligula, Agrippina, Julia
(some sources call her
Livilla) and Drusilla:

Messalina: Claudius's third wife

Britannicus and Octavia: children of Claudius and
Messalina

Roman Politicians/Ministers

Aelius Sejanus: Prefect under Tiberius

Macro: Sejanus's successor

Sextus Burrus: Prefect under Claudius
and Nero

Seneca: Philosopher, leading
politician under Nero

Tigellinus, Otho and
Anicetus: Nero's henchmen

Passienus Crispus: Friend of Tiberius and
Caligula, Agrippina's
second husband

Narcissus and
Pallas: freedmen, powerful
politicians during
the reign of Claudius and
Nero

PRINCIPAL EVENTS

AD 15:   Agrippina born
AD 19:   Death of her father Germanicus
AD 31:   Death of Sejanus
AD 39:   Exile of Agrippina
AD 41:   Return of Agrippina
AD 47:   Agrippina and Nero return to Rome
AD 54:   Nero becomes Emperor
AD 55:   Clash between Agrippina and Nero over
          Acte. Death of Britannicus
AD 59:   Murder of Agrippina
AD 68:   Death of Nero

Chapter 1

'I shudder as I tell the tale'
Virgil, *Aeneid*: II.204

Was I in at the end? Naturally! Did I witness her murder? Of course I did! Did I survive? Well, I am here to tell the tale. Nevertheless, I sense the hidden meaning behind such questions. Yes, something in me died with her. I am only glad that, before we parted, she explained who she really was. I am Parmenon, servant to the Goddess, Domina Agrippina. When a star falls from heaven it never falls alone. I fell with her.

They tried to make it look like an accident, but of course it was murder. The monster Lucius Domitius Ahenobarbus, known as Nero, is a matricide, was a matricide, will be a matricide as long as time runs.

Truth will out, be it in a blaze of fire or creeping like water through fissures and cracks. Domina was hardly cold in her grave when leather bags were hung on Nero's statue. Do you understand the significance of that? It means that Nero should be stitched into such a bag and thrown into the Tiber, the just fate for an assassin! A baby was abandoned in the forum, with a tag on its cradle reading: 'I WON'T MURDER YOU BUT I LEAVE YOU SO WHEN YOU GROW UP YOU WON'T MURDER ME'.

Domina's statues were torn down but a wit daubed an inscription on one of the plinths, a quotation from the Classics: 'I am disgraced, but you are ashamed.' I especially liked one piece of graffiti for its cleverness: 'A novel calculation: Nero= slew his own mother.' A Greek must have written that. (Thank the Gods for the Classics.) Greek numbers are designated by letters of the alphabet, so to put it simply: Neron, in Greek, is equivalent to 1005; the phrase, 'slew his own mother' also comes to 1005. Nero would take some time to work that out, if he ever did.

Others were more blatant. Dartius, a performer of farces, at the end of one his shows, shouted: 'Farewell, Father! Farewell, Mother!' But, instead of waving goodbye at this point, Dartius imitated the gestures of drunkenness and swimming. It brought the house down though Dartius had to flee Rome by dead of night. The hypocrite Nero staged games to mark the death of his 'Pia Mater' – Agrippina had to be mourned. Nero, following the advice of his creature Anicetus, put on a splendid festival, the climax of which was a tightrope-walking elephant. Oh Gods, can you imagine it? An elephant walking a rope? Was that the imperial salute for the daughter of Germanicus, his own mother?

Let me tell my story from the end rather than the beginning. As in all things, it takes a woman to destroy another. In Domina's case, it was that tasty morsel Poppea, wife of General Otho until she caught Nero's eye. Poppea was a ripe grape ready for the plucking, with her beautiful face and a body so rich you'd groan at the very sight of it. Poppea the pretty; Poppea the petulant; Poppea with her sun-gold ring of curls; Poppea the spider; Poppea the assassin! Poppea was determined to share Nero's bed. To achieve that she had to surmount a number of obstacles, which she did with consummate ease. Now, Poppea could easily remove her own husband as well as Nero's wife; after all, in Rome, divorce was as common as murder. Otho was only too willing to give up his wife, whilst Nero and Octavia couldn't stand the sight of each other. Both Octavia and Otho were quite prepared to leave the stage to the gorgeous, pouting Poppea, but not Agrippina. A woman who had survived the intrigues of Caligula, the machinations of Claudius, the murderous malice of Messalina? Agrippina was made of sterner stuff. Goddesses do not go into retirement. They either live for ever or die.

So, how do you kill the Queen of Poison? How do you wipe out someone schooled in the harsh atmosphere of the House of Livia, Augustus's great wife? Agrippina knew every poison available. Her cupboards were full of the antidotes which she regularly took. Poisoning in Nero's Rome was becoming virtually impossible. There was a legion of tasters, not to mention spies, in the kitchen. The principal rule at an imperial banquet was to eat only from a dish which had been carefully tasted beforehand. I've seen many a glorious supper come to an abrupt end at the slightest hint of indigestion amongst its guests. So you can understand Nero and Poppea's problem. Right from the start they plotted Domina's murder. However, whilst selling the bearskin is easy, trapping and killing its owner, to misquote the mischievous Petronius, 'is a different kettle of fish'.

There is always the sword and in the end that's what it came to, but how do you bribe someone to kill your mother, an Empress of Rome? So round and round and round the plotters went. Nero loved his mother, you'll say, it must have been difficult for him. Nero loved nobody! His own father once remarked that anyone who inherited his and Agrippina's blood would turn out to be a bad lot. He didn't mean it as a prophecy, just a statement of fact. Oh yes, I've heard about the allegations of incest: the tumbling in the litter, the stains on Nero's clothing. Just bear with me and I'll explain them in due course. It's the murder we begin with.

Agrippina, may the Gods bless her, suspected it was coming. We were in the gardens at her favourite villa at Antium. We were sitting, as we often did, wetting our feet in a fountain, with a bowl of grapes and a jug of wine between us. Agrippina was tense. She sat, as she always did when spinning her web, with her shoulders slightly hunched. A light sheen of sweat glistened on her full face; her black hair was tied tightly back, except for two corkscrew strands which fell over the ears. She was talking to herself, lips soundlessly moving. Now and again she would pause to chew on a grape and squint up against the sun. It was – is – a beautiful place with raised paths, greenery, flower beds, splashing water, shadowy porticoes and fragrant arbours. Just the spot to contemplate your own end.

'We are all murderers, Parmenon!' Agrippina's tone was meditative, almost as if she was speaking aloud but unaware of anyone listening.

I could have objected, asked her to explain. It wasn't the time. Agrippina turned and yawned, displaying those double canine teeth. Her lips were purple, grape-stained. I recalled the accusation that she was blood hungry: a killer born and bred, more ferocious than any animal in the amphitheatre. Those double canines only enhanced such a reputation, giving a slight twist to her lips. Yet this was offset by those lovely, well-spaced, dark eyes which could crinkle in amusement, flirt outrageously or glare in murderous passion.

Agrippina was very proud of her eyes. In her youth she used to remark, 'Let me stare at a man long enough and he's mine.' It wasn't so much a boast as the truth. I mean, listen to dramatists talking about characterisation and developing different personae.

It's nonsense! Most people are simple and boring. Their lives tend to be dominated by a few questions. How they look? Are they healthy? Will they earn a lot of money? Are they in or out of favour? Agrippina was different. You could tell that from her eyes: maternal, soft and tender, cold and dispassionate, amusing, seductive. Her moods could change so quickly. Oh, I concede she was dangerous. Any member of that family was dangerous!

She studied me closely in that lovely villa garden, a faraway look in her eyes.

'Do you accept that, Parmenon? That we are all murderers? How long is my list?'

I gestured with my hand. She flicked a grape at me.

'Come on, Parmenon, tell me. I know you've kept count.'

'Domina, it's so long, it would be easier to say who wasn't on it!'

Agrippina laughed. My mind was already going through the table of names. Drusus, starved to death in his prison beneath the Palatine, reduced to eating the stuffing from his mattress. Sejanus, his strangled, cat-scratched body thrust into a sack and thrown down the Stairs of Mourning. Caligula, his plotting senators drawing their swords, abruptly realising that, despite all the fuss, he really wasn't a god.

'Come on!' Agrippina urged.

I started to recite the litany. I had only listed seven names when Agrippina clapped her hands.

'Enough! Enough!' She smiled, her eyes all soft and kitten-like. 'Aren't you missing some out?'

'Well, there's dear Passienus . . .'

'Oh yes, my second husband.'

'And, of course, there's . . .'

'I know.' She made a moue with her mouth. 'Dear Clau . . . Clau . . . dear Claudius,' she scoffed. 'He did like mushrooms.'

Agrippina sat, swinging her feet, letting the water ripple through her toes, humming a song a gladiator had once taught her. Oh, she looked so beautiful with the sun shining, the air perfumed with roses and the scent of crushed grapes.

'Why?' she asked.

'Why what, Domina?'

'Why did I murder? Why did I kill? She smiled at me with those butterfly eyes like a young girl teasing a teacher. 'Shall I tell you why?'

I glanced away. Her words are the cause of this story. Shall I tell you why? That's where my story begins and ends. For the first and last time, Agrippina, Domina Mea, was going to confess. She looked at me directly, no longer the coquette, the flirt, the imperial wife or mother. This was a soul-wrenching, haunted glance. Never once had Domina ever discussed this. Oh, she'd removed enemies. She'd plotted carefully but . . .

'Why?' I whispered.

I daren't look round. Were the ghosts thronging in? Tiberius with his rotting body? Caligula playing with himself as he made love to the moon? Claudius with his lopsided face and quivering jaw, hobbling through the palace or purple-faced as he choked to death. Britannicus would be there, livid with poison. Would his ghost also carry the gypsum smeared over his corpse to conceal the poison's noxious effects?

'Why?' Domina broke into my reverie.

'Because you had to.'

She pulled a face. 'Seneca could debate that till the sun froze over.' She shook her head. 'Because I enjoyed it? Not really, enemies are like old friends: you miss them when they are gone. No, I killed because I was born to kill.' She stared at me, then burst out laughing. 'Don't sit there scratching that black mop, your shrewd eyes wet with tears.' She prodded me gently on the tip of the nose. 'Do you understand what I am saying, Parmenon?'

'You were born to kill. It's in the blood?'

'The imperial blood is no different from any other. I don't believe I am different from anyone else. No better, no finer.' She splashed her feet in the fountain. 'You don't understand, Parmenon.'

'I am trying to.'

'Don't be petulant.' She wrinkled her nose. 'Think of the amphitheatre. Its awnings are pulled out, the sand is raked, the crowd sits hushed and the gladiators strut into the arena. I always listen for the sound of the iron gate clanging behind them, locked and bolted. There's no going back. They are to stand and fight, live or die. They raise their swords.' She imitated the gesture of a gladiator. '"We who are about to die salute thee!" The Consul or the Emperor returns the salute. Do you know what I do at that moment, Parmenon?'

She didn't wait for an answer. 'I whisper the words back: "We who are about to die also salute you". That's what we are, Parmenon, gladiators. When you're born into the purple, you step into an arena. You either fight or die. It's as simple as that. You can try and skulk away like Uncle Claudius did, and stay in the shadows but, eventually, the roar of the crowd and the whips of the lanistae will drive you into the centre. You either kill them or they kill you.'

I stared across the fountain.

'Well, Parmenon?'

'I thought you fought for power?'

Agrippina did not seem to hear.

'Domina?'

'If you are born into the imperial purple, life and power are synonymous, you can't have one without the other.'

'So you killed because you had to?'

'No, Parmenon, it's different. What you are saying implies choice. We fight, we murder because that's our life. You know when the gladiators separate to choose their opponent – the net man against the swordsman, the Thracian against the Samnite? We are the same. I fought Caligula and, when he was gone, I turned to face my next opponent, Messalina, a victor from her fights. Now it's Poppea. If I won there'd be someone else. If I lose, Poppea will take breath, and wipe the sweat from her brow just as she glimpses the shadow of her next opponent. There are no exceptions.'

'Not even . . . ?'

'No! Caligula slept with me, his sister. Claudius married me, his niece. You're referring to my darling son, aren't you? Can't you see, Parmenon, in the arena, there can only be one victor.'

'I've heard the prophecy,' I remarked.

'Prophecy?' she mimicked. 'You mean, the one from that old charlatan Thrasyllus. He wasn't making a prophecy. He just knew the rules of the game. Shall I tell you how I could survive?' Her eyes had that hard, venomous look. 'Do you want me to spell it out, Parmenon? If I want to survive,' she continued, 'there's only one way.'

'Kill Poppea?'

'No, Parmenon, kill my son!'

A bee buzzed hungrily from flower to flower. The moment had gone. Its peace shattered. Already I could hear the shouts of the workmen as they returned from their midday rest to continue work on the villa. They were re-roofing and patching up the walls where cracks had occurred. Until recently Agrippina had supervised their work but the looming crisis had diminished her interest.

I reflected on what had happened so far. Nero and Poppea were busy in Rome with little communication between Agrippina and her son. Domina had sheltered at Antium and waited for news. Eventually the silence was broken: Nero was coming south. He intended to stay at one of his villas at Misenum or Baiae. His cronies were coming with him: Otho, Anicetus and, of course, the lovely Poppea. Would there be a reconciliation between mother and son?

Agrippina and her old friend Acerronia had discussed the matter excitedly: perhaps the old times were returning and Nero was missing his mother. Perhaps Poppea's influence was on the wane! The clouds were lifting. I'd been present at such meetings, lying on my couch in the triclinium, with Acerronia chattering away and the actor Callienus sulking if Agrippina did not lavish her smiles on him.

To be truthful I had been hopeful too. Antium was pleasant enough but it wasn't Rome, and I missed the turbulent crowded streets, the smells of the cookshops, gossiping with the gladiators or strolling through the forum listening to the chatter. Nero had been very busy with building work on the Palatine, a new chariot course with unique mechanical devices. I'd have liked to have seen them. However, things weren't changing for the better. Agrippina, in her clear but elliptical way, was able to see the brutal reality of the situation. We might all kiss each other, clasp hands, swear eternal oaths of friendship but it was a charade. Agrippina was in the arena of the amphitheatre, the corpses of her past enemies strewn about, and her new opponent Poppea striding towards her. And what of Nero? Her only son, born feet first, the cause of so much physical and spiritual pain? That golden boy with his red-gold, curly hair, moustache and beard cut in the Greek fashion, those popping blue eyes in that chubby, child-like face.

'Would you?' I asked. 'Could you kill him?'

Agrippina snapped her fingers. 'Like that, Parmenon.' She plucked up a grape and squeezed it between her fingers. 'You forget the ancient laws of Rome. A parent has rights over his or her child's life.'

'But could you?' I insisted.

Agrippina's eyes grew misty. 'No,' she murmured. 'No, I could not, not him.'

'But you are in the amphitheatre,' I insisted. 'Your enemies are helmeted and masked. They carry swords and shields. Blood, sometimes, is not thicker than water.'

'You're wrong!' she replied hoarsely. 'Many years ago I was friendly with Volusus, a Thracian gladiator, one of the best. He fought like a dancer, shifting this way and that, flitting like a shadow around his opponents. One day I went to see him fight. There were four pairs to start with; eventually only one remained. The crowd tensed with anticipation. The combat had lasted for hours and it was now late afternoon. You could taste the blood in the air. People were so excited that a number collapsed from sunstroke, refusing to leave their seats and seek shelter. Volusus had fought like one possessed. You know the way of such events? A gladiator kills his opponent, then searches for another. I'd noticed, and so had the crowd, that Volusus had deliberately avoided a certain fighter. I was intrigued. The remaining gladiator was a mere neophyte, a Dacian with only two or three victories to his name. Volusus was of the same nationality.' She plucked at the grapes. 'The Dacian was a retiarius, a net man, who had won his fights more by luck than skill. He came in stumbling. Volusus danced away. Time and again the net was cast only to miss. The crowd turned ugly. Volusus could have finished him off, you could see that. People were becoming impatient. They wanted an end, to stream out to the taverns and discuss the day's events.' She paused and watched a butterfly gently hover on the early afternoon breeze. 'That's what Volusus was,' she declared. 'A butterfly, floating in the arena. He was like a dream walker. The retiarius was exhausted. He made a final cast, stumbled and the net flew out of his hands. He lunged, but Volusus blocked the blow and sent the trident whirling out of his hand.' Agrippina stretched out her arm, thumb extended. '"*Hoc Habet, Hoc Habet*!" the crowd roared. "Let him have it, let him have it!".' She paused.

'And?'

'Volusus didn't give the death blow. He just threw his shield and sword down and walked away. He was the darling of the mob but you know what they are like when the blood lust is up? "*Hoc Habet! Hoc Habet*!" came the roar, but they weren't shouting for the Dacian's death now: that little bastard had recovered himself. He picked up his trident and ran towards Volusus who turned, defenceless. He didn't stop his opponent driving the barbed blade into his throat, and in a few minutes he was dead, blood pouring out of the wound. The crowd was hostile but the Dacian had won. He was given the laurels of the games. Afterwards I made enquiries and discovered that Volusus and the Dacian had once been lovers.' Agrippina got to her feet. 'I don't need to tell you the moral of the tale, Parmenon. I can sympathise with Volusus.'

She slipped her feet into her sandals and picked up the empty wine goblet. 'The day is drawing on,' she murmured. 'I must see what those lazy workmen are doing!'

Agrippina's story about Volusus haunted me for the rest of that week. Nero might be Emperor of Rome but she had him in her power. She could, if she wished, strike hard and deep but she had lost the will. Perhaps something in that tangled mind of hers had cried 'Enough!'.

The subject of a possible rapprochement with Nero dominated the conversation of the household. Agrippina, the consummate actress, played along with them. Members of Nero's entourage visited the villa bringing tokens and gifts, which Agrippina seized eagerly, listening attentively to the news of her son. But, after that conversation with her in the garden, I saw it all through different eyes.

There was also talk of a great banquet. I wondered if the monster was preparing something spectacular: he was so good at hosting parties. On one notorious occasion, the guests were invited into a triclinium painted completely black. The walls, the floors, the ceiling, the tables, even the glass and silverware, were all as black as night. The chairs and couches were carved in the form of funeral slabs lit by those little lamps you see hanging above a tomb. Every dish, somehow or other, was tinted black. Negro boys, naked as they were born, served the meals.

You can imagine the terror of the guests, who had been promised a supper party to remember. But Nero let them all return home unscathed. From what I could gather most of them were in a state of near collapse but he had kept his promise; they would never forget that supper party for as long as they lived!

Such horror stories, coupled with Agrippina's fears, alarmed me. One morning, as she swam in the villa's pool, I stood on the edge watching her beautiful body streak through the water, her skill and speed reminding me of a dolphin. I was giving her my usual lecture on the need for prudence.

'You should come in!' Agrippina called out, ignoring all my pleas for caution with her son. She stood naked on the far side of the pool, the water pouring off her.

'I prefer watching you,' I called.

'A legacy from Caligula,' she shouted. 'When you are exiled to an island, the only way to get off is to swim around it.'

Callienus appeared. He had been ill with a fever. He sat on a stone seat, cradling a cup in his hands and stared mournfully at his mistress.

'Don't drink too much!' Agrippina called. 'You've got duties tonight.'

She winked at me and disappeared again beneath the water.

'I'll drink what I bloody well want!' Callienus growled.

I ignored him. He was a good-looking Greek actor,

but his pretty face was always spoilt by a scowl. Agrippina left the pool. She dried off and quickly dressed. Acerronia came out, complaining about the workmen. Agrippina, drying her hair, half-listened, more interested in finding out what we were eating that night.

'Piglet cooked in honey,' Acerronia replied. 'I've found some quite old Falernian in your cellars.' She stomped off.

'Isn't it strange?' Agrippina mused.

'What is?'

I had come round the pool, but Callienus had slunk away. Agrippina was always lecturing him about how much he drank.

'I'd forgotten about that wine. I bought it from a vineyard owner who used to live nearby. He was a strange man, who kept lambs in his house.'

'When did you buy the wine?' I asked.

'Ah, it was when I was courting Claudius. We came here for one of our pleasant little weekends. He did like his wine.' She grinned. 'Almost as much as mushrooms!'

Now, I don't believe in portents but at that moment something strange happened. An owl flew across the garden chased by other birds. I shivered and touched the tip of my penis for luck. Agrippina watched the harassed bird seek shelter in a line of trees.

'Approaching death,' she remarked. 'Isn't an owl in daylight a harbinger of impending doom?'

It was as if the sun had slipped behind a cloud.

Looking back, of course, I realise that owl was no natural occurrence: one of Nero's spies must have been nearby with the poor bird in a cage, and released it at that moment. I joked and tried to pass it off but Agrippina remained tense and watchful.

The incident marred the atmosphere at supper. Agrippina drank too much and indulged in a heated argument with Callienus. There was nothing that little bum boy liked more than flouncing off and he did so now in style.

'Let him go.' Agrippina made a gesture. 'I'm tired of his scowling face. Now, let me tell you about Tiberius. Do you know he used to swim on Capri with little boys who had been trained to nibble at him from under water?'

Acerronia burst out laughing. Agrippina ordered the lights to be doused. As the servants had been dismissed, I was engaged in this task when I heard a terrible crash.

Agrippina's bedchamber was at the back of the villa. It was a small annexe built on the corner and flanked on either side by a two-storeyed building. She never really told me the reason why she had chosen this chamber. Most people like to sleep on the roof. Agrippina, however, always preferred to shelter at the rear of the villa on the ground floor. This bedchamber had been specially built, with a ceiling made of slats of wood, not like some fence, but fashioned out of the best cedars of Lebanon with small gaps between so you could glimpse the moon and the stars. Agrippina was a devotee of the moon: she loved its light and, in the fourth quarter when it was full and strong, would often sit and study it.

Well, by the time I reached that bedchamber, the roof had gone, and Callienus with it. The roof had collapsed, crushing the bed and the Greek under a mass of fallen timbers and rubble. Agrippina and Acerronia joined me. The noise had roused the rest of the villa, and lamps and torches were brought. Some of the slaves became hysterical, but Agrippina remained calm. She wrapped a cloak about her and just stood in the doorway, staring at the masonry which had buried her lover.

The following morning I investigated the 'accident'. It would appear that the builders on either side of the bedchamber had piled up masonry on the flat roofs. For some unknown reason this had slipped and fallen, bringing down the timber ceiling to crush Callienus to pulp. The Greek certainly lost all his looks and beauty. A piece of timber had smashed his head as easily as it would a nut. Another had crushed his legs. Agrippina ordered his mangled remains to be sheeted and the corpse was taken down to the beach. A makeshift funeral pyre was hastily assembled and drenched with oil. Agrippina herself took the torch and set it ablaze. She made the libation and muttered the prayer. The sea breeze caught the flames and soon reduced it all to ash. Afterwards Agrippina refused to leave. She dismissed the slaves but asked me to stay.

'Was it an accident, Parmenon?'

'No, Domina. Some of the workmen have disappeared. Oh, there was some rubble left on the roof but not enough to cause such damage. I checked the ceiling joists.'

'And?'

'The beams had been weakened and the clasps broken. I would guess five or six men climbed on the roof during the night, probably carrying sheetloads of rubble, though it was the beams which killed poor Callienus.'

'The rubble was tossed on?'

'Yes, Domina. The beams simply fell in. With a drop of over three yards, Callienus didn't stand a chance.'

'Who ordered this?'

'You know who,' I whispered. 'Domina, you are in the arena, but your opponents have struck first. The scene was well prepared: the portent of the owl in the afternoon, followed by an unfortunate accident. The assassins glimpsed Callienus's lamp, and no doubt thought that you and he had retired for the night . . .'

Agrippina held her hand up. 'I don't want to hear any more.'

She walked down to the funeral pyre. I thought she was going to say a few more words, but she went round it and stood at the edge of the sea, allowing the water to lap about her sandalled feet. Above her the sea birds called. I followed but stood behind, and watched her shoulders shake; one of the few times in her life that I saw Domina Agrippina, daughter of Germanicus, truly weep.

'Don't you hear them, Parmenon?'

'Domina, it's only the sea birds.'

'No, Parmenon.' She turned, wiping the tears from her cheeks. 'The ghosts are calling my name!'

Chapter 2

'The leader of the enterprise is a woman'
Virgil, *Aeneid*: I. 364

We waited like the gladiators in the arena. Nero's spies surrounded the villa, whilst I wouldn't trust most of the household servants and slaves as far as I could spit. As day followed day, ominous auguries and signs manifested themselves. Agrippina's nerves drew taut. She snapped more often and I would frequently find her on the promontory overlooking the sea, brooding deeply as if Neptune could tell her the future. It was growing difficult to tell friend from foe in the dappled half-light of imperial politics. One morning a servant ran in screaming that the chickens wouldn't eat, an awesome portent. Agrippina sprang to her feet, her face contorted with fury. She ran out

21

to the yard, picked up two of the offending chickens and threw them down the well.

'If they won't eat,' she screamed, 'then let the bastards drink!'

Nero's spies amongst the servants were delighted at this outburst. More strange stories circulated: a strange black dog was seen bounding across the villa gardens; a snake fell from a roof beam; a cock crowed in the dead of night.

I tried to divert Agrippina. One evening I hired one of those wandering physicians, more comical than a clown. This character claimed to be a Greek who followed the teachings of Cato. I brought him into the triclinium, where Agrippina and Acerronia were nibbling at roast meat and copiously drinking wine.

'Tell the Domina,' I said to the Greek, 'about your theory.'

Well, I tell you this, the charlatan was better than a tonic. He called himself Aeshcypolus, claimed to have studied in Athens where be became a devout disciple of that old kill-joy Cato. I knew what was coming next. The rogue theatrically gestured at the platters and plates strewn across the tables.

'Don't eat that rubbish,' he pronounced. 'Drink juniper-wood wine and keep a pomegranate close by to combat colic and worms.'

Agrippina's face was a treat. She gaped open mouthed.

'Cabbage!' the man trumpeted. 'Eat cabbage, Domina! It eases the bowels and facilitates urination. Carefully washed and crushed, cabbage will cure ulcers and open sores and dispel tumours. Fried in hot fat, and taken on an empty stomach, cabbage will cure insomnia. Cabbage juice will also cure deafness and, if the same is rubbed on your private parts, heightens sexual pleasure . . .'

Agrippina threw her head back and bellowed with laughter. It was marvellous to see and hear: a truly merry laugh which began in the stomach, echoed through her chest and throat and brought life back to the eyes and face. Acerronia joined in. It became so infectious that I sat down on the edge of a couch, my shoulders shaking. I threw a purse at Aeschypolus and told the silly bugger he could sleep in one of the stables.

'See, I told you,' the fellow lugubriously added as I steered him towards the door. 'Even the mention of a cabbage will dispel the humours and lift depression.'

Well, that was too much for Agrippina. She was laughing so much she slipped onto the floor. I got rid of Aeshcypolus and returned to the triclinium. Agrippina's face was a joy to see. The tears rolled down her cheeks in long black lines of kohl. She got up and washed her face in lotus water, wiping herself carefully. She tried to thank me, took one look at my face and burst out laughing again. A good hour passed before she composed herself. Our wandering physician had released the tension which was tearing her soul apart. At last she composed herself, dabbing at her eyes with a napkin.

'So much for auguries and portents!'

She caught her breath, her face serious. I asked if I should bring the cabbage doctor back.

'No, no.' Agrippina lifted her hand. 'I've had enough, Parmenon. The laughter has helped. I thank you.'

She asked Acerronia to fill three wine goblets with Falernian mixed with yolk of pigeon's egg to clear any impurities. She lifted the jewelled goblet and toasted me with her eyes. She sipped, staring at the floor. The oil lamps began to gutter and go out. I started to call a slave but Agrippina tapped her hand against the cedar table.

'I like the darkness,' she whispered. She lifted her head and stared at me. '"Anything born of myself and Agrippina",' she declared, '"can only be odious and a public disaster".'

'That's not true,' I replied quickly. 'It was vicious of your husband to say such a thing.'

'My first husband,' Agrippina pouted back. 'Domitius Ahenobarbus. He was born drunk, and he died a drunk. What an ignoble end for a noble family. Anyway, that's what he said when Nero was born.'

'Perhaps he'd heard about the portents?' Acerronia declared.

'It was a difficult enough birth.' Agrippina rolled the wine cup between her hands. 'It was a breech delivery. The baby took days to come, and was eventually born on the eve of Saturnalia, feet first. The midwives had a field day clacking and tutting.' She sighed. 'An Egyptian soothsayer told me that Nero would become Emperor and kill his mother.' She smiled through the tears in her eyes. 'Do you know what I replied, Parmenon? Let him kill me as long as he rules!' She laughed quietly. 'Yes, it's true, my son does come of rotten stock. Ahenobarbus means Bronze Beard: it suits Nero. What do the wits say? "Beard of bronze, face of iron, heart of lead".' She sipped from the wine.

'Soothsayers are two a penny,' I declared.

'And don't I know it!' Agrippina retorted. 'You can make signs and omens out of anything. You've heard the story, haven't you? How when Nero was a boy that bitch Messalina sent assassins to smother him.'

'Yes, yes, I've heard that,' I scoffed. 'A snake supposedly appeared and frightened them off. They thought it had been sent by the God Apollo.'

Agrippina chuckled deep in her throat.

'Was it true?' I insisted though I knew the answer. I'd only heard about this incident, whereas I was actually present the night Messalina truly did try to kill both Nero and his mother.

'Yes and no.' Agrippina laughed. 'The assassins Messalina sent were cowards. They crept into my son's room and saw the snake.' She fluffed one of the cushions. 'It was as harmless as a flea: one of those Egyptian house snakes you train to kill rats and mice.' She saw the expression on my face and burst out laughing. 'The rest of the rumour was due to me and those cowardly assassins weren't going to contradict my story. So instead of one snake, there were half a dozen, long, curling, hissing pythons sent by the Lord Apollo.' She made a rude sound with her lips and played with one of her pearl earrings.

'Do you believe in the Gods, Parmenon? Come on,' she urged. 'Do you really believe in them or are you a secret follower of the Christus and his gaggle of mad-cap Jews and slaves? The gang who believe that their crucified God came back to life three days later. Do you believe such nonsense?'

'No, I don't. I don't believe in the Gods, or the Elysian Fields, in Hades or the Underworld. How can we believe in a religion which elevates a man like Claudius to be a god. He couldn't even piss straight.' She laughed and then lifted her head as if listening carefully.

'Why is it so silent?' Acerronia murmured.

'Like the grave, eh? That's what happens after death, Pamenon, just a black nothingness, extinction!'

'Do you regret anything?' Acerronia asked, then bit her lip as if ashamed of her question.

'Regret?' Agrippina blew her cheeks out. 'I wish I could meet my father the great Germanicus. I wish he was here now. He'd teach my son a few lessons. Or even my mother. When my father took over the legions in Germany, the soldiers mutinied. They were terrified the Germans would annihilate my father and cross the Rhine. Mother went on the threatened bridge, holding me or one of her other brood in her arms, and shouted at the soldiers to do their worst. "Burn it!" my mother taunted. "Kill me! Slay Germanicus's child!".' Agrippina sipped from the goblet. 'The soldiers listened to her. I once asked Mother what she would have done if they had fired the bridge. "Oh," she replied. "I'd have jumped." There's one thing about our family.' Agrippina leaned across and plucked at a grape. 'We are good swimmers.'

Swimming, cabbages, Agrippina's story in that shadowy triclinium are still fresh memories. Domina finished her wine and went off to sleep in her new bedchamber. I stayed behind with Acerronia, thinking that perhaps she might agree to a kiss and a cuddle. She was truly drunk though and fell into a deep sleep, an untidy bundle on the couch, so I left her, and returned to my own chamber and stared out at the night.

Agrippina's story about her mother symbolised all our fears. We were at a crossroads between life and death and wanted to know what our fate would be. I wondered how long the waiting would go on. However, the next morning, Agrippina's principal spy in Rome, her boat-master Creperius, arrived. He was dirty, dishevelled, unshaven and stank like a tanner's yard. He almost fell off his horse in the courtyard. Agrippina herself helped him into the baths, shouting at the servants to bring food and wine which she insisted they taste first. Creperius, soaking in soapy water up to his neck, sat and gaspingly sipped at the wine.

'I thought you were dead!' Agrippina protested.

She sat by the edge of the bath, feet in the dirty water, glaring down at this most faithful of agents.

'Where's Sicculus?'

Creperius opened his eyes. He was a horse-faced

man with scrawny, red hair; submerged in the water, he looked even more like the nag he rode with his long, wrinkled face creased into a smile. He sipped again at the wine.

'Sicculus is dead!' Creperius stared round the room, peering through the billowing smoke.

'There's only myself and Agrippina present,' I reassured him. 'Whilst the door is locked and bolted from the inside.'

'I had at least a dozen spies in my son's household!' Agrippina exclaimed.

'Well, we're all gone now,' Creperius replied without opening his eyes. 'Do you remember Roscius the actor? He won't be treading the boards anymore; his bowels became ulcerated and corrupted his whole flesh, turning it to worms. He hired slaves to bathe him but all his clothing, hand basins, baths and food were infected with the flux of decay.' Creperius splashed the water. 'Roscius spent most of the day in a bath, but it was no use: the vermin continued to spill out of every orifice in his body.'

'Poison?' Agrippina asked.

'Of course!' Creperius laughed. 'Probably administered by one of Poppea's servants. Naturally, I became very careful about what I ate and drank.'

'And Sicculus?' I asked, recalling the small Sicilian with his mop of black hair and laughing face.

'I searched Rome for him,' Creperius retorted, 'but there was no sight of him. Rumour says Nero's agents caught him, cut off his eyelids and locked him in a chest bristling with spikes. The only reason

I know that much is because a joke is circulating that Sicculus's death was due more to insomnia than pain. After that, I decided to leave Rome. I have been hiding out for at least a week. When I thought the time was ripe, I used what silver I had, bought that horse and fled.'

'So, it's happening,' Agrippina whispered.

'Oh, yes it's all happening. Publicly, Nero calls you "the best of Mothers". Secretly he's plotting furiously. You haven't got a friend left in Rome: anyone you favour has either been bought or killed. If you returned to the city, you'd never leave it alive.'

'And who is the moving spirit behind this?' Agrippina asked. 'It can't be my son? Somebody has seized his heart and caught his ear.'

Creperius opened his eyes and smiled lazily. 'Domina, I think you mean a different part of Nero's anatomy. Poppea is now queen of the day as well as queen of the night. She is Augusta in everything but name.'

'And my son?' Agrippina was eager to change the topic of conversation.

'He loses himself in the usual revels. Disguised as a slave, he puts himself at the head of a band of roisterers, and they roam the streets after nightfall.'

'Tigellinus!' Agrippina exclaimed.

'Tigellinus is one of them. He's Master of the Revels. They waylay passersby, rob and strip them and then hurl them into sewers. They haunt shops, inns, taverns, houses of ill-repute. No woman is safe. Do you remember Senator Julius Montanus?' Creperius wiped the water from his face. 'One night Nero, in disguise, attacked his wife. Montanus defended her and gave your son a good whipping. The Emperor just ran away. Montanus later realised who he had attacked and went to the palace to apologise. The silly idiot should have kept his mouth shut. All your son said was: "You struck Nero and still dare to live?" Montanus recognised the threat and committed suicide. Your son now wanders Rome with a troop of gladiators to defend him.'

'Why?' Agrippina asked. 'Why such stupidity? Doesn't Seneca have any control over him?'

Creperius's face became tight. He pulled a towel from the edge of the bath and wiped his face.

'Domina,' he whispered hoarsely. 'Nobody knows what's coming. Nero is changing. He's becoming uncontrollable and vermin like Tigellinus urge him on.'

'Caligula!' The word was out of Domina's mouth before she could stop it.

'Yes,' Creperius agreed. 'They are whispering that Caligula has returned.'

Agrippina's fingers flew to her cheeks. She stared fearfully across the steam-filled room as if she could see Caligula, 'Little Boots', her mad, corrupt, obscene brother who believed he could make love to the moon.

'Impossible!' Agrippina shook her head and got to her feet. 'That's impossible! We'll talk tonight, Creperius. I'll hold a banquet in your honour!' And she fled the room.

Agrippina soon recovered herself, summoning the cooks and servants, issuing orders for the banquet that same evening. We did not eat in the triclinium but in a marble enclave on the east side of the villa overlooking the sea. It was a beautiful, early spring evening, with the weather growing soft and balmy. Agrippina acted as if she was still Empress of Rome. The marble walls were brought to life by a myriad of oil lamps and candles. The floor was swept, washed and covered in golden sawdust. Tables and couches were draped in silk and gold, ivory tasselled cushions were scattered about small polished tables set aside for the wine.

'Always keep the wine in full view covered by a cloth,' Agrippina warned. 'It keeps away both flies and poisoners.'

Only four of us were present. Domina, myself, Acerronia and Creperius. Agrippina's chefs did us proud. Accompanied by every sort of wine, there were mantis prawns, African snails, mussels and shellfish cooked in Chian wine, Trojan pig, gutted, roasted and stuffed with meats and different kinds of fish; even a lamprey outstretched on a platter with shrimps swimming all about it. Agrippina looked magnificent in pearl earrings and necklace, dressed in a pure white stola fringed with purple and gold with matching sandals. She lay on the couch like a young woman pretending to be Venus, waiting to be carved in stone by one of Rome's master sculptors. Wine was passed round, and toasts were made, while Creperius gave us the gossip of Rome. A young actor,

Appius, whilst showing off, had thrown a pear in the air and caught it in his mouth only to choke to death; a madman, Macheon, had climbed onto the altar in the Temple of Jupiter, uttering wild prophecies before he killed himself and the puppy he carried; the traffic in Rome was worse than ever.

'It would wake a sea calf,' Creperius murmured. 'Litters, wagons, there's no order.'

And then he said the words that I was to remember, later.

'Your son Nero is disgusted with the city. He claims there is nothing wrong with Rome that a good fire couldn't cure.'

A cold breeze wafted in, chilling the sweat and silencing the conversation. All I could hear was the distant roar of the sea, the surf pounding the rocks, and the cry of the gulls as they swept in before the sun finally set.

Agrippina had listened carefully to Creperius's chatter, allowing the servants to finish their tasks. Once they were gone, she unfastened the pearl ring from her right ear lobe. She dropped it into a small jar of vinegar and watched it dissolve.

'Cleopatra did this once,' she murmured. 'She took a pearl worth one million sesterces and watched it crumble.' She smiled. 'An offering to the Gods.'

'I thought you didn't believe in them,' I retorted. Agrippina shrugged one shoulder. 'Gods,' she whispered. 'Or just the approach of darkness? Well, Creperius, what other news from Rome?'

'Seagulls are regarded as a delicacy. Amerlius has

gone into mourning because one of his lampreys died.'

Agrippina made a cutting movement with her hand.

'The real gossip,' she demanded. 'What of my son, the Emperor?'

'He's still being advised by Seneca.'

'Our great philosopher,' Acerronia mocked.

'Burrus commands the Praetorian Guard.'

'I put him there,' Agrippina snapped.

'Otho's back from his travels.'

'Is he now?' Agrippina's lip curled. 'And does he still shave every hair of his body to make a toupee for his bald pate? Or rub his testicles against any sacred object he can find so as to make them stronger and more potent.' She laughed. 'If that succeeded I really would believe in the Gods!'

'Tigellinus is also a rising star.'

'May the Gods help us all if Tigellinus takes over.' She paused, head down, staring from under her eyelids. 'And Poppea Sabina?'

Creperius sipped at his wine. I studied him carefully. A wild thought occurred. What if he had been bought? Was he really Domina's faithful spy and servant or had Nero seduced him like he had the rest? Creperius's watery eyes shifted towards me. He must have read my thoughts, for he shook his head slightly.

'Poppea Sabina?' Agrippina demanded.

'She rules the Emperor's heart,' Creperius retorted. 'Nero's wife Octavia remains lady of the shadows.

Acte,' he sniffed at the mention of the Emperor's former mistress, 'is no more than a wisp of smoke. Poppea walks Rome as if she were a goddess. She covers her face with a veil: her constant prayer is that she dies before the pure whiteness of her skin is tinged with age.'

'I'd be happy to arrange that,' Agrippina murmured.

'She bathes every day in the milk of asses. The Emperor has arranged for four hundred of these beasts to be kept stabled for her use. Her porphyry bath is filled with the stuff. She spends hours examining her body in long mirrors of polished silver. Crocodile mucus is bought for her hands and her body is dried with swansdown, her tongue stroked with black ivy sticks to make it soft and velvety. She has masseurs from Africa, perfumers from Cyprus, the best dressmakers from Alexandria. She uses saffron powder to make her hair turn amber and has launched a new perfume, her own recipe, ambergris.' Creperius gestured towards the jug of vinegar. 'Only the finest pearls from the Red Sea will do for Poppea. Her shoes are of pure white kid, and their soles are gold-leafed. When Poppea walks, her feet tap like a dancer coming onto the stage. They say she practises every movement of her eyes, her mouth, her face, her hands. She knows all there is of love-making.'

'And, of course, Nero is entranced?' Acerronia spoke up.

'He's infatuated. Poppea is now divorced from Otho but still plays the reluctant maid.'

Creperius picked up a piece of shellfish. Agrippina seemed fascinated by a point beyond his head.

'They are coming for me, aren't they?' Domina whispered.

I half rose from the couch. Agrippina's face had a stricken look. Her gaze had shifted to a shadowy corner as if she could see things we couldn't.

'Who's coming, Domina?' I murmured.

'They are all there,' she replied. 'Dark-blue rings round their eyes, mouths gaping . . .'

'Domina!' I said harshly.

She broke from the reverie. 'So what, Creperius, is our little milkmaid saying to my son?'

'Domina, this is only gossip.'

'What is she saying?' Agrippina's voice rose to a shout.

'Poppea demands if Nero is really Emperor of Rome. "The true ruler is your mother," she rants. "All the important decisions are still hers".' And then Creperius repeated Poppea's most bitter jibe, '"They call you Empress Nero and your mother Agrippina Emperor of Rome".'

I looked at my mistress. She sipped at the Falernian, rolling it round her tongue as she did when she was deeply engrossed. This was a fight to the death: Poppea was a deadly adversary.

'Poppea,' Creperius continued, 'is supposed to have given your son a gift wrapped in silk. When Nero undid the bundle all it contained was a golden coin displaying your head. "Why is this?" Poppea hissed.'

'And?' Agrippina broke in.

'To give your son his due, Nero was confused. "I am an artist", he replied. "That's all I care about". Poppea knelt at his feet. "And your mother?" the little hussy persisted, "saves you the trouble of being Emperor. She is always reminding the people, not that she's Nero's mother, but Germanicus's daughter: that's more important than your poetry.'

'Who told you this?' I asked, fearful of the effect this conversation might have on Agrippina's raw nerves.

'It's chatter,' Creperius replied defensively, 'but the proof of the dish is in the eating. If I am wrong, why doesn't Nero come here? Why doesn't he invite Domina back to Rome?'

Agrippina slammed her goblet back on the table.

'Parmenon.' She pulled herself up from the couch and stared across at me. 'How do you think it will come?'

'What?' I asked innocently.

'My death.'

The supper room fell quiet. Even the sea seemed to hear her words, the roar of its waves now hushed.

'He won't go that far,' Acerronia intervened. 'He would be accused of matricide! To kill the daughter of Germanicus!'

'No, he wouldn't do it,' I replied, 'but others might do it for him.'

'How?' Agrippina's voice grew strident. 'Advise me, Parmenon, how?'

'Not by poison: they'd have to get too close, and

they know that you take every known antidote. Besides, the finger of suspicion would be pointed firmly at him.'

'The dagger?' Agrippina asked.

'Too blunt and bloody,' I retorted. 'Again the trail will lead back to him. No, Domina, I think we've had our warning. An accident. Something which can be explained away like a collapsing roof.'

Agrippina laughed abruptly.

Creperius spoke up. 'Or perhaps the August Nero will allow his honourable mother to live in peaceful retirement?'

'Nero will,' Agrippina offered. 'But Poppea won't. My father always advised, "Know your enemy!" If I were Poppea, I would be plotting my rival's death. She's no different.' Agrippina looked at me archly. 'She's the gladiator I have to kill.'

'We could strike first,' I continued. 'Kill Poppea. Poison her asses milk. Put some filthy potion into the powder with which she adorns her face and hands.'

Agrippina shook her head.

'No, she'll be waiting. The others would seize the opportunity to accuse me.' She beat on the table top with her fingernails. 'What will happen?'

'Exile?' Acerronia spoke up. 'Perhaps the Emperor will exile you to some distant island or the wilds of Britannia?'

'We could flee,' I urged. 'Go north to Germany, and seek the protection of one of the legates?'

Agrippina wasn't listening.

'Bring Salvara,' she murmured. 'Hurry!' She snapped her fingers. 'I want her now!'

Salvara was a witch, a local wise woman who lived in a hut amongst the pine-clad hills behind the villa. I left and sent servants to fetch her. I was surprised when they returned immediately with the old woman between them. She was a bony bundle, dressed in rags stinking of the unguents and potions she distilled. Youthful clear grey eyes full of mockery gazed out of Salvara's lined face.

'I was already on my way,' she announced, her tone cultured and refined. I recalled rumours that, many years ago, she'd played the great lady in Pompeii.

'How did you know?' I asked.

'I'd like to say I'd divined it but the news is all over the countryside that the Augusta has received a messenger from Rome, and a festive banquet has been held.' She cocked her head slightly. 'Yet I can hear no music or singing.'

'It's not that type of banquet,' I replied. 'The Augusta waits.'

I took her down the colonnaded portico. Agrippina had been drinking more quickly, her face was slightly flushed, her eyes enlarged and glittering. Salvara bowed and squatted before the table.

'I knew you would need me.'

She undid her small leather sack, laid out the bones on the floor and, opening a small stoppered phial, sprinkled these with blood. Without asking permission, she took Agrippina's goblet and sipped from it before mixing the wine with the blood.

Salvara stirred the bones, praying quietly to herself. I have never believed in the black arts, although I have seen many tricks that would take your breath away. Some of the best mountebanks in the empire have performed their games before me. Agrippina was as sceptical as I, but Salvara, like Joah the Jew, was different: there were none of the tricks, the theatrical gestures and the high drama of the professional charlatans. Only an old woman crouched before Domina, staring down at the bones, crooning softly to herself. The song was like a lullaby a mother sings to a fretful child. My eyes grew heavy. I shook myself and looked around. Creperius and Acerronia lolled on their couches as if they'd drunk deeply. Agrippina only had eyes for the witch. The chamber grew very warm, and a wind blew in, dry and sharp like that from the desert.

'What do you see, Mother?' Domina asked. 'Has the veil lifted?'

'What do you want me to see?' came the sly reply.

'My fate.'

'Death!' came the answer.

'We are all to die, Salvara, but how, why, when?'

'When, I cannot say.'

Some of the oil lamps guttered out. The darkness around Salvara grew more intense.

'Will I be reconciled to my son?'

'Before you die you shall be reconciled,' came the tired, slow reply.

Salvara had her eyes closed, rocking herself backwards and forwards, her fingers pressed to the floor.

'And whom should I fear?'

'The master of the sea.'

'The master of the sea? Will I drown?'

'You shall not drown, Domina, but be wary of the master of the sea!'

'Neptune?' I called out.

Salvara wasn't listening. 'You shall be reconciled, Domina, and receive your son's sweet embrace and loving kiss. But, remember my words, be careful of the master of the sea!'

The old woman's head drooped. The warmth dissipated. Agrippina, her eyes brimming with tears of joy, toasted me silently with her cup.

Chapter 3

'No one ever becomes depraved overnight'
Juvenal, *Satires* II. 83

Agrippina was a changed woman. Salvara had said that she would be reconciled with Nero, so she thought it was only a matter of waiting. Once again the villa became a place of light, and musicians and dancers were hired. Agrippina spent more time out in the garden, tending flower beds, gossiping with Acerronia. It was all sun, no shadow. I tried to advise her to act prudently. She may have heard, but she certainly didn't listen. She spent more time on her appearance, hiring hairdressers, buying perfumes and pastes. She even went out to apologise to the chickens and made us all laugh with the little mime she concocted. I hadn't the heart to remind her that

41

she was still in the arena and the game had yet to begin. Would Poppea give up? I knew Nero for what he was: a spoilt, depraved actor who could play any part the mood suited him. I was troubled by the phrase 'master of the sea'. What had Salvara meant by that?

Not being superstitious, I decided it was only a matter of logic. Since no one would dare draw a dagger, or so I thought, against the daughter of Germanicus, and poison was ruled out, Agrippina's death would have to appear an accident. I took matters into my own hands. I patrolled the garden at night, checked doors, paid out money for information to the pedlars and tinkers who wandered the roads.

Antium became busier as the weather improved and the people left the city to take the sea breezes. Our next visitor was that doddering old fool, the banker Quintus Veronius with his balding head, perpetually dripping nose and eyes which looked as if he never stopped crying. He'd made a fortune in the Egyptian corn trade and spent most of his wealth raising peacocks. He'd once made the mistake of inviting Caligula to dinner. Our madcap Emperor arrived and spent most of the evening shooting at the birds from a balcony. The peacocks died and Veronius had a nervous breakdown. He'd retired to Campania and spent his life in mourning until Caligula's murder. Veronius was a fool, who could be used by anyone. He arrived at the villa in his cumbersome litter as if it was a chance visit, but of course, he'd been sent deliberately. The news he brought only delighted Agrippina further.

'Oh yes, oh yes.' Veronius slobbered over his wine. 'The Emperor, Augusta, is full of your praises. He's banished two actors from Rome for their lying attacks on your Majesty.'

'And Poppea?' I asked wearily.

'She's seen less and less. There is news,' Veronius continued, 'that Nero is to visit Baiae.'

Every wrinkle disappeared from Agrippina's face, which became as smooth and creamy as that of a young girl.

'He'll visit me,' she murmured, 'or he'll invite me to his villa. You wait and see.'

Veronius continued his journey and Agrippina's preparations became more frenetic. At last it happened. A bireme arrived on the coast. Officers of the Praetorian Guard marched up the shingle, along the white, dusty trackway and presented themselves at the main door of the villa. They delivered their invitation. The Divine Augustus, Nero, Emperor of Rome, intended to celebrate the feast of Minerva in his imperial villa at Baiae, and he wished Agrippina, 'the best of mothers', to be his honoured guest. If I hadn't stopped her, Agrippina would have kissed them to death. Both officers stayed with us overnight, saying that the bireme would take Agrippina and her household across the bay the next day.

The villa was transformed: servants scurried about; chests and coffers were packed and taken down to the beach. Agrippina emptied her wardrobe, fiercely debating with Acerronia which shoes she should wear, which dress would best suit the occasion.

I travelled lightly, taking just my tunic, sandals, sword, writing implements and a small casket which carried antidotes to the best-known poisons. I also sought the company of the two Praetorians. Former centurions from the German legions, they were only too pleased to be away from the court and to sample the best wine from Agrippina's cellars whilst sunning themselves in the garden. I introduced myself and let it be known that my father had been an officer in the Second Augusta. For a while we chatted. They were honest men, more interested in fighting, women and wine than in court scandal. Nevertheless, I picked up something: they found it hard to look me in the eye, and if I mentioned Poppea they became tight-lipped. When I reminded them that Agrippina was the daughter of the great Germanicus, they looked away, as if more interested in the flowers and herb plots. I had learnt enough. These men were not party to any plot but they had ears, quick wit and could sense the undercurrents of the court. I returned to the villa and urged Domina to be careful. Agrippina, however, was at her most stately.

'Parmenon, you are like an old fishwife!' she snapped. 'The Emperor has come to Baiae. My son has returned.'

'It could mean your death!' I hissed.

Agrippina strode across, shut the door and returned with her eyes blazing. She stood only a few inches away from me. I could smell the herbs she used to sweeten her breath and noticed how the wine had purpled the corner of her lips.

'I don't care, Parmenon. If I die in his arms that's enough for me. Do you understand?'

It was what I had always suspected. Agrippina loved Rome and power, the adulation of the legions, the right to appoint and dismiss, to grant life or death. Nero, however, she loved above all.

We left late that afternoon. Our slaves carried our baggage down to the beach where the marines were camped. We were taken out to the boat and, sails unfurled, the bireme turned, canvas snapping, oars splashing, to make its way across to the waiting glory of Baiae.

Agrippina lounged on a couch in the stern, flanked by Acerronia and Creperius. The sea was calm, just that gentle, undulating movement which always curdled my stomach. I ignored my seasickness and stared at the mist curling across the water. I was aware of the snapping sail, the creak of the rudder, the oarsmen ready to bend and pull, the cries of the pilot, the sharp orders of the captain. Could this be an ambush, I wondered? A trap? Yet the Praetorians seemed relaxed enough. They were dressed in half-armour and wouldn't relish an accident at sea. The mist lifted, the afternoon sun grew stronger. Baiae came into sight, that den of sin, the playground of the rich and powerful. Green-topped hills overlooked white shingle and dark-green pines, the sun flashed on gleaming marble. Orders were rapped out.

Agrippina prepared herself, trying to remain calm as, shielding her eyes, she studied the beach.

'There's a procession!' she exclaimed. 'Look, my son's coming to meet me!'

I followed the direction of her eyes and saw the flash of standards, the sheen of gold. I glimpsed soldiers, slaves in white tunics, silk-caparisoned litters, following a group of men walking down onto the beach. Agrippina was as excited as a girl waiting to greet her parents. As the bireme was expertly beached, a guard of honour ran up, a troop of Praetorians who helped Agrippina ashore.

'Mother!' Nero came running down the beach, arms extended.

Agrippina hastened to meet him. They met in the most tender of embraces. He kissed her on the cheek, neck and breast before kneeling to hold her hand to his cheek. I studied the Emperor closely. He had got fatter, his reddish hair had been allowed to grow and was carefully coiffed and curled along the brow and nape of his neck. The barber had dusted it with gold. His cheeks and jowls were heavy, his neck thicker. He glanced past Agrippina. His perpetual frown, due to his short-sightedness, cleared and his popping blue eyes crinkled in a smile. I noticed his red-flecked beard and moustache and that he was dressed in the pale-green tunic of a lyrist. He got up, his pronounced paunch making his legs look even more spindly. He tightened the white silk handkerchief round his throat.

'To protect my voice,' he explained.

Nero wore no other ornamentation except an exquisite emerald monocle which hung from a gold chain round his neck. Nero had seen me clearly enough but he elegantly held up the monocle and peered.

'Welcome, Parmenon.' As he spoke, his voice squeaked and he looked alarmed and tapped his chest carefully.

He grasped his mother's hand and walked over to me, studying me in that affected manner.

'Your Emperor welcomes you.'

His hand snaked out. I fell on my knees and he patted me on the head affectionately, as if I was a spaniel, before adding insult to injury by brushing past me to greet Acerronia and Creperius.

'Oh, you can get up now, Parmenon,' he called over his shoulder.

I got to my feet, embarrassed by the mocking laughter from the small group which had accompanied Nero. They were all there. Seneca, the self-proclaimed great philosopher, grasping the folds of his toga as if he was to deliver a panegyric from the rostrum – Seneca of the balding head with the thick heavy features of a wrestler. He did not join in the laughter but raised his hand in salutation. Beside him was Burrus, dressed in elegant half-armour, his severe face impassive under close-cropped hair, and a look of distaste on his thin lips. He was a born soldier and ever ready to act the part. Tigellinus, dark as a Nubian, thin-featured, his eyes bright with malice, and that constant smirk on his ugly lips. A figure came from

47

behind him: Anicetus, small, sallow-faced, dressed in a purple gold-lined toga, his arms hanging down like those of a monkey; the deep lines on each side of his mouth only increased the likeness. He'd led the laughter. My heart froze. I had forgotten about Anicetus: as Admiral of the fleet based at Misenum, he was one of Nero's 'masters of the sea'. He was the Emperor's former tutor and he hated Agrippina with all the passion of his evil soul. For a short while I caught all their enmity, malice and hostility. From the likes of Anicetus, it came hot and bubbling; from Seneca and Burrus, it was cold and businesslike.

Behind me Nero was calling Agrippina the 'best of mothers' and profusely thanking the Praetorians and the captain of the bireme. It was all pretence! The blue sky, the dark line of greenery, the white shingled beach, the laughter and the greetings were a sham. We'd entered a trap. This was a death chamber: Agrippina would be lucky if she left with her life. Nero, however, was cavorting about. A tray of cups were distributed and toasts exchanged. Nero led his mother off, his arm round her waist, his head resting on her shoulder. They made their way from the beach up to the waiting litters, where the silk folds were pulled aside. Nero solicitously helped his mother up and climbed in with her. The Praetorian Guards, resplendent in their armour, circled it in a ring of steel. Tigellinus cracked a joke, and Anicetus bawled with laughter. Catching the word 'litter', I knew that they were resurrecting the old scandal that Agrippina had tried to seduce her own son whilst riding in a litter through Rome. The procession moved off, along the tree-lined trackway towards the imperial villa. Acerronia and Creperius took advantage of a second litter, but I decided to walk. Seneca and the others put as much distance between themselves and me as possible, but Burrus hung back. I decided not to waste time on niceties.

'How dangerous is it?' I asked. 'Has the Augusta anything to fear from you?'

Burrus grabbed my wrist and squeezed it tightly. 'Remember this, Parmenon,' he whispered back, his dark brown eyes unblinking. 'No soldier of mine will lift a sword against the daughter of Germanicus.'

'But others might!'

'I can only answer for Burrus,' the Praetorian Prefect replied, 'not the rest of the world.' He released my wrist and walked quickly to join the rest.

We reached the tree-line and entered the broad avenue which cut through to the imperial villa. It was the first time I had been there since Nero had spent a lavish fortune turning it into a palace of the Gods. There were marble columns, glittering pavilions, gleaming white stone statues, gardens filled with every possible variety of shrub and tree. Torches and lamps were carefully placed to fend off the darkness. Everywhere, because of the feast, stood statues of Minerva in copper and bronze, garlanded with leaves and fresh flowers.

Agrippina and her household were given their own pavilion in the imperial grounds. If show was anything to go by, Nero did regard her as the 'best of mothers'. No expense had been spared, no honour ignored. Even Agrippina was impressed by the sumptuous luxury of her reception and the quarters provided. The walls and floors of the pavilion were adorned with mosaics or lined with rare marble and mother-of-pearl. Exquisite diamonds, specially imported from the mountains of Asia Minor, had been lavishly used to decorate her private apartment. Agrippina's bed was of scented wood, inlaid with gold and covered with the richest oriental tapestries, embroidered with pearls from Palestine in Arabesque designs. The walls of this luxurious bedchamber were lined with panelling, containing revolving tablets of ivory. These were set on pivots and could be turned to display different pictures. In the ceiling, a hidden machine could, at a touch, spray perfumes, whilst through the room ran a special conduit full of fragrant water. Agrippina was ecstatic. She really believed such opulence was an eloquent testimony to Nero's love for her. The Emperor himself escorted her into the pavilion and showed her its glory before making his farewell, adding that we would all meet at a specially prepared banquet that evening.

'You see!' Agrippina exclaimed, once the imperial party had left. 'Don't you see, Parmenon, this is a fresh beginning.'

'We are to return to Rome?'

'We are to return to Rome.' She smiled and, clapping her hands, shouted to the servants and slaves to make her quarters ready.

I supervised the baggage being brought in. I had

a quiet word with Acerronia and Creperius. Everything was to be checked – the wine, the perfume, the sheets, the coverlets – for any trace of poison. I went outside. Dusk had fallen but the garden lights shed a golden glow, and I glimpsed armour: Burrus had apparently ringed Domina's pavilion with a suitable guard. I trusted the Prefect but what of Nero?

Agrippina spent the rest of the day preparing herself. She bathed in the marble tub, Acerronia rubbing precious cream and perfume into her skin. She piled her hair up, holding it in place with jewelled pins and small ivory combs. She dressed in a white stola fringed with purple and gold, a lapis lazuli gorget round her throat, gold bangles on her wrists and ankles. She looked beautiful and spun on her heel, hands extended.

'Look, Parmenon!' she cried. 'How can any son resist a mother like this?'

I could have wept at the sheer pathos. Agrippina looked as brilliant as some rare jewel. Yet here was the great Domina, Agrippina, daughter of Germanicus, mother of the Emperor of Rome, having to act like a courtesan to obtain what was naturally hers, Nero's affections.

The Emperor, of course, played his part well and responded in kind. We dined in a special pavilion of silken cloth, the air sweet with roses and honeysuckle. The tables were arranged in a horse-shoe fashion with couches, covered in gold and silver cloth, ranged along the side. Torches, candelabra and scented oil lamps lit the darkness and, as Nero proclaimed, created an artificial day in Agrippina's honour. He escorted her to the place of glory. I was left at the foot of the table. I was glad to be there, so that I had a good view of the rest. If Agrippina had decided to gather all her enemies together in one place, she couldn't have done better. Seneca, Tigellinus, Burrus, Anicetus and, of course, smooth-skinned Otho smirking behind his hand. Only the golden Poppea was absent.

Musicians in the background provided music. Jugs of wine were circulated once again, and toasts were made. I saw Nero wink down the table at Anicetus and my blood ran cold. This feast may begin with laughter but it would end in tears, even death. I tried to appear distracted, as if more concerned with the nearby aviaries carved in the fashion of a temple, full of rare singing-birds, or the marble basins full of live fish which the guests could pick out for cooking. Servants and slaves of both sexes, the most beautiful Rome could supply, solicitously tended to every want. I tried to catch Agrippina's eye but it was futile. She was only interested in Nero. As far as she was concerned, everything else was like the air we breathe, hardly to be noticed.

At last the banquet itself began. Fish, poultry and game were brought in, followed by a roast pig stuffed with live quails which flew away when the chef slit its belly. A troop of cooks entered, preceded by a line of musicians playing flutes. The chef carried a whole boar on a huge silver salver. When this too was cut, it was seen to be stuffed with pheasants, inside which were quails, which in turn were filled with ortolans. After each course the attendants returned, allowing us to wash our hands and face in perfumed water.

We then solemnly processed to a second pavilion where the tables were even more sumptuously laid out. From the poles hung golden lamps in which burned scented oils. We were crowned with roses and, behind each guest, a slave wafted perfumed feather fans. Sherberts were served, mixed with snow and tinged with the lightest of white wines. Dancers from Antioch entered and performed a sensuous ballet to the lilting tunes of zithers and flutes. The evening became more raucous. Guests got to their feet, staggered outside to be sick and returned to gorge themselves even more. Others helped themselves to the dancers or slave girls. In the corner of the pavilion Otho made noisy love to one of the slave girls whilst another looked on and encouraged the coupling pair. Creperius and Acerronia sat opposite me, both of them deep in their cups. I wondered if their wine had been laced with some potion or powder. I ate and drank nothing. All I was aware of were flushed, sweaty faces, glittering eyes, raucous music and the shouts and cries of the revellers. Like all the guests, I had been searched to ensure I carried no arms but I'd managed to seize a carving knife and place it under my couch. All the time I watched Nero and his mother. Sometimes they kissed, rubbed noses, held each other's hands. On one occasion Nero shared her couch and laid his head on her breast. I could tell he was playing a part for the onlookers. Now and again Nero would flash a sly smirk at one of his cronies. They, in turn, tried to draw me into conversation, wishing to share a joke or tidbits of gossip from Rome.

Anicetus came and sat on the edge of my couch, cradling his wine cup, his little monkey face wreathed in a shifty grin.

'You are solemn, Parmenon,' he slurred.

'I'm worried, Anicetus.' I pulled myself further up. 'Do I need to be worried?'

'Worried?' Anicetus mocked. 'Parmenon, why should you worry? Here is food, wine, music and, above all, the company of your Emperor!'

I smiled at the trap.

'The Emperor is always in my thoughts,' I retorted. 'He is the beginning, end and substance of my being. I am, as you know, the Emperor's most loyal servant. Do we have anything to fear, Anicetus?'

He rose, tapped me patronisingly on the shoulder and walked away.

A slave girl came up and crouched beside me. She was a mere child really and I could tell from her olive skin and sloe eyes that she was Egyptian. She offered to share my couch, but when I shook my head, she pouted and walked away. My eyes were only for Nero and his mother. The night seemed to drag on for an eternity. At last the wine had its effect: one by one the guests succumbed, sprawled on couches or on the floor. Nero was no different. Agrippina eventually looked in my direction. Just for a moment her mask slipped. Perhaps she'd realised her son's extravagant praises were as false as they were empty. She smiled, gently extricated herself from her son's drunken embrace and got to her feet. I accompanied her out into the perfumed darkness.

'Was there ever such a feast, Parmenon?' she called out over her shoulder. 'Was there ever such a son?'

'Domina!' I urged, coming up behind her. 'Domina!' I hissed, seizing her wrist.

She dragged it away and lifted her hands, fingers splayed. In the light of the torches her eyes had a hard look. She brought her other hand up as if in prayer.

'Please don't, Parmenon! Don't spoil it for me. If I am to go into the dark, let me go happy.' She touched the side of her head. 'Let me take my dreams with me.'

And, spinning on her heel, she walked into the night. I trailed behind to make sure but she reached her pavilion safely. The waiting slaves, holding torches, escorted her in. I noticed the guards sheltering under the trees and recalled Burrus's words, 'No soldier of mine would draw their sword against the daughter of Germanicus.' I was about to walk away when I heard a rustling in the bushes and paused.

'Don't look round!' a voice whispered hoarsely. 'Just listen!'

'What is it?' I asked.

'Don't talk, just listen!' The voice paused. '"Oak and triple bronze",' it whispered, '"must have encircled the heart of the man who first committed a frail boat to the cruel sea".'

I recognised the quotation from one of Horace's odes.

'Is that all?' I called back.

'"Brute force, without judgement, collapses under its own weight".'

Another quotation! There was a faint rustling and the mysterious messenger had left. I stood, my hand going to my mouth. That bitch Salvara! She was obviously in Nero's pay, and had only to wait for Agrippina to send for her. She'd done exactly what that copper-headed monster had told her to. Without her words, Agrippina would never have come to Baiae. Salvara had blinded my mistress, given her false hope, baited the trap and Agrippina had walked straight into it. The two quotations were a warning: put together, it became clear something dreadful was to happen at sea. Even Salvara's reference to a 'master of the sea' agreed with this. An accident, in fact murder, was planned. Once it was over, Salvara's warnings would be used to demonstrate that Agrippina's tragic death was fated. Years later, I caught up with the old bitch and cut her throat.

I spent that night tossing and turning. Once it was daylight, I went for a walk in the mist-strewn gardens. The musicians had long retired whilst the slaves and servants were helping themselves to the remains of the feast. Of the revellers there was no sign, but a chamberlain assured me that they had all been carried to their beds. I went across to Agrippina's villa: she, too, was sleeping.

The rest of that day was what I'd call a ghost day.

The sun didn't show itself till the afternoon. Matters were not helped by an eerie atmosphere in the imperial villa. Nero didn't appear until, white-faced and red-eyed, he paid a courtesy visit to Agrippina. They cooed and laughed together until he left, saying the bireme would be ready later that day to return my mistress to her villa at Antium.

'From there,' Agrippina excitedly explained, 'I travel to Rome. Apartments have been prepared for me in the Palatine Palace. We've had enough of the countryside, eh, Parmenon?'

She gave me a warning look. I nodded and made preparations to leave.

Darkness had fallen by the time we congregated on the beach. Two lines of Praetorians held torches to light the way along the shingle. It was a lovely, cloudless night, with the moon riding high and a stiff sea breeze proving a welcome relief after the perfumed air of the villa. I had not attended the small leaving banquet, which Nero had stated was a private affair. He escorted his mother down to the boat, holding her affectionately by the hand. The rest of the coterie gathered around as Nero embraced his mother, kissing her lips and bosom.

'These breasts,' he murmured, 'once suckled me.'

Members of the court also made their farewells. They all ignored me except Burrus who clasped my hand and wished me health. I was about to pull away when he dragged me closer.

'"With you",' he whispered, '"I would willingly live! With you I would willingly die!"'

I couldn't make out his face in the darkness yet I recognised this further quotation from Horace. Danger was all about us.

'*Iacta alea est!*' I replied. 'The die is cast!'

I joined Agrippina and the rest as we were taken out to the waiting bireme. I clambered aboard and stared around. The ship seemed seaworthy enough but no Praetorians were present and the captain and the pilot were not dressed in their usual uniform but in simple tunics and sandals. I glanced back towards the beach, where a ring of torches surrounded the would-be murderers. Even before it happened, I knew where the danger would come from. Agrippina stood in the prow, eyes fixed on the shore. Nero called out something. The breeze caught his words but it didn't conceal the mocking laughter. Agrippina blew kisses and walked away to take her place on a couch under an awning in the stern.

Orders were rapped out, and the ship glided silently round. The slop of oars sliced the water rhythmically, each stroke measured by the captain marking the time. A breeze wafted across to us the smell of pines and perfume. The bireme picked up speed, cutting through the water. As the torchlight on the beach disappeared, a strange silence descended. Agrippina lay on the couch under the awning, with Acerronia kneeling on one side, and Creperius on the other. I walked along the ship, my eyes searching every corner. I could see nothing wrong. Had it been built to capsize? But that would endanger the lives of the crew as well. Were they in the plot?

'Parmenon!' Agrippina called. 'Stop stalking like a cat, you are making me nervous.'

I ignored her. She called again, as I climbed the steps to where the captain and pilot stood. I tried to engage them in conversation, but they busied themselves about their duties. I walked to the rail and stared at the approaching bank of mist.

'Why did no Praetorians accompany us?' I asked. 'A guard of honour?'

'I don't know. I was just given my orders,' the captain grumbled.

I left the platform and went down the steps. Agrippina and Acerronia were discussing the events of the night before. Now and again Domina would break off to give instructions to Creperius over what to pack when they left for Rome. She was annoyed with me. I still felt tense at the sense of pressing danger. I looked up, to see that the captain had moved to the rail, and was staring out into the night. He carried a lantern lashed to a pole. Was he signalling?

'Domina!' I hissed.

'Parmenon, either be sick, go to sleep, or sit down!'

The sea breeze shifted. I heard a slight creak, and the sound of oars. The captain on the bridge was waving the lantern. I raced up the steps and ran to the rail, staring out into the night. As the mist parted, I gasped in terror. A huge warship, a massive trireme, oars out, its prow carved in the shape of the cruel face of an eagle, was bearing down, intent on ramming the bireme.

'Agrippina!' I screamed.

Commotion broke out below, where some of the rowers had now glimpsed the monster which was about to smash us. I heard a sound behind and turned, drawing my dagger. Without hesitation, I thrust it straight into the pilot's stomach. The half-raised club dropped from his hand as he slumped, choking on his blood. The captain lunged, flinging the lantern at me. I ducked to one side and lashed out with the dagger, cutting a deep jagged slash across his chest. I ran down the steps, but it was too late: the trireme struck us with a mighty crash. The awning covering Agrippina collapsed, and one of the poles dealt Creperius an ugly blow on the side of his head. I could do little for him. I pulled the awning up and dragged Agrippina from her couch. Acerronia was screaming, and I slapped her on the face, pulling her to the side. Figures loomed out of the darkness. The trireme was now pushing the bireme, threatening to either tip it over or crush it beneath its weight. The night air was rent with screams. I ripped Agrippina's stola from her shoulders, pushed to the side of the bireme, already dangerously low in the water, and tipped her over. Acerronia and I joined her in the cold water.

'Swim!' I screamed.

Agrippina needed no second bidding. Light and swift as a dolphin, she struck out, putting as much distance between herself and the sinking bireme as possible. I followed, but Acerronia, behind me, was spluttering and calling out. Agrippina was a splendid swimmer, but Acerronia was not. I glanced back, saw lantern lights and heard the calls of officers on the trireme. Treading water, I saw Acerronia panic. She swam back towards the trireme, straight into the pool of light thrown by the torches and lanterns.

'Help me!' she screamed. 'Help! I am the Empress!'

An oar moved towards her: the usual tactic employed to drag a man from the sea. Acerronia swam towards it. The oar moved viciously like a club and, instead of allowing Acerronia to grasp it, struck her viciously on the side of the head. Acerronia spun round. For a few seconds I glimpsed her white face above the water before she sank. Agrippina was calling out to me. I swam in the direction of her voice.

'An accident?' she spluttered.

'Murder,' I replied.

I seized her by the arm, allowing the waves to float us away from the trireme. I stared out, but the bank of mist had now thickened. I caught glimpses of distant lights and recalled that the pearl fishermen often came out here at night. I struck out in their direction, Agrippina following. The fishermen already knew something was wrong. As one of their craft, a torch in its prow, came thrusting through the water towards us, we called out. Voices replied. I grasped an oar, making sure Agrippina did likewise and strong burly hands plucked us from the sea.

The oyster men had no idea whom they had picked up, until Agrippina stretched out her hand, displaying the imperial ring. She was nursing a wounded shoulder and a cut to her cheek, but the physical wounds were nothing to those inflicted on her soul. She sat in the boat, a haggard, ageing woman, dripping with sea water, staring sightlessly into the darkness. I bribed the fishermen with some of the coins I still had in a purse stitched to my belt to cross the bay into the Lucrine Lake. They happily agreed, navigating its narrow channel and crossing a sand bar which protected us against pursuit. We landed safely, and, half-carrying Agrippina, I staggered along the beach and up the trackway to her own villa. I aroused the servants, who took one look at Agrippina and knew what had happened. Even as I shouted orders, most of them backed away, owl-eyed, pale-faced, and within the hour most of them had fled. I placed Agrippina in the triclinium and brought metal dishes full of burning charcoal, towels, napkins and heavy military cloaks from the stores. I made her strip off, then dried and changed her before wrapping a blanket round her. I warmed some wine and forced her to drink. The villa fell quiet except for the occasional patter of feet, and the howling of a dog. Agrippina sipped at the wine before being violently sick. I moved her to another part of the room, where we sat on stools.

'You are still wet,' she murmured. 'Dry yourself off.'

I stripped, changed, wrapped one of the blankets round me and rejoined her. Agrippina had now grown more composed. She stared out through the window at the starlit sky.

'We are creatures of the night, Parmenon,' she whispered. 'It's finished, isn't it?'

'It's always been finished,' I replied. 'Ever since Poppea walked into Nero's court.'

She sighed. 'They'll have to complete the job, Parmenon. They won't let it rest. The slaves and servants have fled. Poor Acerronia.' A tear trickled down her kohl-smeared cheek. 'And Creperius, gone with the rest.' She nudged me. 'You should flee too. They'll kill you. They won't allow any witnesses to survive.'

'I'll stay. My life, Domina, is yours.'

She turned, her eyes wrinkled up in a smile, that dazzlingly beautiful woman I'd met so many years earlier.

'You are good, Parmenon.'

She kissed me lightly on the lips and brushed my face with the tip of her finger.

'If I had listened to you . . .'

'You can still do that,' I urged. 'You could flee, seek refuge with the legions.' My voice faltered.

She pressed a finger against my lips.

'You and I both know that's not possible. Every road and trackway will be watched and sealed.' She put down her wine and stretched her hands towards the charcoal brazier. 'Isn't it strange, Parmenon? We first met on the feast of Minerva, at the games in the amphitheatre near the Campus Marius.'

I cradled my own cup. My mind going back . . .

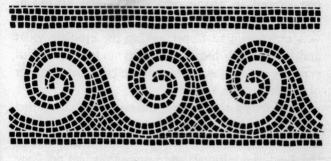

Chapter 4

'Woe is me: I think I'm becoming a God'
Suetonius, '*Lives of the Caesars*': *Vespasian*

'*Sic Habet! Sic Habet!* Let him have it! Let him have it!'

The crowd thundered in one great roar, people on their feet leaning forward, thumbs pointing to the ground: the populace of Rome shrieking for a man's life. I watched the arena, where Sullienus, in Thracian armour, had brought down Callaxtus the net man. The latter hadn't fought very well; he had been clumsy and frightened, although admittedly, I myself was not the most stalwart of warriors. Although it was early spring the amphitheatre was hot and close. The stench of cooking sausages, oil, human sweat and blood seeped everywhere.

Sullienus turned, sword raised towards the imperial box draped in purple and gold. I was sitting at the back. The Emperor was not present: Tiberius was ensconced to Capri, taking his cronies, vices and power with him. Rome was under the careful scrutiny of Sejanus, Prefect of the city, Commander of the Praetorian Guard.

As Caesar's right hand, Sejanus also controlled the secret police, which is where I come in. My father had died, his remains buried somewhere in the Teuterborg forest, and my mother had not long survived his death, wasting away to skin and bones. Before she died, though, she had hired a scribe and dictated a letter on my behalf to her distant kinsman Sejanus. He hadn't bothered to meet me himself, but had delegated the task to one of his minions. I had expected a posting in the army, as I had done some military service or, in view of my education, a benefice in the courts or treasury. Instead Sejanus's minion (I forget his name but remember his face), sat on the corner of a table and scrutinised me carefully.

'You don't look Roman.' He got up and walked round, examining every inch of my close-cropped head. 'Swarthy, aren't you? Are you sure you're Roman? I'd wager you were Numidian or Mauretanian?'

'I'm Roman. My mother's family are of Spanish blood.'

'Ah,' the Minion replied. 'I see you can read and write, have done service with the auxilaries and that your father was killed in Germany?'

'He was a centurion,' I replied. 'In the Second Augusta until he was swept up in Varus—'

'Shush!' The Minion tapped me on the shoulder. 'The first lesson of the imperial court is that you never mention Quintilius Varus, his legions, or his defeat.'

He walked away as if still shocked by my utterance. I sat and stared. The Minion was correct. No one wanted to know about Varus, and how he had led his legions into snow-bound forests only to be ambushed. They say the massacre took almost a week as the Germans broke the legions and hunted them down amongst the dark, demon-infested trees. When Germanicus invaded, to reclaim Rome's honour and its lost eagles, he found the remains of Varus's armies strewn over miles: bones heaped in glades; skulls nailed to tree trunks; the charred flesh of those burnt on altars or sacrificed in wicker baskets.

'So, you are a kinsman of Dominus Sejanus. But a very distant one, aren't you? I've done a little research on you, Parmenon. They say you are surly, taciturn, but a good listener. Is that true?'

'I am listening to what you say,' I replied.

The Minion laughed at my joke.

'We need men like you, Parmenon. His excellency Dominus Sejanus needs eyes and ears. Would you be his eyes and ears, Parmenon?'

I knew all about Dominus Sejanus. 'You mean a spy, an informer?'

I kept my face impassive, but I was angry. I may

be many things, but I am no traitor. The Minion was insulting me. His excellency Dominus Sejanus was insulting me but ... I had no family, no prospects, no money. Moreover, if I refused this offer, I had no doubt something rather unpleasant would happen. Men like Sejanus don't allow you to refuse such a proposal and then walk away.

'I would be his excellency's faithful servant,' I replied and made a secret sign with my fingers, a childish trick to ward off the effect of a lie.

'Good!' the Minion exclaimed. He shifted his cloak and sat down behind his desk. It was a tawdry little chamber in an outbuilding of the Palatine Palace. He picked up a piece of parchment.

'Do you know Domina Agrippina?'

'Which one?' I replied.

The Minion laughed. 'The younger one. Sixteen years old and sweet with it, so the men say.'

'You are talking about the daughter of Germanicus?'

I enjoyed doing that. The Minion furrowed his brow, realising his mistake. He could joke with impunity about many things but nobody joked about our great Roman hero Germanicus, the general who'd invaded Germany to retrieve Rome's honour.

'Ah well.' The Minion cleared his throat. 'Domina Agrippina needs a scribe, a secretarius.'

'And you need a spy?' I added.

He raised his close-set eyes, a sly grin on his face.

'You are very blunt,' the Minion whispered.

'I want to be very clear about what I am to do.'

'I think you know full well,' the Minion replied.

'Let's see, in a week's time on the feast of Minerva,' he clicked his tongue, 'his excellency will chair the Games held in the Divine One's honour. Agrippina and her family,' he smirked again, 'what's left of them, will be his excellency's guests in the imperial box. You'll receive authorisation to join them there, and can introduce yourself to Domina Agrippina.'

'What happens if she doesn't want me?'

'I don't give a fart whether she wants you.' He mimicked my voice. 'Or likes you. You'll carry a letter, sealed by his excellency, stating very clearly that you are now a member of her household.' He scratched the side of his cheek and wafted away a buzzing fly.

I stared behind him at the bust of Tiberius, the Divine One, sitting on its plinth. The sculptor hadn't simply flattered: he was guilty of a downright lie. The head looked like that of a young Greek athlete, the hair brought forward to fringe the noble brow, the long nose, deep-set eyes and generous mouth. I'd seen Tiberius from afar. His skin was scabby, his right ear stuck out, he had lost his teeth and his breath, so they said, reeked like a sewer. Naturally I kept such observations to myself. The Minion pushed a scroll across, followed by a very small leather bag which clinked. I was hired. I took both letter and money, and a slave ushered me out through the back entrance.

So, there I was, on the feast of Minerva, sitting in the imperial box watching a man prepare to die. In fact, I hadn't really followed the fight. I was more concerned by Domina Agrippina who also sat, next to her two sisters, on one of the raised benches at the back. I wondered about her brother Gaius Caesar – known as Caligula or 'Little Boots' – until I recalled that Tiberius had decided to take him to Capri.

I was fascinated by Domina. She was only sixteen but acted as if she was twice that age. She was dressed in the usual finery: a white stola, and a brocaded shawl across her shoulders which carried a small hood that she'd pulled up over her black glossy hair. Another of Sejanus's minions had introduced me to her. I kissed her perfumed hand and delivered the commission. She undid the purple cord, read the scroll, tossed it to lie between her feet and totally ignored me. I studied her face, with its high cheekbones, the nose just a little too long, the slight enlargement of her right cheek due to her double canine teeth, and her lower lip jutting out as if in a pout. It was the eyes which held my gaze. I couldn't decide whether they were dark-blue or black but they were large, lustrous and full of life. She'd peered at me as if she was short-sighted, though this was only a mannerism she'd developed. Nevertheless, with those long eyelashes, it gave the impression that she was just waking from a deep, sensuous sleep. As she watched Sullienus, now and again the tip of her tongue would come out. Apart from that she sat impassive, hands clenched in her lap. Abruptly she turned and said, her voice surprisingly low, 'Are you wondering where my husband is?'

'Domina,' I replied. 'That is none of my business.'

'Yes, it is,' she retorted cheekily and moved slightly towards me.

I smelt her perfume, faint but aromatic, reminding me of sandalwood.

'That is your business, isn't it, Parmenon? Spying? Aelius Sejanus will be asking you, "At the games, where was the little bitch's husband, Domitius Ahenobarbus"?'

She talked as if we were alone in some private chamber. Agrippina was cunning, and she'd chosen her moment carefully. Everybody else was shouting, and stamping their feet, eyes fixed on the arena, including the spy who would no doubt be spying on me to make sure that I spied on Agrippina.

'My husband,' she continued, eyes widening, 'is in some brothel on the road to Ostia. He'll no doubt be drunk with his head in a whore's lap. He smells like a goat and he acts like one but I can't really complain as our Divine Emperor himself chose my husband. I, however, reserve the right to choose my bed companion. Now,' she smiled. 'What do you think? Should Callaxtus die?'

'Domina, he should live.'

'I agree.'

She stretched out her hand, thumb pointing to the ceiling of the imperial box.

'*Vivat!*' she cried. '*Vivat!* Let him live! Let him live!'

Heads turned. I moved the stool, peering through the assembled notables; the generals, the senators, the priests and Vestal Virgins. I looked for Sejanus's lean, saturnine face, his iron-grey hair combed carefully forward, his gentle smile, those wide-spaced eyes. He, too, had heard Agrippina shout. He turned, a smile on his lips, scratching the tip of his nose, and narrowing his eyes as if searching out who was shouting against the crowd. He saw Agrippina, winked and lifted his hand. I moved my stool to stare down into the arena. Sullienus had taken his helmet off. He stood sweat-soaked, sword up in salute, waiting for Sejanus's sign. The Prefect stretched out his hand, thumb extended. I knew he was about to give Callaxtus life but at that moment the fallen gladiator did something very stupid. Whilst Sullienus's back was turned, probably because he could no longer stand the tension, Callaxtus picked up his trident and lunged at his opponent's exposed thigh. Sullienus was too quick – perhaps he had seen the shadow or heard a sound? – and, stepping nimbly to one side, he turned and drove his sword straight into Callaxtus's bare throat. The crowd roared its approval. Sejanus's hand dropped. He shrugged and got to his feet, arms extended to receive the salute, not only of the victor, but the approval of the mob. Agrippina sat and shook her head.

'Fool!' she whispered to me. 'But most men are fools, aren't they, Parmenon? They think with their balls and lack all patience.'

She turned away, joining the plaudits for Sejanus. I looked down at her feet. The scroll she'd tossed there had disappeared.

After the Games I followed her back to the Domus

Livia on the Palatine. The house had once belonged to Augustus's wife but she'd now died and been turned into a God. Well, not exactly, as her son Tiberius was reluctant to grant her the honour, but the people considered her as such. They regarded Livia as the model of chastity. I suppose they were right, for every other woman in her family had taken lovers with the same greed and gusto as a starving man snatches bread. The Domus was supposed to be a palace, but Tiberius, or rather Sejanus, had let it fall into disrepair. Steps were chipped, the paintwork was flakey, the baths were dusty and dirty, the water system cracked and there was a general shortage of money shown by the empty oil lamps, faded cushions, stained couches, and tables and chairs which rocked when you touched them.

Agrippina had a chamber on the first floor overlooking a dusty courtyard. I was invited there as soon as she returned. She lay on a couch beneath the window, leaning against the headrest, staring up at the ceiling, her sandals and shawl tossed on the floor. She tapped the side of the couch.

'Come here, Parmenon.'

I stared. Yesterday I had been wandering the narrow lanes of Rome, and now a member of the imperial family was asking me to sit on the edge of her couch.

'Come on!' she urged. 'Sit here! I won't bite you.' She grinned mischievously. 'Yet!'

I took a step forward.

'No, first open the door, quickly! See if anyone's in the corridor outside.'

I obeyed but the gallery was empty. Dust motes danced in the pale afternoon sun which streamed through one of the high windows. I closed the door.

'Again!' Agrippina whispered. 'Open the door quietly and look down! Do it quickly, quietly!'

I obeyed but still saw no one there. I closed the door and she beckoned me over. I sat on the edge of the couch and stared down at her. She looked even more beautiful: her eyes had turned a dark blue, her skin had the sheen of porcelain, her lips seemed fuller and redder. I wondered what it would be like to kiss her.

'If Livia was still alive,' she murmured, pulling herself up and resting on her elbow, 'and she walked through that door, you'd be strangled and I'd be off to exile. You're uncomfortable, aren't you? You are almost sitting with your back to me, having to twist your neck round. Do you know who taught me that? Livia! She had a genius for making people feel uncomfortable: she taught me a lot more as well.' She gently pushed me off the couch. 'Kneel down.'

She sat on the edge of the couch, and I knelt on the floor before her. I could have refused, I was a free-born Roman citizen, but I was fascinated. I had never expected this to happen. Agrippina clasped her hands before her.

'You are Parmenon,' she began. 'And you are related very slightly, may the Gods be thanked, to that human spider, that vile viper, the Prefect Aelius Sejanus. He's a very, very dangerous man, Sejanus. Our Emperor's dark shadow! A man of infinite ambition. You know he wants to be Emperor? Oh yes! He has pretensions enough. After all, if the line of Caesar can produce an emperor why not that of Sejanus?'

'Yes, but—' I protested.

'But, but what?' she mimicked. 'Who's in the way! Livia's been dead two years. My father twelve!'

'Your brothers?'

'Drusus is in prison. He's been lowered into a pit called the Sepulchre. Sejanus arranged that. They are going to starve him to death. And Mother? You are going to ask about my mother, aren't you?' she continued. 'And my other brother Nero. Well, I'll tell you where they are. Nero's in Pontia and Mother's on Pandateria, a little island. They say she's gone mad, and they had to restrain her so forcibly she lost an eye. Can you imagine that, Parmenon? The kinswoman of Caesar Augustus, with her eye knocked out by a centurion, being force-fed by sweaty ex-gladiators, and roaming the rocks like a mountain goat?'

'What about young Gaius?' I replied.

'Oh, you mean "Little Boots". Well, he's with the old fox in Capri. Only the Gods know what's happening to him. Anyway!' She moved a lock of hair away from her forehead. 'I've told you enough. You can now trot back to Sejanus and report all the juicy bits.' She clicked her fingers. 'Go on!'

I remained kneeling.

'Go on!' she repeated.

'If I do, you die!'

'Aye, Parmenon, and so do you.' She ruffled my hair with her fingers. 'We are both trapped, aren't we? You go and tell Sejanus's minions what I have said and I'll join my mother, or brother, on some lonely island.' She pointed to the floor. 'Or my other brother Drusus in the cells below. As for you, Parmenon, as time passes Sejanus will start to wonder. Why should young Agrippina open her heart to a stranger? Can this Parmenon be truly trusted?'

I strained my ears and hoped the gallery outside was empty. This remarkable young woman had trapped me.

'Do you know why I chose to sit here, Parmenon? Because that door is thick and there are no ledges outside this window. I've also checked the walls and floor carefully. No spy-holes, no little apertures for the ear. So, what are you going to do, Parmenon? Choose life or death?'

'I am . . .'

'What are you going to say, Parmenon?' she mocked. 'That you are only a servant, a scribe? You are only a flea on Sejanus's table.'

'Why are you doing this?' I asked.

'I don't know. I am taking a gamble. I watched you at the amphitheatre. You don't like bloodshed, Parmenon.'

'I always think of my own skin.'

'No, Parmenon, somewhere you've got a soul and a heart. I rather like you, you don't act like an informer or a spy. So, let me draw you deeper into the net. We haven't got much time. At the moment everybody's drunk after the Games – nothing like a little blood is there, Parmenon, to whet the thirst and stir the cock – and Sejanus's spies will be slaking themselves before they remember their duty. That's their great mistake: blood blinds them. Such is Rome under Tiberius. Have you heard the poem, Parmenon?' She closed her eyes.

> '"Tiberius is not thirsty for neat wine.
> What warms him up is a tastier cup,
> The blood of murdered men".'

I shivered. Agrippina was muttering treason. Both of us could be handed over to the executioners to be strangled, our corpses tossed down the Steps of Mourning before being thrown into the Tiber.

'He's mad,' Agrippina continued. 'Tiberius is mad; either that, or possessed by a demon. Perhaps both. Do you know what my father told me, Parmenon? When Tiberius was a general, he used to study his maps in his tent the night before a battle, and suddenly the lamps around him would abruptly go out.' She made me jump as she snapped her fingers. 'Extinguished just like that! Tiberius always took it as a sign that his demon was nearby and he'd be lucky in the coming fight.'

'Domina,' I stammered. 'You shouldn't tell me all this.'

'I'll tell you more, Parmenon. Tiberius is the great Augustus's successor but he spent most of his early manhood sulking in exile. It turned his mind. He wants to kill and kill again. My father is dead, my mother and two brothers will soon join him and, if Sejanus has his way, I and my sisters have got –' she coolly shrugged her shoulders '– perhaps a year, certainly no more than eighteen months. Go out and check the gallery again, Parmenon. Stay there for a while before coming back.'

I obeyed her command. I closed the door behind me and tried to stop trembling. Agrippina had sent me out to test me. Any sensible informant would have fled like the wind, certainly not to Sejanus but down to Ostia to beg, buy, do anything to gain passage to the western isles or beyond. My face was coated in sweat. My stomach was clenched so tightly I thought I was going to vomit. It was like being woken up from a deep sleep by a jug of cold water splashed over your face. I was no more than twenty-three years of age and so far my life had been like that of a dream-walker, an observer of what was happening around me, but feeling very little. My father killed, my mother a sickly woman who had died before her time. Friends and acquaintances were merely people I talked to, dined or slept with. In an hour all this had changed. I walked up and down the gallery drawing deep breaths. Why, I kept asking myself? Why was Agrippina telling me this? It was all true, of course. Tiberius was a sick, bitter man. The stories from Capri depicted him as a monster. One story currently doing the rounds of the taverns of Rome was that a fisherman on the island had caught an enormous mullet, and eager to please his

Emperor, he towed the fish up the trackless cliffs and surprised Tiberius. The Emperor was furious at being disturbed. He ordered his guards to wash the fisherman's face with the mullet; its scales skinned him raw and the poor fellow screamed in agony, 'Thank the Gods I didn't bring Caesar the huge crab I also caught.'

Tiberius sent for the crab, had it used in the same way, before his hapless victim was thrown from the cliff top. A party of marines stationed below dealt with the fisherman, as they did others sent hurtling to their death, whacking him with oars and boat hooks. The poor man's corpse was left a bloody mess upon the rocks. In Rome the hunger for blood was no different. The prisons were full, and those detained were deprived of light, food, even conversation. Some of the accused, on being warned to appear in court, felt so sure the verdict would be guilty that, in order to avoid public disgrace, they stayed at home, took a warm bath and opened their veins. If Sejanus's police suspected this might happen, the house was raided, the poor unfortunate's wounds were bandaged and he was hurried off to prison. A few senators, knowing they were going to be accused in public, drank poison openly, toasting their colleagues whilst cursing Caesar's name. Their corpses were always displayed on the Steps of Mourning, before being dragged by hooks along the muddy lanes of Rome to the Tiber. Men, women, even children were imprisoned. Sejanus often toured the prisons, where one of his victims, half-mad from the torture, begged to be put out of his misery.

'Oh no,' Sejanus replied. 'We are not friends yet.'

Such thoughts heightened my anxiety, standing in that dusty gallery of the Palatine Palace. I decided to flee. I was not one of the powerful ones of Rome so why should I be troubled? I stopped and stared back at Agrippina's room. If I returned to that chamber, I could die an excruciating death, yet Agrippina was right, for if I reported her conversation, the same fate awaited me. I heard a footfall on the stairs and stepped into a shadowy recess. A slithering, soft sound, someone taking their time, coming up slowly, stealthily. Was Agrippina playing some cruel game? I peered out and recognised Metellus. I'd been introduced to him in the imperial box at the Games. He was a balding, narrow-faced scribe, responsible for ordering stores and ensuring the kitchen was well supplied. However, he wasn't mounting those stairs like a scribe, more like the spy he was. He came onto the gallery and tiptoed by. I held my breath. He stopped at Agrippina's door and listened carefully. Satisfied, he withdrew and slipped back down the stairs. I made my decision, or rather Metellus had made it for me. I waited until I was sure he wouldn't return and crept back into the chamber. Agrippina was sitting where I had left her, tapping her foot as if listening to some invisible tune.

'Well?' she asked, raising her head.

I was about to kneel in front of her but she tapped the couch beside me.

'You are with me, aren't you, Parmenon?'

I nodded. She pulled down the front of her stola, exposing her beautiful breasts, their nipples dark and enlarged. She took my hand and pressed it against her left breast, her face only a few inches from mine.

'Swear, Parmenon, by earth, sea and sky!'

I found it difficult to speak. My throat had gone dry. It was a strange sensation, my hand clasped against that beautiful breast, her lovely lips not far from mine, juxtaposed to the silence of the room, the terrors beyond the door, Metellus waiting like some snake.

'Swear!' she hissed.

I took the oath, and she kissed me full on the lips, pushed my hand away and re-arranged her stola.

'What's the matter, Parmenon? Are you shocked?'

'No, Domina, frightened. Metellus is slinking like a fox outside.'

'Foxes can be trapped.'

Clearing her throat, a mannerism employed whenever she was excited, Agrippina snuggled closer.

'Tiberius is Emperor,' she whispered. 'He's mad, bad or both.' She smoothed her face. 'But, there again, I'm no different. We have rotten blood in our veins. Tiberius's son was poisoned.'

I started.

'No, be still.' She tapped my knee. 'The Emperor's true son is dead and that's the end of the matter. Tiberius, therefore, has several possible heirs: Gemellus who is weak; or one of my elder brothers.

However,' she sighed, 'we must consider them, like my mother, as dead. That leaves me, my sisters and "Little Boots".'

Her voice took on a mocking tone as she referred to her brother, the seventeen-year-old Caligula, who was now Tiberius's house prisoner on Capri.

'Tiberius,' she continued, 'is worrying enough. Sejanus, however, is the more pressing danger. He's Prefect of the city and commands the Praetorian Guard. The Senate are a claque and his bosom friends command the German legions. Sejanus has spun a web in which everyone is caught up. What he'll do next is try to get rid of Caligula, myself and my sisters before we can beget any children. We'll soon be arrested for treason, and either exiled or imprisoned. And then we shall certainly be executed, probably sooner rather than later.' Agrippina paused as if she had forgotten something. 'Yes, yes, that's how it will go. Once he's finished with us, Sejanus will turn on Tiberius, and the Emperor will go into the dark. Sejanus will marry Tiberius's widowed daughter-in-law and have himself proclaimed Emperor.' She tapped her foot and cleared her throat.

'So, what can you do? Flee Rome?'

Agrippina threw her head back and laughed. 'Flee Rome, Parmenon? We wouldn't get as far as the Forum.' She pinched my arm. 'Don't you have any life in those veins, a heart which beats? Haven't you heard of a blood feud? Tiberius and Sejanus have struck at my family. Now I will strike at theirs.' She waggled a finger like an aged housewife telling her husband off. 'Where's the weakness in all of this, Parmenon?'

'You've thought all this through, haven't you?' I asked.

She grinned. 'The weakness, in fact, is Sejanus himself. Tiberius regards Sejanus as too low-born to pose any real threat. However, our Emperor, by nature, is very suspicious. At the moment he puts up with Sejanus because he once saved Tiberius's life. They were dining out in some cave and there was a rock fall. Tiberius believes he has a debt to pay. He must now be made to realise that this debt is cleared and Sejanus is his greatest enemy.'

'How will you do that?'

'We must get to Capri.'

Agrippina got up, walked to the door and opened it.

'You will arrange that, Parmenon. In the meantime, ask Metellus to come up!'

I looked up in surprise.

'Go on!' she urged. 'Tell him I need him now!'

I obeyed her command and went down the gallery. I could hear shouts, doors opening and closing. The festivities after the Games were now in full swing. I slipped downstairs into the gallery below, where servants and their girls were milling about, some much the worse for drink. Metellus was sitting at a table, tapping his fingers as if mystified by what had happened.

'Domina Agrippina will see you now!' I declared.

'Will she? Where has she been? Where have you been?'

'I've been nowhere,' I slurred, pretending to be tipsy. 'You'd best go upstairs now.'

Metellus scraped back the stool and followed me up. I went along the gallery and knocked on the door. Agrippina opened it, almost dragged the fellow through, then slammed it shut in my face. I stood wondering what was to happen. I heard Agrippina laugh, the clink of cups. Was she playing some game? I tried the handle but the bolts were in place. I was walking down the gallery when I heard the screams, terrible piercing yells, so strident they quelled the clamour below. I ran back towards the door and pushed against it. From inside I could hear the clatter of noise as if a violent struggle was taking place. The alarm was being raised. Two Praetorian guards came running up, swords drawn. Burly fellows, they shoved me aside. Using the pommel of their swords, they hammered on the door, from behind which came Agrippina's screams and yells, and the sounds of a scuffle grew more strident. Stools and benches were used to force open the door and I followed the soldiers into the room. Metellus lay sprawled on the floor before the couch, a gaping wound in his chest. Agrippina, her tunic covered in blood, knelt beside him holding a dagger. Her stola had been ripped, and she had scratch marks on her face. She pushed her hair back and stared wildly at the soldiers.

'He tried to rape me!' she hissed. She pointed to the goblets lying in a pool of wine in the middle of the room. 'He was drunk.'

She caught my gaze and, for a second, I saw the

smile in her eyes. She got to her feet still holding the dagger.

'Is this the way –' she yelled, '– to treat the daughter of Germanicus? Am I some common whore to be pawed at by servants?'

Her maids appeared. Agrippina yelled obscenities, asking them where they had been. They tried to reply but Agrippina threw the dagger on the floor. She crumpled on the couch, put her face in her hands and sobbed bitterly. The soldiers, both outraged and fearful at what had happened, grabbed Metellus's corpse and flung it through the window onto the courtyard below. I decided it was time to act as if I was the Domina's secretarius. Water and towels were ordered. I thanked the soldiers and asked them to leave. Once they had, Agrippina got to her feet and allowed the maids to dab at the cuts on her face and hands. She seized a moment in the hustle and bustle to beckon me over.

'Go, tell Sejanus's minions,' she whispered, 'that I am of the blood imperial. I have been attacked! A lowling has tried to rape me. I demand to see the Emperor!' She grabbed my hand and pulled me closer. 'Use your wit, Parmenon. Act as if you were truly Sejanus's spy. Tell the truth!'

I left immediately, threading my way through the passageways of the Palatine Palace across the parklands. Darkness was falling, and torches and lamps were being lit. I found the Minion in the same chamber in which we had first met. I suspect he already knew what had happened but when I gave him the details his face paled. He plucked at his face and sifted the parchments on the table.

'I see. I see,' he muttered. 'You'd best stay here.'

An hour passed. The darkness deepened, the light from the oil lamps gutted out. At last the Minion returned.

'His Excellency will see you now!'

Chapter 5

'I wish the Roman populace had only one neck'
Suetonius, *'Lives of the Caesars'*: Caligula, 30

'So, she wishes to go to Capri?'

Sejanus lounged on a couch, one arm on the head-rest, a wax writing tablet on his knee. A small tripod next to the couch held quills, ink and pumice stone. He put the tablet down and glanced at me, fingers laced. Sejanus was at his most avuncular: patrician, his grey hair carefully combed, smiling eyes, slightly hooked nose, his face freshly shaved and oiled.

'I've heard what happened.' He smiled. 'Do you believe it?'

I recalled Agrippina's advice.

'No, I don't, Excellency.'

Sejanus furrowed his brow. 'I am glad you said that.

Neither do I. Metellus was a cold fish, who prefered little boys to women so why should he try and rape Agrippina?' He clicked his tongue.

I was standing about three yards from him. I hoped he couldn't smell my fear.

'But Agrippina acted foolishly. Surely she would have known about Metellus's preferences? Let me think this through.' Sejanus reflected. 'Agrippina sent you to bring Metellus to her room, and then locked the door. Almost immediately she started to scream a yell and when the Praetorians broke in, Metellus, one of my spies, was found with a dagger thrust through the heart. Now Agrippina is acting the hysterical bitch and pleading to be sent to Capri to complain to the Emperor.' He sighed. 'To be perfectly honest I suspect the Divine One won't believe her either.'

He lowered his head and clicked his tongue. I stared round the marble room. Purple and gold drapes hung against the walls and two crumbling gravestones, a memento mori, perched at either end of the couch. Was it Sejanus's idea to terrify visitors or had this been the great Augustus's writing chamber? The furniture was exquisite, much of it of Egyptian design, as were the statuettes – an Apis bull, a Hermes, a dancing girl – and a silver lamp-stand carved in the shape of a tree. Agrippina later explained that it was all looted from Cleopatra's court. At the time I didn't really care, only aware of the warmth and the brooding silence. The drapes moved slightly, and I glanced down and caught sight of the toe of a boot peeping out beneath. Sejanus was no fool: he appeared to be frightened of no one but the chamber was full of guards, their swords drawn, ready to protect him or to carry out his slightest whim. He continued to click his tongue, an unnerving sound: sometimes fast, sometimes slow it seemed to echo the beat of my heart. I stared down at the floor and studied the mosaic which was of Demeter rising from the corn fields.

'I am wondering,' Sejanus smiled, 'dearest kinsman, if you are part of this plot?'

He picked up a bell and rang it vigorously. A door in the wall opened and the Minion stepped through. Sejanus didn't even bother to turn his head.

'Who's in the chamber below?' he demanded.

'Tibullus.'

'Ah yes, our self-styled poet who thinks he is a new Virgil. Any progress?'

The Minion shook his sweat-soaked face.

'Take my kinsman Parmenon down.'

The Minion snapped his fingers, and I followed him out. The chamber beyond was pitch black except for a torch flickering at the bottom of the steep, sharp steps. The Minion grabbed me by the arm and bustled me down.

'Don't be frightened!' he sniggered.

I wished I'd fled. Agrippina's plot was doomed to failure. Sejanus had realised what she was up to. She wouldn't be travelling to Capri and I was about to end my days in a place like this. We reached the bottom of the steps and went along a poorly lit corridor which debouched into a circular chamber, where I saw men dressed like gladiators and satyrs, the masks over their faces made all the more grotesque by the leaping torchlight. The smell was as fetid as that from an open latrine. The grotesques moved away to reveal the outstretched body of a man on the table.

'He's not a prisoner,' the Minion sniggered, pointing at me. 'At least not yet. Just show him.'

One of the grotesques pushed me forward. Tibullus, or what was left of him, lay outstretched on a table. He was completely naked. He had lost consciousness but the vinegar-soaked gag in his mouth would have blocked his screams. Blood soaked both him and the table, oozing from small puncture holes in his body. I froze in horror. The table top beneath was covered in a forest of small spikes. Tibullis was literally being tortured to death by a thousand cuts. Each time his body was moved and turned, the nails either dug afresh or cut deeper into the open wounds.

'He wrote a poem, Tibullis did,' the Minion explained. 'What we are trying to discover is who paid him?'

'I didn't!' I snapped, trying to hide my fear.

'No, of course you didn't. But you get the message?'

'Very clearly.'

'Good, good.' The Minion put a scented pomander to his nose. 'Do remember what you've seen.'

I stared at the torturers, at their sweat-soaked,

balding pates, eyes glittering behind the masks. They were full of a malicious enjoyment at the sight of another human being torn to pieces. I followed the Minion up the steps back into Sejanus's chamber.

'Is Tibullus still alive?'

'Yes, Excellency.'

'Well, he won't be by tomorrow morning. Right, Parmenon, were you party to this nonsense with Domina Agrippina?'

'To some extent,' I replied.

Sejanus glanced expectantly at me. 'You need to do better than that, kinsman!'

'Domina Agrippina was hysterical,' I lied. 'She recognised who I really was as soon as she met me at the Games. "I am your secretarius," I announced. "No," she hissed. "You are a spy!" She returned to the palace, where she started to make extravagant promises about what she could do for me.'

'And?'

'Excellency, I pretended to listen to her, until she told me to get out. Metellus went in to see her.' I shrugged. 'The rest you know.'

'And would you send her to Capri?' Sejanus asked.

I stared across at the secret door, which the Minion had closed. I took a step forward and one of the drapes moved.

'No, Excellency, I wouldn't risk it. Only the Gods know what kind of mischief she could get up to.'

Again the clicking tongue. I was in a cold sweat: the next few seconds would decide my life.

'So, what do you advise, kinsman?'

'According to public report,' I blurted out, 'a woman of the imperial family was attacked, the daughter of Germanicus. I saw the outrage on the soldiers' faces: Agrippina's story will be believed.'

Sejanus, cupping his chin in his hand, nodded.

'If you do send her to Capri,' I continued, 'it could be dangerous. But if you refuse, you can be sure that some spy will carry the story to Capri and the Emperor might think someone is trying to hide something.'

'Very good! Very good!' Sejanus smiled. 'Kinsman, pour yourself a goblet of wine.'

He pointed to the small dresser which stood between two pillars. I obeyed.

'No, not for me!' He barked as I started to fill a second cup. 'You may be my kinsman, but it doesn't mean I trust you.' He held up his finger, displaying a large amethyst ring. 'I carry poison in this ring, and you could do the same. Come on, sit in the chair. You look sly enough, Parmenon, but have you the brain to match? Tell me what you would advise, kinsman?'

I sat on the stool a few paces from him.

'If you send an ordinary messenger,' I replied, 'the Emperor may still misunderstand.'

'What do you know of the Emperor?'

'Very little, your Excellency. I am merely a speck of dust under his sandal.'

'Yes, yes, you are and I am that sandal.'

'Then, Excellency, I would advise that you send the only witness to the incident, namely myself.'

Sejanus clapped his hands. 'Very good, Parmenon. You will leave by trireme first thing tomorrow morning. You'll go dressed in a tunic and sandals, with a cloak and nothing else.' He paused. 'Agrippina will try and give you a letter. What do you do then?'

'I'll be reluctant to accept it so she'll bribe me. I will take it and hand it over to one of your men.'

Sejanus's face crumpled into a smile.

'Good and when you get to Capri?'

'I will tell the Emperor, the Divine One, exactly what I told you: that Agrippina is becoming hysterical and Metellus was innocent of any crime.'

'And the rest is up to your sharp wit. However,' Sejanus picked up the wax tablet and pointed to where the secret door was, 'my servant will accompany you. Give him Agrippina's letter and he will study it carefully. He will also be my witness at your meeting with the Emperor so he'll be able to report everything that you say. Be warned, when you go into the Emperor's presence, make no reference to any religious belief or astrology. You must kneel and not raise your eyes. Above all, do not hold the Emperor's gaze. He believes it's one way demons can enter his soul. If possible, study the Divine One closely. When you return to Rome, I want to know everything you've seen and heard. Oh, by the way, Parmenon.' He pointed to the goblet I was cradling. 'That's the very best Falernian, so drink it up.'

I did so quickly.

'You are safe for now,' Sejanus murmured. 'However, my servant has his orders and if he suspects you of the slightest treachery towards me, you'll never see Rome again. You may go!'

I was at the door when he called my name. I turned, to see that Sejanus was now sitting up on the edge of the couch. His face had lost that gentle conspiratorial look.

'You did very well, Parmenon. Much better than I expected. You should celebrate with more wine tonight. You are a very lucky man.'

A guard took me back to Agrippina's quarters. Darkness had now fallen and the gardens were lit by torches and lanterns. Praetorian guards patrolled in full view whilst others were hiding beneath cypress trees, in porticoes or recesses in the walls. My guide, a Praetorian officer, was dressed in half-armour and stank of sweaty leather. As we went through a side door leading to Agrippina's quarters, the man hauled me into the shadows. I heard the scrape of metal and felt a sword tip press into my throat just beneath the chin.

'What's this?' I murmured. 'I have done no . . .'

The man pushed me up against the wall.

'Can you be trusted?' he asked.

Gods, I was on the verge of hysteria! 'Trust?' I yelped. 'In this viper's nest? Trust whom?'

'Leave him be,' a woman's voice urged.

The man stepped back.

'You have a few minutes,' he whispered and left, closing the door softly behind him.

Agrippina stepped out of the darkness. She was swathed from chin to toe in a dark-blue military cloak smelling of horse piss and stables.

'Quickly, tell me all!' she urged.

'I could have been killed!' I hissed. 'You knew Sejanus wouldn't believe your story.'

'Of course I did,' came the calm reply.

'You could have told me what to say.'

'Now, now, Parmenon.' Agrippina's pale face peered at me. She stood on tiptoe and kissed me on the lips. 'You are like a gladiator returning from the arena and complaining that you have won. If you had been killed what use would you be to me? I told you to tell the truth. You did so and survived.'

'Why did you kill Metellus?' I demanded.

'That's one thing Sejanus doesn't know. I suspected Metellus had heard me complaining of Sejanus so he had to die. It was also a way of bringing both myself and you to Sejanus's attention. That's the way of things, Parmenon. When you deal with the blood imperial, you either survive or go into the dark. Metellus had to die. I had to catch Sejanus's eye. He's not going to let me go to Capri, is he? He's going to send you?'

'How did you . . . ?'

She laughed softly. 'It's the only logical thing he could do.'

'What about that guard?' I pointed to the door.

Agrippina put her arms round my neck. 'He loves me, Parmenon. He fought with my father in Germany. He's held Germanicus's daughter in his arms, fondled my breasts, run his hand in the secret part between my legs. He'll die for me if necessary.'

'But you are married?'

'Oh, Parmenon, you are such a fool.' She pressed her body against mine. 'And yet you are doing so well. We are here to survive, Parmenon. I'll fight with every weapon I have.' She let her arms fall away and stepped back. 'Can't you see that? Now you are off to Capri, where you are to tell the Emperor the truth: that I murdered Metellus because I was hysterical.' She clicked her tongue. 'Did Sejanus do that?'

'Yes, he did.'

Agrippina laughed. 'So, what's the next step, Parmenon?'

'I am to leave tomorrow. Any letter you give me must be handed over to the Minion.'

'Sejanus really thinks I'm a hysterical, stupid woman!' The words were spat out, each one full of hate and malice. 'One of these days,' she added, 'I'll make him face the truth.'

'Why did we have to meet like this?' I asked. 'In the dark?'

'Because they'll be watching you, Parmenon. If you came straight back to report to me, they'd suspect your allegiance. So, come and see me tomorrow morning before you leave. I'll give you the letter to the Emperor and something else.'

She brushed by me and was gone. The door opened and the Praetorian officer stepped through. He took me by the elbow and pushed me up the steps, along to the servants' quarters, a refectory with trestle tables and stools. The Praetorian introduced me and turned to where a greasy-handed cook stood at the end of the kitchen.

'He's got loose bowels,' he sneered. 'Either that or he's so frightened he almost crapped himself. Give him something light to eat.'

He joined in the general laughter and left, satisfied that he could explain the slight delay in bringing me from Sejanus's chamber to this refectory, where possibly every man, woman and child was in Sejanus's pay. I ate some highly spiced stew and rye bread. I remember the meal well: I found it so difficult to eat, my hands kept shaking from fear and elation. I felt as if I had been put through a fire but come through unscathed.

A sleepless, restless night followed. In my dreams the ghouls clustered in. I was walking through Rome' but every street and lane flowed with blood. Sightless eyes in severed heads perched on pikes gazed beseechingly at me, their lips still moving, spurting out blood as well as guttural sounds. I woke in a sweat, took some wine and returned to a more peaceful sleep. I once discussed such nightmares with Domina. She winked and nipped my cheek.

'It proves you have a conscience, Parmenon,' she mocked.

'Don't you dream, Domina?'

'I sleep like a baby,' she replied.

The next morning she certainly looked unruffled and unperturbed, when a servant took me up to her quarters. The room where Metellus had died was now cleaned and cleared. Servant girls thronged about, so I had to be prudent: most of them, if not all, were in Sejanus's pay. Agrippina played her part to perfection. She led me over to a window recess and took a small scroll from beneath the shawl round her shoulders. She glanced down into the courtyard.

'Your escort is waiting. Give this to my brother Gaius and no other. Tell him his sister loves him.' She moved so her back was to the rest of the room. 'Tell him,' she continued slowly, 'to play the man and act the part. Remind him of the herbarium I sent him. He is to study it closely for the source of his deliverance is in Capri.'

She turned as if to walk away but came back.

'Oh, and tell the Emperor that Sejanus wants to become Drusus: that's why Drusus has gone away.'

I stared perplexed. Drusus, her brother, was in a dark hole beneath the Palatine. She blew me a kiss and walked over to one of the servant girls, shouting for water and napkins and the clearest mirror they could find. I went down to the yard. The Minion was waiting, with a small cohort of troops and one of those huge four-wheeled carts to carry our baggage and other supplies for the Emperor in Capri.

'You are ready, kinsman?' the Minion mocked.

He looked me over from head to toe. I was dressed in a dark-green tunic and a rather threadbare cloak I had bought in the market place. He threw me a clinking purse.

'When you return to Rome you really must visit my tailor.'

I caught the clinking bag, and saw that his hand was still outstretched. I gave him Agrippina's letter, he broke the seal and studied it carefully.

'Nothing treasonable,' he sighed. 'More's the pity. Here!' He tossed it to a servant. 'Take that to His Excellency!' He gestured at me. 'Come on! Ostia awaits!'

I was given a sorry nag to ride. We left the Palatine by side gates and made our way through the narrow, stinking streets towards the gate to Ostia. It was late March. The sun was beginning to strengthen but really the seasons made little difference in Rome. It was always busy with merchants' carts, pedlars' barrows, the cookshops and wine stalls, the jostle and bustle of an empire. Soldiers forced their way through the crowds. Sailors and marines, up from the docks, searched out the ladies of the town. Fruit and vegetable-sellers shouted and sold their produce whilst trying to evade the market police. Astrologists, soothsayers, magicians and conjuring men clustered about. I heard at least thirty different tongues being spoken. I wondered if it was the last time I'd see this city. Some wit cracked a joke about the nag I was riding but I ignored him. We were soon through the city gates, onto the broad road to Ostia.

A trireme was waiting at a well-guarded quayside, Tiberius's personal craft. It was a grim-looking vessel, it flew the imperial colours, but its sails were black and white, and the marines and officers on board were all dressed in dark leather corselets or tunics. It was the quietest ship I have ever sailed on and provided an insight into Tiberius's suspicious mind. No one trusted anyone and the best way to keep your head was to have a quiet tongue. We were welcomed gruffly aboard, and our baggage was stowed away. Orders rattled out and we were soon leaving the quayside, as the trireme's prow, curved in the shape of an eagle, sliced through the water. The fishing smacks and pedlars' boats kept well away from our vessel, recognising the colours: the red and gold prow, the silver gilt along the rail and the dark sails.

The sea was calm, the winds favourable, the journey short; I was pleased to see the Minion was as seasick as I. At last Capri came into sight. Tiberius had chosen the island well. It was only a short distance from Rome, but well protected by its soaring cliffs which allowed only one natural harbour. Even as the trireme skimmed towards this, I glimpsed the armed men on the cliff tops. The Minion whispered to me that the Emperor had constant lookouts posted there with beacons at the ready, vigilant for the hint of any danger, any threat to the Emperor. Tiberius truly hated Rome. He viewed it as a place full of devils and went there as little as possible. He had even failed to return for his own mother's funeral: her corpse had begun to decompose before Tiberius allowed the funeral rites to take place. Sometimes he travelled to outskirts of Rome, issuing orders, receiving envoys and quickly departing.

Tiberius also hated religion. He had no time for the Roman Gods or any others and neglected the temple ceremonies. He was, however, deeply interested in the science of the Chaldeans: the soothsayers, diviners and oracle-tellers who might predict the future. The most famous, Thrasyllus, had once promised that Tiberius would be Emperor. Consequently, Tiberius took such men and women seriously. But woe betide any whom Tiberius considered charlatans. They were invited to Capri and, once they had completed their business, were taken down the steps along the cliff edge. If Tiberius was unhappy with his soothsaying guest, a burly guard had secret orders to tip him onto the rocks below. A sinister, ominous place!

The trireme soon docked, and ran down its gangplank. I had been in many harbours and ports throughout the Roman world, but found Capri was the quietest. Everything was closely regulated, and there were none of the usual swaggering sailors or tempting courtesans. We were welcomed by the commander of the Emperor's bodyguard, a stocky, thickset man, dressed in full armour. At first I thought he was the usual dim-witted bully boy until he clasped my hand, and I saw that the eyes beneath his heavy brows were bright and cynical. He looked me over from head to toe.

'Another of Sejanus's creatures,' he murmured. 'I am Macro.' and withdrew his hand. He nodded at the Minion and ordered us to follow him.

Capri had been taken over completely by the

Emperor. Macro explained, as we followed the path up to the cliff top, that there were twelve villas in all for the Emperor, his guests and household. Gardens and temples had also been laid out and built. We were given apartments in a villa not far from the harbour. Macro informed us we had an hour to make ourselves ready before the Emperor would see us.

'So soon?' I asked once Macro had left.

'Tiberius doesn't like visitors,' the Minion replied. 'Though he'll be eager for news from Rome.'

'I thought . . .'

'What?' the Minion demanded.

'Macro already seemed to know that I would be I coming here?'

The Minion gave a shrug. 'You have your orders. Make sure you follow them.'

We washed and changed, then ate some white bread and grapes. Macro returned and we were led across the island to a white, marble-colonnaded villa perched high on the edge of the cliffs. It was cooled by breezes which also wafted in the perfume of exotic plants from the garden.

Tiberius met us alone in a small atrium which overlooked the garden. I glimpsed a sparkling fountain and the curtain wall, beyond which was the death-dealing fall. Tiberius sat between two pillars leading out to the garden. He didn't recline on a couch but on a soldier's camp chair. He was dressed in a purple and gold-fringed toga, with a simple bronze chain around his neck. He kept playing with the silver tassels on the cushions beneath him. Despite Sejanus's warnings, I glanced up at him quickly. Tiberius looked hideous: although balding at the front, his dark hair clustered thickly round the nape of his neck, his nose was twisted slightly to the left, the jutting upper lip was made worse by the rotting teeth, and a weak chin gave his face a bitter, sneering look. His glowering dark eyes blazed in contrast to his skin which was a dirty-white like that of a whore who'd painted her face, emphasized by the fetid ulcers which covered his body. Years earlier Tiberius had tried to burn these off by cauterising them with a fiery iron. Such a clumsy cure had only made matters worse. Tiberius reminded me of a leper.

We had to wait until Macro finished his whispering. Tiberius pushed him away and beckoned us forward with his fingers. We knelt on cushions before him, heads down.

'You come from Rome?'

'Yes, your Imperial Highness,' the Minion replied. 'And we bring felicitations . . .'

'Enough of that!' Tiberius barked like a centurion on a parade ground. 'I'm not interested in Rome or what it thinks of me. But I understand my good friend Sejanus has undergone some sort of crisis?'

The Minion stiffened. I hid my smile of satisfaction. I was correct: Macro had known why we were here. Was this a good augury? I closed my eyes and thought of Agrippina's face. I prayed to whatever gods there were that I would survive this ordeal.

'Well, come on!' Tiberius urged.

The Minion spoke quickly, describing Metellus's death. I looked away, trying to distract myself. In the garden beyond grew asparagus and cucumbers, Tiberius's favourite vegetables. They were kept in boxes on wheels so they could be taken in and out of the sun according to the weather. Sometimes he would go for days, eating only these or radishes from Germany. I half listened to the Minion's lies, until a shadow passed in front of the column. Tiberius told the Minion to be quiet. Forgetting myself, I looked up. The new arrival was tall and stoop-backed, with long-fingered hands which dangled like the claws of an animal, their nails curved and dirty. The newcomer's face was sallow and pitted and, like Tiberius, he was bald at the front with a thick crust of hair on the nape of his neck. He came and stood by Tiberius like a faithful dog.

'My good nephew, Gaius!' Tiberius murmured.

By then I had lowered my eyes. 'Little Boots' certainly didn't resemble Agrippina with his dull face, muddy-coloured complexion and eyes like those of an opiate-drinker. Slobbery-lipped and loose-jawed, Caligula looked like an imbecile.

'Continue,' Tiberius murmured.

The Minion did so in a few halting sentences. Tiberius tapped his silver-gilded sandal, an ominous sound like that of a drumbeat accompanying a victim to execution.

'And you are Parmenon?'

Again the Minion stiffened. Tiberius's tone seemed to be more friendly.

'Yes, your Imperial Highness.'

'And you can vouch for all this?'

'I know the truth, Excellency.'

'The truth?' A short, barking laugh. 'If you know the truth, Parmenon, you are, truly, a very fortunate man. You are both dismissed!'

We got up from the cushions, bowed and backed out of the chamber. The Minion was very restless. Red spots appeared high on his cheeks and his agitation only deepened as Macro told him to wait whilst beckoning me to follow him. I crossed the small atrium. Macro pushed me into a doorway, told me to stay there and walked off. The door opened and a hand dragged me inside. Gaius Caligula grinned at me. Believe me, they were a family of fine actors! Gaius's face had changed, it was no longer slack and vacuous, his eyes were a strange light-blue, and his mouth and jaw more composed. He grasped me by the shoulder, and I smelt his wine-drenched breath.

'Well? Does she love me?'

'Agrippina . . . ?'

'Not her! Drusilla!' Gaius snapped, referring to the younger sister.

'Of course, your Excellency!'

Gaius wetted his lips. 'And what do you think of the old cadaver?' His eyes widened and he giggled behind his fingers. 'That's what I call Tiberius. Did you see his face?' he continued. 'There are bits dropping off. The Gods should call him home, eh?' Gaius's eyes gleamed.

Was he mad, I wondered? Or had he taken some juice which stirred his soul and excited his wits.

'You'll see such sights here, Parmenon, believe me! I don't like your companion,' he continued breathlessly. 'Sejanus's turd dropped hot from his anus.'

I stared round the room: it was some sort of writing office with one window overlooking the garden.

'Oh, don't worry,' Caligula reassured me. 'The cadaver can't hear us. Right, what did Agrippina say?'

I delivered Domina's message, and Gaius almost did a jig from foot to foot.

'Got him! Got him! Got him!' he murmured.

He danced away, a grotesque sight with his tall, stooping figure and his strange hair, leaping from foot to foot, hands raised like some priest in a trance. He danced back to me.

'Say it again! Say it again!'

I delivered the full message. Caligula was quick. In spite of his excitement, he'd already memorised it and, opening the door, he pushed me out. Macro was waiting, helmet under his arms. He stretched out his hand. I noticed the bracelet on his wrists, which bore a carving of Castor and Pollux. I had seen a similar one in Agrippina's chamber. Macro drew me close.

'You did well there, Parmenon.'

'How did the Emperor know?' I gasped.

Macro stepped away, playing with the bracelet.

'Because he's a God.'

And, turning on his heel, he led me back to join the Minion, who was in a state of almost nervous collapse: one moment sitting on the marble stone wall bench; the next walking up and down.

'This has never happened before!' he whined. 'Never before!'

I looked round the atrium. Macro had disappeared. The door to Tiberius's chamber was guarded by two burly German ruffians who stood, shields in one hand, drawn swords in the other. The Minion came up and clapped me on the shoulder.

'I hope that bitch hasn't been up to mischief.'

I clicked my tongue and smiled. 'Don't be frightened,' I mocked.

Another hour passed. The doors of the chamber were thrown open and Macro beckoned us forward. We walked in. Tiberius looked as if he hadn't moved. Gaius was standing beside him, immobile as a statue. We went to kneel before them.

'Not you!' Tiberius's voice grated.

I looked up. Tiberius was gesturing at the Minion. He pointed with his thumb over his shoulder at the garden wall.

'You certainly know how to lie!' Tiberius accused. 'You lied to your Emperor! So, let's see if you can fly as well!'

And, before the Minion could protest, the two German auxiliaries who had followed us in, grasped him by the arm and dragged him out into the garden. They pulled him to the edge of the parapet and tossed him over. Dreadful screams shattered the silence. Tiberius made himself comfortable on the chair.

'You see, Macro,' he joked. 'I told you he couldn't fly!'

Chapter 6

'No sober man dances, unless he is mad'
Cicero, *Pro Murena*

For a while the Emperor sat in silence as if savouring
what had happened. Caligula had stepped back so the
Emperor couldn't see his face, shaking with giggles.
The two German mercenaries watched the body fall
and then left.

I heard a singing bird trill out its sweet song, and
the buzzing of a bee, which surprised me as it was
so early in the season. I could only wonder whether
I would be next?

'Kneel back, Parmenon.'

I did so.

'Look at me! Forget Sejanus's advice! Look at
me!'

I did so. The Emperor studied me closely.

'Are you a kinsman of Sejanus?'

'A very distant one, Excellency.'

'And can you fly, Parmenon?'

'No, Excellency, I can only swim.'

The Emperor threw his head back in a neighing laugh. 'Are you a liar, Parmenon?'

'Excellency, I do not know what the truth is.'

'Ah, quite the philosopher. Now, Parmenon, relax, you are not going to fly. Just repeat your message.'

Caligula had moved even further back, his face now alert. He shook his head imperceptibly and tapped his cheek. 'Do not mention me,' he was saying.

I learnt a lot during that interview. Caligula was acting to survive. He was plotting against the Emperor. Macro, who must have seen his secret gestures, was his accomplice. I repeated the secret message, Agrippina's last words to me. Tiberius's face grew livid.

'Do you know what she means about Drusus?' he snapped.

'I don't understand, Excellency. Drusus is a prisoner in the Palatine.'

'She wasn't talking about that Drusus,' Tiberius retorted. 'My son was also called Drusus!'

I swallowed hard. Of course, I'd forgotten that. On his death the rumours had come thick and fast. Many said Tiberius's son had died of overindulgence, whilst other rumours claimed he'd been poisoned. Tiberius took a nut, crushed it in his hand, daintily picked out the fragments and ate them.

'I have a strong hand, Parmenon. Do you know I can poke a child's head and smash his skull?'

He didn't wait for an answer.

'Macro!' He summoned the commander of the guard forward.

'I want letters despatched to Rome. Our friend Parmenon will stay here for a few months. Well, well, we've got business, we've got business!'

I was dismissed with a flick of the fingers. My enforced sojourn at Capri had begun.

Tiberius moved as carefully as a spider weaving its web. He enjoyed the game: he sent letters to Sejanus swearing eternal friendship, and extending his condolences on the death, 'from a fever', of his Minion. He wrote that he wanted me to stay for a while. He even began to hint that Sejanus would be given tribune powers and be allowed to marry Tiberius's widowed daughter-in-law, Drusus's wife. At the same time, passage to and from the mainland was strictly controlled. For the rest I discovered how bizarre Tiberius's existence on Capri really was. Sometimes he could be indulgent, at other times ruthless. A soldier who stole a peacock from the aviary was crucified on the cliff tops. On another occasion when Tiberius was being taken by litter from one villa to another, the bearers stumbled over a bramble bush in their path: the centurion responsible was flogged within an inch of his life.

Tiberius's sexual exploits fascinated me. Capri was a hotbed of sexual intrigue. Macro was married to a beautiful, dark-haired girl called Aemilia. To win Caligula's favour, Macro acted as her pimp and Aemilia was a constant visitor to Caligula's villa. Tiberius's practices, however, were more bizarre. All the rumours about him were true. He had his own private bawdy house where sexual extravangazas were staged for his secret pleasure. Young men and women from all parts of the Empire, adept in unusual sexual practices, would be encouraged to congregate before him in groups of three or four to excite his flagging passion. This bawdy house consisted of a number of rooms decorated with the most obscene pictures and statues available. It even boasted a small library with erotic manuals from Egypt so these sexual athletes could learn exactly what was expected of them.

Macro led me on a tour of all this, like a Roman taking a provincial visitor round the city. The rooms were opulently decorated, drenched in perfume, furnished with couches and stools for the Emperor and his coterie of favourites. Spy-holes had been drilled in the walls, floor and ceiling. The 'Sexual Athletes', as Macro called them, were confined to their own private apartments. They wined and dined on the most exquisite aphrodisiacs and were under strict orders to save their energies for the Emperor alone. Macro also took me into the woods. Special glades had been set aside where boys and girls, dressed as Pans and nymphs, prostituted themselves in caves or grottoes. No wonder the wits had re-named Capri 'the Place of the Goat.' Macro hinted at other obscenities.

After from my initial interview with the Emperor I became, to all intents and purposes, Macro's creature. On one occasion he asked about Agrippina. Was she well? How did she look? Her husband Domitius? Had she taken new lovers? I was pleased I could tell the truth: I knew nothing.

'What will happen?' I asked, trying to change the topic of conversation.

'Be careful,' Macro warned. 'Tiberius can be excitable and as changeable as the moon. Letters have been despatched to Rome with conflicting messages. Sejanus doesn't know whether he's on his head or his arse, if he's still the Emperor's favourite or not.'

Macro scratched the tip of his nose.

'Tiberius could play this game for months, even years. He might forget it or change his mind.'

'And me?' I asked.

'Are you so desperate to get back to Agrippina?' Macro sneered. 'Quite a little courtesan, isn't she? Her brain teems like a snake pit. You should be careful, Parmenon. Tiberius might decide he can't do without Sejanus.'

'And Caligula?' I asked.

Macro breathed in.

'According to all the rules, Gaius Caligula should be dead. To understand Caligula you have to understand Tiberius's mind. I can speak to you bluntly, Parmenon, because no one would believe you if you were to repeat what I say. Tiberius is nourishing Caligula as he would a viper; that young man is to be Tiberius's revenge on Rome.'

'And yet you support him?' I bit my lip immediately.

'Do I?' Macro taunted, drawing his brows together. 'I support no one, Parmenon, except the Emperor. You are new to this game, aren't you?' He drew closer. 'Remember the first and only rule: keep your mouth shut!'

I soon grew tired of Capri and I missed Agrippina. I would have loved to have sent a message but that would have been dangerous, even foolish.

At the beginning of October I was still wondering how I could arrange my departure from Capri when Macro aroused me before dawn on one cold, dark morning.

'Get dressed!' he urged. 'Quickly, we are for Rome!'

Two biremes stood ready in the harbour; one full of marines dressed in half-armour, a savage-looking bunch totally under Macro's command; the second bireme contained members of Tiberius's own personal guard. We clambered aboard and within the hour were heading for a pre-arranged spot somewhere to the south of Rome. No imperial colours were shown and Macro took advantage of the sea mist, as well as the early hour, to keep well clear of the normal shipping lanes. The pilot guided us in, and both biremes beached in a sandy cove some miles south of Ostia. We came ashore like an invasion force: scouts were sent out; fires were lit and breakfast cooked; sentries were deployed. We spent the rest of the day bringing supplies ashore whilst spies crept in from Rome. The news they brought was favourable, the Senate was to meet the following morning.

Once darkness fell Macro marched his troops along the coastline. It was still dark when we reached the Viminial Gate, where Macro displayed the imperial passes and we were allowed entry. How strange to be back in Rome! I was desperate to see Agrippina but Macro's orders were strict: the will of the Emperor was to be carried out and I was Macro's accomplice. The marines and bodyguard marched to the Palatine where Macro concealed them in a small park. He took off his own armour and, in the torchlight, washed and shaved and put on clothes appropriate for a visitor to the Senate. We went up the Palatine, into the exquisitely beautiful heart of Rome with its fluted columns and finely carved statues. The great temple of Apollo, built of gleaming Parian marble, its vast doors inlaid with ivory, dominated this lavish concourse. The Senate was scheduled to meet that morning.

I felt giddy, slightly nervous. It was such a bewildering contrast to the solitude of Capri with its tangled woods, sinister secrets and silent villas. Dawn broke. Macro, easily hiding his tension, sat on a marble bench at the top of the steps leading into the temple; whilst the officers of the marine guard and I stood behind him. The sky turned a blue-pink as the sun began to rise. The braying of horns and conch blasts shattered the silence as the city came to life. Senators appeared, dressed in their white togas, with scribes and house retainers behind, carrying parchment and leather bags. They all stared nervously at Macro who nodded but sat impassive.

Sejanus, of course, had heard the news of our arrival and came hurrying up with his entourage. No longer so calm and self-possessed, he looked red-eyed and wary. Macro rose to meet him, but Sejanus waited at the foot of the steps until his Praetorians deployed around him in a semi-circle: a grim threatening ring of steel. The soldiers were dressed in their red and leather kilts, greaves, boots, embossed breast-plates, and plumed helmets. Each carried an oblong shield, and all had their swords drawn.

'Macro!' Sejanus raised his hand in salute. 'I heard you had come from Capri. I was growing impatient. The Emperor has sent messages?'

Macro took a scroll from beneath his toga and beamed.

'Aelius Sejanus, Prefect of the city!' he proclaimed. 'I have brought fresh honours from your Emperor. You are to be given tribunician powers. The Emperor is eager you use your authority to root out sedition and treason in the city.'

Sejanus seemed to swell in relief. Macro came down the steps, and they clasped hands and embraced. Sejanus grabbed the scroll from Macro and pushed by him, smiling triumphantly at me as he swept into the temple. Macro watched him go and coolly re-took his seat. The news, of course, had soon spread through the wealthy quarters, and other senators now came hurrying up, eager to learn the news. They ignored

Macro as they poured through the huge doorway. Once this was closed, a sign that the session was about to begin, Macro turned to his officers.

'Bring the lads up!' he ordered.

The men hurried off. I heard the blowing of whistles and then Macro's marines, followed by the Emperor's bodyguard, came up the steps and deployed in the great courtyard before the temple of Apollo. The Praetorian officer in charge of Sejanus's guard became nervous. His anxiety deepened as more armed men appeared led by Laco, Prefect of the Night Watch.

'Don't be anxious!' Macro called and got up.

The Praetorian Guard now broke rank, some resheathed their swords. Macro handed their commander a letter.

'Fresh orders from your Emperor!' he proclaimed. 'You are to be praised and rewarded. Your first duty is to return to camp.'

Their commander quickly read the letter, shrugged, rolled it up and stuck it in his belt. Then, without a by your leave, he ordered his men to fall in and marched them quickly away.

Their position on the steps was now taken by Macro's men. He plucked me by the arm.

'Let's join our worthy senators,' he grinned. 'Sejanus is about to learn his future.'

We entered the temple by a side door, and a worried-looking priest led us along the marble corridor into the huge assembly chamber. It was arranged like that of an amphitheatre with tiers of marble seats which flanked a soaring statue of Apollo the Hunter. The senior Consul, Regulus, was already on the rostrum. Sejanus was seated to his right on the lowest tier, surrounded by his coterie, smiling like a triumphant general. Mennius had already begun to read out Augustus's letter, which was full of praise for Sejanus. Macro and I stood within the doorway, watching as the Senate sat in silence, nodding in agreement at the praise being heaped on the Emperor's favourite. Mennius droned on, but imperceptibly both the tone and tenor of the letter had changed: now trivial complaints surfaced about Sejanus. The smile faded from the favourite's face, as the other senators sat puzzled. A few began to withdraw from Sejanus, just a slight shift. Mennius paused and then resumed reading the letter, in which Tiberius confessed to fears about his own safety, stating that he was an old man and needed fresh troops on Capri to guard him.

Mennius thundered on, warming to his task, slowly quoting Tiberius's words. '"Much as I would wish to come to Rome, I find myself unable to do so due to fears for my safety. It would be too dangerous for me to be within reach of the man who has betrayed me."' Mennius paused. '"Aelius Sejanus! I demand his arrest for high treason!"'

Chaos and consternation broke out. The doors at the back of the hall opened, and tribunes and centurions poured in. Macro laughed quietly as some of the senators scampered away like puppies. Sejanus stared in shock.

'You have heard your Emperor's wishes?' Mennius called. 'Sejanus is to be arrested!'

When a man like Sejanus falls, it is as sudden and as quick as a star dropping out of the heavens. The very people who'd applauded and greeted, fawned and flattered him when he first entered the Senate that morning, now turned on him. Blows rained down, he was kicked and shoved whilst his close adherents tried to flee. As Macro pushed his way through, I seized the opportunity to slip away.

Agrippina was in her quarters, sitting by a window and pretending to read. She greeted me as if I had only been away a few hours. By now the news of Sejanus's downfall had spread and, from the yard below, came the sound of running feet, shouts and cries. Agrippina put down the scroll she had been reading, a copy of Horace's *Odes*. She smiled and, standing on tiptoe, kissed me on the cheek. She was paler and thinner, those dark eyes more rounded.

'What's happening?'

'Sejanus has fallen,' I replied. 'He's been arrested. Macro, I suspect, will become Prefect of the Praetorian Guard. Tiberius has begun the attack.'

Agrippina put her hands together, closed her eyes and smiled. She lowered her head and glanced at a group of serving girls in the far corner of the room.

'Do you hear that?' she yelled. 'Sejanus has fallen. It's prison for him and all his followers.' She walked forward. 'Now's your opportunity to confess! Which of you are his spies?'

The girls huddled together. Agrippina advanced

119

threateningly. 'Come on, now's your chance to confess. If I find out later, it will be the strangler's noose.'

Three girls stepped forward.

'I thought as much.' Agrippina pointed towards the door. 'Get out!'

The maids fled. The upset and chaos had reached the gallery outside, and there were shouts of despair, the sound of doors being kicked open and closed. I looked out through the window: already people were fleeing the Palatine with bundles on their backs. The reign of terror had begun. Agrippina walked back, eyes glittering. She caught at my arm and made me sit on the couch beside her.

'Are you safe, Domina?'

'For the time being, yes.' She smiled coldly. 'Sejanus hated my family so we can hardly be regarded as his friends. And how is our August Emperor?'

'Rotting,' I replied. 'Though his brain is still sharp and his reach is long.'

Agrippina played a tattoo on her knee with her fingers.

'He will die soon enough. And what of my sweet brother Gaius?'

'A dog,' I replied. 'The Emperor's faithful shadow.'

Agrippina breathed in noisily. 'So, he still plays the part?' she murmured.

'Domina, your brother is insane. Anyone who stays in Capri for long . . . !'

'He can be managed, he will be managed,' she replied.

'Well, what's this?' A man, his hair and beard the colour of copper, lurched through the door. He was dressed in a tunic and toga which were purple stained, and, despite the early hour, he carried a deep-bowled cup. One of his sandals was loose and it slapped on the floor as he staggered across to Agrippina. He stopped to paw at one of the serving girl's breasts.

'Domitius,' Agrippina cooed, her voice and smile full of false sweetness. 'Domitius, you've been partying again, haven't you?'

She went across to him. He glared over her shoulder at me.

'Who's that?' he slurred. 'He's too ugly to be a lover. And what's happening outside? There are soldiers everywhere with drawn swords and there's a corpse in the yard. Someone stabbed him in the back.'

'Sejanus has fallen.'

Agrippina ordered me with her eyes to leave the couch, as she steered her drunken husband towards it. 'You are too tired,' she soothed, 'for all this excitement.'

She loosened the cup from his hand, put it on the floor and persuaded him to lie down on the couch. For a while she stared contemptuously down at his drunken face.

'Drunken sot!' she declared. 'He'll sleep for hours and wake with a headache.' She came over and grasped my hand. 'Parmenon, the blood-letting has begun. You must keep a still tongue in your head, and say nothing about Capri, the Emperor or my brother Gaius. And you must keep your distance from Macro!'

'Is he your lover?' I blurted out.

'I have no lovers, Parmenon. Only men I have to deal with.'

'And me?'

'Why, Parmenon, you are my right hand. We are one.' She glanced towards the door. 'Go and see what happens to Sejanus and report back to me. Remember what I have said!'

She pushed me out of the room. In the corridor she held me back.

'You have done well, Parmenon.' Her voice was excited. 'You and I are locked together like spokes in a wheel: don't you understand that?'

A scream echoed up the stairs. One of the soldiers was helping himself to a slave girl.

'You left me vulnerable,' I accused.

'Don't moan!' Agrippina's face turned ugly. 'Remember the arena. You wanted to enter, so now you must fight or you die. Do what you have to!' Her face softened. She waggled her fingers, like a little girl saying goodbye, and went back into the room.

The Palatine was now in uproar. Macro, using the Emperor's warrant, had ringed the entire hill with troops from the Urban Cohort. These had already caught some of Sejanus's followers who were being led off to the city prisons with bound hands and bloody faces. A few members of Sejanus's personal bodyguard had attempted resistance, only to die in an untidy, bloody heap in a corner of the square. Macro's men recognised me and I was let through. I raced up the steps leading to the great enclosure of the Temple of Apollo, where there were more corpses and ever-widening pools of blood. Severed heads already decorated the spikes which fringed the Stairs of Sighs.

In the colonnades I glimpsed the bodies of more victims, strung up from iron torch-holders and left to swing softly in the morning breeze. I reached the temple doors where Macro stood surrounded by his officers.

'You have been to see Agrippina, haven't you?' Macro sneered. 'Clever and quick as a rat, eh? You should . . .'

His words were drowned by a roar from inside the temple. Sejanus, a parody of what he had been, was dragged out, his face bloody, his clothes torn. As he was pushed towards Macro, I saw that his mouth was nothing but a bloody mess: the clicking tongue had been silenced for ever. Macro stared, head to one side, as if he couldn't really believe what he was seeing.

'Well, well, Sejanus,' he sighed. 'Life is like a game of dice.'

Sejanus's eyes turned to me with a flicker of recognition. I hardly recognised his bruised and battered face. The hair had been torn from his head, oozing cuts sliced his arms and shoulders, there were even teeth marks where his enemies had bitten him. He opened his mouth in a hideous moan.

'What's that?' Macro asked, leaning forward. 'You

want to see the Emperor? Rome can no longer tolerate such treason.' His voice rose. 'Bring him with
me!'

Macro gestured at me to follow, in what was
supposed to be a triumphant procession across the
Palatine to Sejanus's palace. Macro swaggered in
front surrounded by his guards, their shields up
and swords drawn. Sejanus, now bound by ropes,
was led like a reluctant horse, as the assembled
mob hurled abuse at him. Men, women and children
pushed and shoved at him, pelting him with rotten
food and other missiles, spitting and cursing at the
Emperor's fallen favourite. Our journey became a
trail of blood, until even Macro tired of the fun.
The guards drove the mob off as we entered the
colonnades. We crossed a garden, went down some
steps and I found myself in the same torture chamber
I'd visited when I had first met Sejanus. The guards
were left in the corridor. Macro's officers, myself
included, watched as the prisoner was made to squat
on a stool. The executioners stepped forward, their
faces covered by ghastly animal masks. A noose was
placed round Sejanus's throat, and a small, steel rod
was slipped through the knot, which the executioner
slowly turned. I glanced away, as terrible groans and
gasps came from the dying man. One of Macro's men
joked about eyes popping out. Sejanus's feet beat the
floor to the jeers and laughter of the onlookers. Once
it was over, hooks were fastened to the corpse and
it was dragged out along the passageway, through
the city and thrown down the Steps of Mourning.

The mob were encouraged to tear and pluck at it, so viciously that the executioner had difficulty in finding a piece of flesh big enough to place the hooks in to drag Sejanus's corpse down to the Tiber.

As the old year gave way to the new, the killings, proscriptions and denunciations gathered pace. It was the age of the informer and spy. Every week Tiberius sent a list from Capri denouncing his enemies, even his friends. Father turned on son, brother against brother. Some men acted nobly. One senator, when accused of being a friend of Sejanus, rose in the Senate and proclaimed.

'Yes, I was and so was Tiberius. I was proud of being Sejanus's friend. What treason is there in that?'

His courage and ability saved him. Others were not so fortunate. Agrippina and I became silent observers of the mounting horror. She refused to leave the palace but stayed in her quarters or walked in the garden.

'Will the Emperor now show mercy to your mother and Drusus?' I asked.

Agrippina was painting a doll, a gift for the daughter of one of her handmaids.

'Tiberius never forgets and never forgives. He will compromise. Gaius and his sisters will survive but there will be no mercy shown to the rest.'

She held the doll up, her tongue half-sticking out of her mouth as she painted its face.

'I'll keep quiet and hide deep in the shadows.' She put the brush down and wiped her fingers on a rag.

'It's going to be a pretty doll, isn't it, Parmenon? If I can't have children at least I can look after those of others.'

'Why can't you have children?'

'You could have taught them grammar, Parmenon. I should have said, won't.' Her eyes became fierce and hard. 'I'll never have children whilst that monster on Capri lives. Until he's dead, no one's safe.'

Agrippina's prophecy was as shrewd as it was accurate. Apicata, Sejanus's estranged wife, wrote a letter to Tiberius denouncing her dead husband as the murderer of Tiberius's son Drusus. She then took a warm bath, opened her veins and escaped the Emperor's vengeance. The news drove Tiberius to the edge of madness: no possible rival was safe. On Pandateria, Agrippina's mother was starved to death. Her brother Drusus was never released from prison; he died a starving madman, tearing and eating the stuffing from his own mattress.

More deaths occurred. Tiberius's old colleague, Sextus Letillus, opened his veins when the Emperor denounced him but promptly closed them, thinking he might escape with a begging letter. When he received Tiberius's reply, he quickly opened his veins again and announced that he welcomed death. One senator took poison in the Senate, drinking it cheerfully whilst he denounced Tiberius's cruelty and rapacity. Another senator, Sabinus, was executed and his body exposed on the Steps of Mourning. His faithful dog brought food every day and placed it close to the dead man's mouth. Even when the corpse was thrown into the Tiber, the animal plunged into the water and kept it afloat before the admiring gaze of the people, who saw it as a clear sign of the dead man's innocence.

Youth and innocence were no defence. Sejanus's children went under the knife. His son was old enough to know what was happening, but his young daughter, distraught, kept asking everyone what she had done wrong and where was she being taken? As she was a virgin, the executioner violated the girl immediately before strangling her. Both corpses were exposed to the public view.

I tried to draw Agrippina into conversation about what would happen next but she shook her head. She never mourned her mother or brother: that was too dangerous and could be taken as treason. She grew thinner, paler. She went to bed late and rose early, busying herself with humdrum tasks. I was aware of her tension. Sometimes she would let me embrace her or hold her hand but then she would push me away. Some days she'd disappear and come back red-eyed, with bruises on her arms and legs. I suspected she was visiting Macro, Rome's new master, and her only link with Tiberius. Days, months and years slid one into the other. If Agrippina kept free of the politics of Rome, she also ensured I did the same. I was never entrusted with any secret tasks or sent on mysterious errands. Instead I became her steward and secretary, kept busy organising stores and purchasing goods. Occasionally I would be sent out to her villa at Antium to check that all was well there.

'You've done well,' she once remarked. 'What you did in Capri, Parmenon, was more than enough. I will keep you like an arrow in my quiver. Hidden from public gaze until the time comes . . .'

Chapter 7

'O fairer daughter of a fair Mother!'
Horace, *Odes*: I:16

Early in the spring of Tiberius's last year, just after a Roman force had been ambushed and cut to pieces by the Frisians on the empire's northern border and the survivors cruelly tortured, Agrippina dropped her mask.

At first I thought it was the break in the weather: a sudden, glorious spring had transformed Rome in bursts of golden sunlight, fresh flowers, and sweetness in the air. The blood bath had begun to abate; the list of proscriptions appearing less often in the Forum as Tiberius became more engrossed with the security of Rome's frontiers. The change in Agrippina began almost imperceptibly, but once I had noticed it, I realised that her spirit had revived. She met me early one afternoon, in one of those flowery grottoes so lovingly designed by imperial gardeners. She'd been reading poetry again and talked about visiting the theatre. She looked round like a young girl ready for mischief, placed her reading tray on the turf seat beside her, got up and put her arms round my neck.

'Parmenon, I am pregnant!'

She seemed so excited, so full of life. I tried to hide my jealousy. 'Which means,' I replied sourly, 'Tiberius must be dying.'

This was one of those bitter remarks which slip from your tongue before you can think. It was also highly dangerous. On any other occasion Agrippina would have been angry but today she drew me closer, those dark eyes bubbling with laughter.

'Parmenon, you should be an astrologer. The monster is dying!'

Now I was nervous. I pulled away and went to the edge of the arbour and stared round the garden. Agrippina was always cunning: there was no one about.

'You don't believe me do you?' she asked. 'Parmenon, the old cadaver is dying at last. I doubt if he'll last till summer.'

'How do you know this?'

'Oh I do. But you have fresh orders: you're to visit Tiberius.'

'Orders?' I demanded. 'Is that what I am now, Domina, your lackey?'

'Parmenon, Parmenon.' She held her stomach. 'Believe me, if I thought Tiberius would live, I would never have conceived.'

'How?' I whispered.

'Oh the usual way,' she laughed. 'Domitius got into my bed and I gave him free rein.'

'No,' I contradicted. 'Tiberius?'

'The queen of all poisons, Parmenon. Aconite.'

I stared in disbelief. Agrippina, even then, had an interest in the collection and mixing of poisons. Aconite, ground from herbs grown in the Alps, was rare, powerful and went under many names: wolf's-bane, woman's-bane. Its effects were very much like dropsy: alternating bouts of heat and chill, numbness of the limbs, tingling in the mouth and throat, giddiness, loss of feeling.

'Caligula?' I asked.

'He's quite the gardener.' Agrippina could hardly stop laughing. 'You know how Tiberius likes his vegetables? Well, he encouraged Gaius to be a gardener and my darling brother faithfully followed the Emperor's orders. "Little Boots" has got more poisons than I have in my cupboard. Remember the message you took to Caligula about his salvation being on Capri? It was a reference to Aconite specially grown there. Gaius has been killing Tiberius drop by drop, mixing it with his snails and cream, and a little with his wine.' She giggled behind her fingers. 'Sometimes it was even mixed in with dishes of horseradish and we all know how much Tiberius likes his radishes!'

'He might be caught?'

'Caught? Someone else will take the blame.'

'I thought Tiberius took antidotes to all poisons?'

'He does. He's a regular medicine chest. You've heard the phrase, "creaking doors hang longer". Tiberius has so many ailments he doesn't really know what's happening.' She stepped closer. 'Aconite, if fed long enough, will overcome any antidote. Gaius has simply increased the usual dosage.'

'And why now?' I asked, looking furtively over my shoulder.

'Oh, don't be so nervous, Parmenon. Macro knows everything, and this garden is guarded by his best men.'

'Why now?' I repeated.

Her face became grave. 'If Tiberius lives, Parmenon, he'll take all our necks. Can't you see that? In the years that have passed since Sejanus's death, Tiberius has started to reflect and regret, wondering whether Macro was part of a more sinister plot. With my mother and two of my brothers dead only my two sisters and I are left, apart from Gaius. Tiberius might decide to make a clean sweep.'

She plucked a parchment from beneath her robe and handed it to me. I undid it carefully: the writing was scrawled like that of a child.

'Tiberius was never good with a pen,' Agrippina declared.

The very first word chilled me: *Proscripti* – the Proscribed. Tiberius spent his time drawing up lists of those he would like to see strangled. The ink on this list was faded.

'It was written some months ago,' Agrippina explained.

The list was long. Some of the men and women on it had already died. After a gap, some new names appeared: Agrippina, her two sisters, Drusilla and Julia, Macro, and Parmenon. I thrust the parchment back.

'When do I leave?' I demanded.

'As soon as possible. At the moment Tiberius is in Campania, roaming up and down the countryside, too frightened to enter Rome, but he intends to sail for Capri very soon. Once he gets back there, he'll return to his death lists. Macro has prepared well for this. He's already been in touch with the generals on the frontiers and their loyalty is assured.'

She went and sat on the seat, crossed her legs and leaned back, eyes half closed, gently rubbing her stomach.

'Tiberius must not return to Capri. He already thinks he's going to die, he's been having visions. A new statue of Apollo, which is to be erected in the Senate library, apparently appeared to him in a dream and said: "Tiberius, you will never dedicate me." There have been fires that are suddenly extinguished or abruptly flare up. Tiberius's pet snake, which he fed with his own hands and was the only creature which would come anywhere near him, abruptly died and was eaten by a swarm of ants.' She leaned forward. 'Caligula would have enjoyed arranging that. I must ask him how he did it. Tiberius is agitated; he left Capri and came up the Tiber in a trireme, posting troops along both banks so that no one could see him. He's presently at Misenum: Caligula and Macro are there with him.'

'What am I to do?'

'Make sure that Tiberius does die,' she whispered. 'And when he does, return immediately to Rome.'

I reached Misenum late the following evening, and it was apparent how grave matters had become. Cavalry units and squads of Praetorians patrolled every path to and from the imperial villa. The house itself was like a mausoleum with everyone tiptoeing around. Macro and Caligula met me in the gardens. The soldier was the same as ever, cynical and mocking, but Caligula had changed. He was now taller, but more stooped, his head balding, his eyes deep-set, a cynical sneer twisted the cruel mouth, and his arms were covered in thick, black hair. He reminded me of an ape I'd once seen in the arena. He was drinking deeply and couldn't sit still, walking up and down the path, staring up at the dark-blue sky. Occasionally, he'd turn away, muttering and talking to someone we couldn't see.

'What's the matter with him?' I whispered.

Macro put a finger to his lips and led me away.

'He's talking to his Daemon, which you must never ask him about. He's drunk, tired and agitated. He still believes Tiberius will order his execution!'

'What's that? What's that?' Caligula came striding back up the path. 'I want to go to Rome, Macro!'

'Very soon, Excellency.'

'I want to see my sister, Drusilla. Have you seen

Drusilla, Parmenon?' Tears glistened in his eyes. 'She's beautiful. She's got breasts.' He pointed to a statue of Venus. 'And her bottom; I always said she had the sweetest bottom in Rome. Have you seen her, Parmenon? I am going to make her Empress.'

I had seen Drusilla on one occasion, a lithe, olive-skinned girl. I'd also heard rumours of how Caligula's aunt had found brother and sister in bed together.

'You can't have ever seen my sister,' Caligula continued, tapping me on the shoulder. 'If you had, you would be full of her praises.' He slurped from the wine cup. 'So, when is the old goat going to die, Macro? And why are you here, Parmenon?'

He turned away and talked over his shoulder. 'Where's Gemellus?'

'Your Excellency,' Macro soothed. 'Parmenon brings messages from your sister Agrippina.'

'Oh, the sly one, the sly one!' Caligula's fingers went to his mouth, deep in thought.

Darkness was falling. The breeze from the sea had turned cold. It brought a smell of olives, figs and salt. The sky was filling with cloud, dark blotches hiding the stars. The trees rustled and shook. I felt frightened. This truly was a place of demons. I wished I was back in Rome.

Caligula took a deep breath.

'It's good to see you, Parmenon.' His tone had changed. He linked his arm through mine as if we were the best of friends. 'Have you ever been to Misenum before? You should come more often: the mussels are marvellous. You are going to have supper

135

with us, aren't you? The old goat thinks if he keeps eating he'll keep living.' He sniggered beneath his breath, stopped and looked at my head. 'You've got a full head of hair, Parmenon. Isn't it a pity we can't exchange heads?'

His face came forward as if expecting an answer. Agrippina had told me to take care over this, never to stare at Caligula's hair or mention his increasing baldness. He tapped his forehead.

'A wasted dome,' he muttered. 'Isn't it, Parmenon?'

I looked over his shoulder. Macro's eyes were watchful.

'Excellency,' I replied. 'You have the face and head of an Emperor. You have the face and head of a God. You are not like us mere mortals.'

Caligula threw his head back in a raucous laugh. He seized my face between his hands and kissed me full on the lips. 'When you first came to Capri, Parmenon, I knew you were touched. He has visions, Macro! I'll never forget what you said.'

Then the lunatic was off, striding up the path, arms swinging, chuckling loudly to himself.

By the time the guards allowed us into the Emperor's supper room, Caligula was transformed, quietly composed. Macro introduced me but all I could see was a figure sitting in the darkness.

'Come here!' The voice was full and strong.

I stepped into the pool of light before the couch and dropped quickly to my knees.

'Who are you? Look at me!'

Tiberius's face was ghastly: it was a dirty white,

with the lines round his mouth more pronounced
and the cheeks sunken. The sores had got worse,
so that now it was a suppurating mess, from which
the slanted eyes gleamed frenetically. I didn't know
whether it was due to the fever, the poison or the
light from the oil lamps. Tiberius scratched one of
the ulcers on his face and touched my cheek.

'Parmenon! Have you brought news?'

'Excellency,' Macro replied. 'He comes from Rome,
where all is well.'

'Now that's a lie. Rome is never well. Sit down,
sit down!'

I took my place on the couch provided. The table
was laid simply, with bread, figs, some apples, cher-
ries, stuffed dates and an amphora of wine. The
meal was eaten in silence. Afterwards the Emper-
or's physician Charicles came in and sat on the
edge of the Emperor's couch. The Emperor greeted
him, hand extended. Charicles's fingers rested on
the Emperor's wrist as if taking his pulse: Tiberius
didn't seem to be aware of this. Charicles looked
at Macro and nodded. Caligula got up and brought
across his own cup of wine, and Tiberius drank from
it. Macro started some innocuous conversation but
I was hardly listening. It was one of the strangest
supper parties I had ever attended. Tiberius began to
groan and moan, gesturing with his fingers for Macro
to keep quiet, and the cup Caligula had given him fell
from his hand. Charicles, assisted by Macro, helped
Tiberius to his feet, and Caligula came to help. I was
instructed to follow as they half carried the Emperor

from the dining-room along a marble passageway to his private bedchamber. No guards challenged us, no one interfered. The bed chamber smelt stale and musty. Once the door was closed, all protocol was dropped. Tiberius was tipped on the bed, his head made comfortable on the bolsters.

'I have done what I can.' Charicles spoke through the darkness. 'I can do no more.'

He left. Caligula lit an oil lamp, hands shaking.

'It must be tonight.' Macro stood on the far side of the Emperor's bed. 'Tiberius must never leave for Capri.'

The Emperor moaned and groaned, his head thrashing from side to side. Macro ordered me to bring a lamp across. He pulled back Tiberius's eyelids and felt the pulse in his throat.

'Weak,' he muttered. 'He'll never last the night.'

Caligula was breathing heavily like an athlete who'd run far and fast, a hoarse, rasping sound which jarred the nerves and prickled the hair on the nape of my neck.

'If he leaves for Capri,' Macro repeated, 'we'll all be in danger!' He brought a sheet up and tossed it across the Emperor's chest. 'We will all stand guard.'

We left the chamber and waited outside. The night wore on, until, just before dawn, Charicles returned. Macro led him into the bedroom, and I heard a shout of triumph. Charicles came out followed by a grinning Macro.

'The Emperor is dead!' Macro grasped Caligula's right arm and raised it. 'Long live the Emperor!'

It was as if the clouds had lifted and the very walls had ears. Within a short space of time the news had swept through the villa. Macro and Agrippina had organised everything well. The Praetorian Guard assembled outside the main entrance, joined by the household as well as visiting senators, as Macro led Caligula out, with me trailing behind. In the presence of all, Macro placed Tiberius's great seal ring on Caligula's finger. The guards drew their swords and clashed their shields, proclaiming Caligula as Emperor. His elevation to the purple was greeted by a roar of approval. I could already see small clouds of dust round the gate as horsemen left for Rome. Charicles crept up beside me, pale, sweaty and shaking.

'What's the matter, man?'

'Tiberius!' The word croaked from the back of his throat. 'He's alive!'

The word spread like a ripple. Macro spun round, his swarthy face pale. Caligula became like a little boy lost, shoulders hunched, he stared open-mouthed then gibbered with fright. Somehow the whisper reached the men below, and the Praetorian Guard became restless. The crowd began to break up and drift away.

'It can't be! It mustn't be!' The words slipped out of my mouth.

All I could think of was Agrippina's face. If Tiberius lived another day, Caligula would go into the dark, his sister with him. I doubted if I'd survive long either.

I ran back into the building and down the passageway. The patter of footsteps behind told me that Macro and Caligula were following. I burst into the bedchamber. Tiberius was standing in his night shift, those hideous eyes glaring at me. He brought his hand up, fingers splayed.

'Where is my ring?' The voice was strong. 'Parmenon, that's your name, isn't it?' He pointed a bony finger. 'You were sent by that bitch in Rome.'

Macro and Caligula followed me into the bedchamber . . .

'Where is my ring?' The voice rang out as if from beyond the grave.

'I have your ring.' I walked towards the Emperor. 'You are dead, Tiberius.'

He blinked. Macro kicked the door shut. I pushed Tiberius back onto the bed. Macro and Caligula came over to help. The Emperor tried to resist but was overcome by weakness once more. Macro pulled the sheet up as Caligula grabbed a bolster. He held his hand out before Tiberius's eyes, so the old Emperor could see the seal ring on his finger. The bolster was placed over Tiberius's face, as Caligula giggled. 'Go to sleep! Go to sleep!' he crooned. 'Go to sleep and leave us alone!'

There was a hammering on the door but Macro had pulled the bolts across. Tiberius was kicking out frantically as Caligula pressed down harder.

'Go to sleep, sweetest Uncle! You are dead, stay dead!'

At last Tiberius's body lay still. Caligula took the

bolster away, and Tiberius's sightless eyes stared up at the ceiling. Macro opened the door and Charicles burst in and went across to the bed.

'You were wrong,' Caligula declared. 'Uncle is dead, isn't he?'

Charicles felt the pulse in the neck. Caligula grabbed Tiberius's wrist and, from beneath his toga he drew a small dagger and sliced the dead man's wrist.

'Watch the blood seep out and let it fall!'

He rushed out into the passageway.

'False alarm!' he shouted like a child playing a game. 'A mistake! He is dead! The Emperor Tiberius is dead, his soul is with the Gods!'

He paused and spoke over his shoulder to that mysterious person none of us could see. He lapsed into the doggerel Latin of the slums but I caught the word, '*Debet, debet*, it has to be, it has to be!' He ran back into the bed chamber and grasped me by the shoulder. He'd changed once more into the powerful, new Emperor, eyes searching, lips pursed as if on the brink of an important decision.

'You have a cool nerve, Parmenon, and courage! I shall not forget!' He glanced round me. 'Oh, put a sheet over that dirty, old man. He's disgusting!'

Tiberius's face was now livid, the ulcers and carbuncles oozing pus.

'Come on!' Caligula declared. 'I want the treasure chest brought out, so that I can give donatives to the guards. Let's burn the old goat and take his ashes back to Rome!'

Within an hour, thanks to Macro's careful work, the surprise and shock caused by Tiberius's recovery disappeared. It was politic not even to mention it. The Emperor had died in his sleep; that was the end of the matter. Fresh couriers were despatched to Rome and the generals on the frontier. Tiberius was dead: Caligula was the new Emperor. Nobody mentioned the co-heir, Gemellus, although Caligula immediately despatched guards to place him under house arrest. Macro looked at me and shrugged.

'It's Agrippina's wish,' he declared. 'Gemellus won't see the year out.'

Agrippina arrived the next day, accompanied by her two sisters Julia and Drusilla. Caligula met them in the main garden. He was dressed in his toga but insisted on wearing the sandals of a dancer, and a floral wreath on his balding head. Macro was trying to school him on how to act appropriately in public, but as soon as he saw his family, all pretence was forgotten. A small banquet was served of stuffed dates, a patina full of elderberries, succulent pig, boiled partridge and stuffed hare, white and red wines. Only his sisters and private entourage were invited. The rest were kept out by the Praetorians who ringed the garden in a circle of steel. Caligula hugged and kissed his sisters. He treated Drusilla as if she was his wife, embracing her, kissing her face, throat and breast, holding her closely, curling his fingers through her black, perfume-drenched hair.

After the banquet, Caligula insisted on giving us

a dance of triumph. I sat at the foot of Agrippina's couch and watched that madman, dressed like a cadaverous Bacchus, cavort and leap about, whilst we all pretended he was the best dancer and singer in the world, excelling even the most professional artiste from Syracuse. He also sang a coarse song about his uncle, which undoubtedly contained very funny lines, and the wine we'd all drank helped us laugh. I glanced across at Agrippina. My mistress wasn't amused. Her face looked fuller with more sheen and colour than I'd seen for many a month. She wasn't looking at Caligula but at Macro, and her eyes had a hard, imperious glare, as if she held the new Praetorian Prefect responsible for this nonsense. Once the Emperor had calmed down, he returned to his feasting, insisting that Drusilla share his couch. Agrippina took me away to the coolness of a cypress grove, where she questioned me closely about Tiberius's death.

'And what do you think of our new Emperor, Parmenon?'

She gestured across to where Caligula, now he'd rested, was busy berating the small gaggle of musicians on what tune they should play for his second dance.

'If the guards see such behaviour,' I replied. 'Rome could have three Emperors in one year.'

'You mean Gemellus?' she demanded. Agrippina followed my gaze sorrowfully. 'Tiberius corrupted him but he can be managed, at least for a while.'

'How?' I demanded.

'You'll see.' Agrippina was gnawing at her lips and patting her stomach.

'You are going to have to keep Caligula alive for quite a while, aren't you?' I asked.

'We will have to ensure that no wife ever bears him a child,' Agrippina acknowledged.

'And your child?' I asked.

'My son,' she declared haughtily, 'will one day be Emperor. Remember my words, Parmenon. Now, let's get my idiot brother off to bed!'

She walked back across the grass and had words with Macro. She urged the almost collapsing Caligula to retire for the night and, half-carrying him, helped by Drusilla, left the party.

Agrippina didn't reappear that night. The next morning I was in the kitchen, listening to a cook describe how to serve milk-fed snails and what sauce to use for young tunny fish, when Agrippina appeared. She looked pale-faced and red-eyed. She imperiously ordered the cook away and told me to follow her out into the garden. She took me over to a small grotto, a stone arch covered by a rambling rose bush.

'We leave for Rome this evening. Our Emperor,' she referred meaningfully to Caligula, 'has now recovered.' She looked at me narrow-eyed. 'He thinks very highly of you, Parmenon, and says he'll never forget your services. You're not thinking of changing horses mid-stream, are you?'

I glowered at her.

'I thought as much.' She smiled and glanced up.

Caligula was walking across the lawn towards us, one arm round Drusilla's shoulder.

'Good morning, Parmenon.' He stopped and stared down at me.

I was dumbfounded. Was this the same Caligula as the night before? The prancing madman? The drunkard pawing at his sister? He was now clean-shaven and clear-eyed. His toga, and the tunic beneath, were spotlessly white. He had sandals, displaying the imperial seal, on his feet, and his hands were scrubbed, with neatly manicured fingernails. Drusilla, on the other hand, despite her olive-skinned beauty, looked as if she hadn't slept a wink the night before.

'Well, Parmenon, is that the way to greet your Emperor?'

I slipped to my knees. He patted me on the head.

'I was only joking. None of that here!'

I re-took my seat, as he hugged Drusilla.

'We leave for Rome. Have you heard the news?' He laughed, a short, barking sound unlike his usual high-pitched giggle. 'The mob are mad with delight. Crowds roam the streets shouting, "Tiberius for the Tiber! Tiberius for the Tiber!" I think it's best if we burnt the raddled goat's corpse here and take the ashes to Augustus's mausoleum.'

He continued with other plans. I was astonished. Caligula spoke lucidly, clearly mapping out the days ahead, and the changes he would bring about in Rome. He deeply regretted that he had not immediately issued pardons: Tiberius's victims were still being strangled in the prisons of Rome. He said he wished to send envoys to Parthia to seek assurances that Rome's borders would be secure. He declared sorrowfully that one of his first duties must be to recover the ashes of his mother and two brothers and give them honourable burial in Rome. Satisfied at his plans, Caligula nodded cheerfully at me and Agrippina and walked back across the grass.

'He's sleeping with her, isn't he?'

'I didn't hear that!' Agrippina sat as immobile as a statue.

'Domina,' I replied. 'If you don't hear it from me, you'll hear it from others. The Emperor is sleeping with his own sister. Is that the price you paid?'

'I had no choice,' Agrippina replied softly. 'He needs Drusilla.' She glanced at me. 'We are all demons, Parmenon. And can you blame us, brought up in the shadow of Tiberius's bloody hand? You never met Livia, Tiberius's mother! One day with her would chill your soul.'

'Did you encourage him?' I asked.

'Encourage him! Encourage him!' She glared at me. 'Do you think I like this, Parmenon?' she whispered. 'Did I ask to be born into the purple? Did I ask to be raised by someone like Livia? To depend, for every breath of my life, on men like Tiberius and Sejanus? To be given to that drunken oaf Domitius in marriage! To be terrified,' – she touched her belly – 'of becoming pregnant lest a demon like Tiberius whip the child away from me! To have a brother like Caligula? To have my mother starved to death, and my brother reduced to eating the straw out of his mattress?' She sprang to her feet, rubbing her arms as if cold. 'Caligula has been sleeping with Drusilla since they were children. They used to clutch each other at night like terrified little rabbits. I tried to stop them, and so did my aunt. Mother suspected but . . .' She shook her head. 'If Drusilla can keep him sane, then let him have what he wants. After all, the Pharaohs of Egypt married their half-sisters.' She glanced over her shoulder at me. 'Anyway, what do you advise, Parmenon?' she asked sardonically. 'That I give him a lecture on morality? Find him a new wife? What?' She stamped her foot. 'What can I do? Separate them? Caligula would take my head. What have you become, Parmenon? A stoic? A philosopher? Weren't you there when Tiberius died?'

She held out her hand which I grasped. She squeezed mine and let go.

'Who advises him?' I asked.

'Macro and myself.'

'And Drusilla?'

'Drusilla has a pretty face and an empty head. She's as vacuous as she's beautiful.'

'Are you giving Caligula drugs?' I asked.

'You know I am: valerian seed to soothe the nerves and help him sleep.'

I stared across the garden. The morning mist was lifting. I heard the clink of metal, the rumble of carts as they were brought out onto the cobbles for the luggage to be stowed. I felt sorry for attacking Agrippina. The imperial court was not a place for morality, just for power and survival.

147

'If the Senate find out,' I replied slowly, 'the Emperor's relationship with his sister could be fanned into a scandal by that gaggle of hypocrites in Rome. They'll start accusing him of being degenerate. He has the blood of Mark Anthony in him. They'll gossip about his ancestor's love for Egyptian ways . . .'

'So?' Agrippina demanded.

'If he is to honour one sister,' I continued, 'then let him publicly honour all three.' I laughed. 'You'd like that anyway. Let there be no distinction between his love for all his sisters. It will cloud people's minds, blunt suspicion.'

Agrippina seized my hand again, gripped it and walked away.

Whatever Agrippina had done with Macro's help, it certainly worked. If anything, Caligula appeared saner than any of them. He entered Rome with the approbation of both Senate and people. He was greeted by the College of Priests and the Vestal Virgins. Glory and honours were bestowed on him. Caligula acted with all the gravitas of Augustus. He refused to have the dead Tiberius criticised and had his ashes solemnly interred in the imperial mausoleum. He stood at the rostrum of the Senate and said he needed their help in ruling. He decreed an end to the treason laws, issued pardons and had the secret police records burnt in the Forum. He brought the ashes of his dead relatives back for honourable burial and promised a period of reconciliation. I was dumb-founded, but everybody was pleased. Caligula had spent the last few years on Capri, and very few people really knew the true nature of the monster they had taken to their bosom. He opened the treasury and lavished rewards on the Praetorian Guard and the legions. Informers and spies were driven from Rome. At banquets and festivals he acted with the utmost propriety.

It was all a charade, of course. I sometimes caught him watching himself in the mirror, practising gestures and still talking to that mysterious, invisible presence behind him.

Chapter 8

'It is difficult to give up a long established love'
Catullus, *Carmina*: 76

Despite my forebodings, Agrippina seemed more relaxed. She moved back with her husband Domitius to his mansion on the Via Sacra. He soon began to display the symptoms of dropsy, but Agrippina didn't seem to care. When I questioned her, she pulled a sorrowful face.

'Domitius has brought his own death upon him,' she murmured. 'I did not ask him to be my husband or to be a drunken lecher, and boorish both in bed and at table. Like a lot of people, Parmenon, he should be careful what he eats and drinks and whose bed he shares.' She tapped her belly. 'I have my son: Domitius is no longer needed.' She changed the subject and refused to discuss the matter any further.

Pregnancy suited Agrippina. She positively bloomed and, as her belly grew bigger with the monster within, she fought to control the monster without. Despite a few mistakes, Caligula maintained his mask and behaved himself. He liked to process in triumph through the city showing himself to be magnanimous and merciful. On one occasion, at a banquet, he stared into a lucent pool of water as if he was concentrating on a mirror.

'I forgive you,' he murmured, lifting his hand, talking to his own reflection. 'I, the Emperor, pardon you!'

He raised his head, eyes half closed, and pretended to be a second Augustus listening attentively to speeches or poetry. The mob loved his grandiose gestures, especially when he staged games in the amphitheatre near the Campus Martius which resulted in the killing of four hundred Libyan lions and an equal number of bears. Agrippina fought to keep him in line. Her two sisters, Julia and Drusilla, were married off: the favourite to Lepidus, a man whom Caligula had also slept with. Caligula's first wife had died when he was on Capri. He married again but soon divorced his next wife. He only had eyes and heart for Drusilla. Lepidus, I suppose, was to act as panderer to the bedroom and head off any scurrilous gossip about the Emperor and his sister. When he wasn't closeted with Drusilla, Caligula pawed and kissed two actors, Mnester and Pallas.

Agrippina watched her brother closely. She made sure he did not drink too much at banquets or leap up to join in the singing and dancing. She relied for help in controlling him on two other people: Caligula's aged aunt, Antonia, and her son, Claudius. I've never really been able to decide whether Claudius was a great fool or a very wise man. Slack-jawed and vacuous-eyed when he talked, Claudius sounded as if he suffered from a stroke. He spat and stuttered as if his tongue was too big for his mouth and, when he walked, dragged his foot behind him. Clumsy in all his movements, Claudius's table manners were no better. He'd gobble his food and slurp his wine. He became known as Claudius the Windbreaker or Claudius the Farter because of his offensive personal habits. Nevertheless, he was a great scholar of the history of the Julio-Claudian House and Caligula would humour him by listening to his droning speeches. Claudius appeared more and more in public, and Caligula even made him Co-Consul, an act of magnamity and clemency which endeared him to the Senate and the powerful ones of Rome.

Claudius's mother, Antonia, was a different dish of onions: sharp and shrewd, upright in her life, she knew the true Caligula. One evening though she berated him too openly at a banquet, and Caligula lost his temper. He cleared the room and leant over his aged aunt, his face a mask of hatred. 'I can do what I like!' he hissed. 'I'm the Emperor!'

Agrippina intervened, pulling her brother away. A short while later Antonia died, some say from poison.

Caligula didn't attend the funeral rites. Instead he feasted and banqueted and watched the pyre burn, all the time murmuring, 'I can do whatever I like! I can do whatever I like!'

Indeed, he did do what he liked. Some of his gestures were noble. A slave woman, who had been racked and tortured by Sejanus but refused to betray her master was given her freedom and the huge sum of 800,000 sesterces. On another occasion I was with Caligula when he visited the public baths – he'd taken a liking to me since Tiberius's death – accompanied by a small retinue of slaves, one of whom carried his linen towels, flask of oil, perfume jar and strigoil. On entering the baths Caligula saw an old man, an ex-soldier, rubbing his back up against the wall, and told me to call the old soldier over.

'I can't afford a slave to clean my back,' the old man explained. 'So, rubbing it against the wall is the best I can do.'

Caligula immediately gave him two of his own slaves as a present. The next time he returned to the baths, at least three dozen veterans were rubbing their backs up against the wall. Caligula roared with laughter and told them to clean each other's back: the Emperor's wit became the toast of Rome. All seemed well. Agrippina now withdrew to her own house. She hired every physician in the city to advise her on what to eat and what to drink, how best to protect the child growing within her. When she wasn't talking to them, she was closeted with me. She'd question me closely about Caligula's moods, advise me what to say, what to do, and warned me to watch for certain symptoms.

'What do you fear will happen?' I asked.

'The same as if a hungry panther burst into a chamber,' she replied.

The panther sprang in the September following Tiberius's death. Caligula was now obsessed with the games and staged a massive spectacle for the citizens of Rome. I rose early, in the still time just after cock crow. I had a light meal of bread soaked in watered wine and prepared Domina's litter and retinue, to take us to the games. Every merchant and food-seller in Rome had flocked to swarm round the gates selling honeyed cakes, spiced sausage, lizard fish and boiled eggs, and the air was sweet with spices and perfumes. I joined Domina in the imperial box overlooking the amphitheatre. Caligula was there with his new plaything, whose name I forget, though as usual the place of honour was reserved for Drusilla, accompanied by her weak-jawed husband Lepidus. We sat behind them, but Agrippina moved so she could watch her brother's face. Caligula was highly excited.

The games started with a mime featuring a dog. The animal was given food which, the audience was informed, was laced with poison. The dog ate it, exhibited hideous convulsions and fell down, to all appearances dead. He was picked up by his master, carried around and laid down on a mock funeral pyre. The man clapped his hands and the dog sprang to his feet. Caligula was beside himself with laughter. He grabbed a purse from Agrippina and threw it into the amphitheatre. He turned round, his face only a few inches from his sister, flushed, his eyes bright and starting.

'Find the name of that poison, Agrippina,' he whispered hoarsely. 'And I'll never use it again!' He jumped up and down clapping his hands.

'The time of the panther,' Agrippina whispered. 'But we've done what we can.'

Caligula loudly applauded the tightrope-walking elephants and those other animals which had been dressed up in male and female costume, but then his mood changed abruptly.

'*Iugula! Iugula!*' he screamed. 'Cut his throat! Cut his throat!' The cry of the mob when the gladiator was down.

The games manager recognised his cue for the carnage to begin. Gladiators poured into the arena to a fanfare of music. The combatants whipped themselves up into a fury by shouting abuse at one another. The music grew more raucous; trumpets, horns, flutes brayed and shrieked and the real bloodshed began. Caligula was beside himself, screaming abuse. As the sun grew hotter, the crowd began to demand a break for their usual refreshments. Caligula, getting to his feet, bawled at them to shut up. He had the awnings removed so the mob would learn its lesson and suffer the full brunt of the burning sun. Agrippina hastily called a servant and poured a goblet of wine – only I saw her add the powder – which she thrust into her brother's hand. Meanwhile, in the arena below, the red-gold sand was littered with corpses. The gladiators, who had fought for hours, were now looking askance at the imperial box, where Caligula had dozed off. Agrippina whispered to the games manager. She ordered the awnings replaced and water and cakes to be distributed to the crowd.

Caligula slept for an hour. When he woke, he was paler, and more composed, taking more interest in Drusilla than in the tally of mounting corpses for the rest of the afternoon. The games finished and he returned to the imperial house on the Palatine, where he had ordered a banquet that was to cost the treasury millions of sesterces. Caligula demanded that Drusilla share his couch, where he lolled, drinking incessantly, whilst every possible dish was served: young kid, pheasant and goose, lamprey and turbot, sow's udders. All the best chefs in Rome had been hired for the occasion, and Caligula led many of the guests on a tour of the kitchens, where they flocked like starving, screeching peacocks, standing on tiptoe, biting their fingernails as they watched each chef prepare a dish. The Emperor had insisted on inviting the 'Victor Ludorum' from the amphitheatre, a burly Thracian with the nickname of 'Lord of the Dolls' because of his sexual prowess amongst the women of Rome.

Caligula was beside himself with pleasure at the consequent revelry and chaos. Musicians and jugglers noisily thronged about and, despite Agrippina's efforts, Caligula joined them. He insisted that the jugglers explain how objects thrown into the air seemed to fly back into their hands. Agrippina ate and drank nothing. She tried to distract her brother with comedians and actors who performed a bedroom farce, 'Love Locked Out', which Caligula watched intently. After the first act, he kissed Drusilla full on the lips and staggered to his feet, before stopping convulsively as if poisoned, staring at an actor wearing a bright red mask. Caligula thrust a hand out towards him.

'So, you are back!' he bellowed. 'Has Tiberius sent you up from Hell? Who invited you here?'

Agrippina half rose from her couch. The Emperor's screams stilled all the clamour.

'What are you doing here?' Caligula demanded.

The actor wearing the mask stood rooted to the spot. Caligula's hand flew up in the air, he gave a loud scream and collapsed to the floor. Agrippina and Macro immediately took charge: the banqueting hall was cleared and the Emperor was hastily carried to his bedchamber, to which physicians, including Charicles, were summoned. As Agrippina supervised their ministrations, I heard her whisper, 'He can't die, not yet!'

Caligula was as white as a sheet, his breath coming in short dying gasps. Indeed, at one point Agrippina had to hold a mirror to his mouth to see if he was still breathing. Charicles examined his mouth and eyes and took his pulse before coming in to the antechamber, where Agrippina, Macro and I had gathered, together with that sly-eyed Greek, Progeones. The inclusion of Progeones was Agrippina's idea. He was one of those hybrid creatures, who seemed neither truly male nor female. Oh, he had a man's face and testicles, but the way he talked and moved, especially the flutter of his eyelids, the turn of his mouth and his high-pitched tone, were more suggestive of a woman. He walked with a better wiggle than some of the best courtesans in Rome. Agrippina had hired him to keep an eye on Caligula when he went visiting in the pleasure houses and brothels of Rome. She trusted him completely, claiming to have enough proof of that creature's execrable habits to have him crucified or strangled a hundred times. I hated him, with his curling eyelashes, dewy glances and affected lisp. I should have killed him that night.

Agrippina led the meeting, as Macro's men guarded the door.

'Well,' she demanded of Charicles. 'Is he dying?'

'I don't believe so, Domina, it's just a fit.' Charicles tapped his forehead. 'More of the mind than the body.'

'Has he been poisoned?' Progeones lisped.

Charicles stared at Agrippina. The valerian was a secret: I begged Agrippina with my eyes not to mention it.

'He's not been poisoned,' Charicles confirmed, 'but he's in a deep sleep. He may die or . . .' He shrugged.

'What can we do?' Agrippina asked.

'If he dies,' Macro broke in, 'Gemellus still

lies under house arrest, a possible heir to the throne.'

Agrippina clutched her belly. During those few tense moments I discovered the full extent of Agrippina's secret ambition: she would have a son, who would ascend to the purple, and when he was Emperor, she would be the one to control him. Anyone else – whoever they were – would simply wear the purple until she and her son were ready.

'No!' She shook her head. 'Macro, send messages to the legion commanders!'

'Oh, they'll be loyal enough,' Macro laughed. 'And the Praetorian Guard take their orders from me.'

Agrippina sat, sucking on her lips.

'Let it be. Let it be,' she murmured.

Agrippina stayed on in the palace where she and Macro managed everything. The news of Caligula's illness spread through Rome, and people grew hysterical, or pretended to, with grief. The Palatine was besieged by mobs eager for news. Five days after that infamous banquet, Caligula awoke. He pulled himself up in bed and stared around, smacking his lips. His eyes were clear with a mischievous, malicious look, as if it had all been a game. As Agrippina carefully explained his illness. Caligula heard her out, nodding wisely, before demanding to be washed and fed and have Drusilla sent to him.

Caligula kept glancing at Agrippina out of the corner of his eyes, and now and again he would wink at me as if we were sharing a joke. I'll be honest, the look on that man's face made me shiver. Whatever soul Caligula possessed before, had died during those five absent days, and thereafter the king of demons controlled his mind.

'So, he said he'd sacrifice himself, did he?' he declared, tapping his chin and referring to a Roman citizen Afraneus. 'Promised to commit suicide if I recovered? Well I have, haven't I, Parmenon?' He grinned and winked, clapping his hands. 'The Gods have blessed me. So, Afraneus must fulfil the vow!'

It was the beginning of the terror.

The following day Afraneus was arrested. Naked, except for a loin cloth, he was paraded through Rome and tossed off the Tarpeian rock. Another official had reputedly offered to fight as a gladiator if Caligula recovered. The Emperor kept him to his promise and made the unfortunate man battle it out in the amphitheatre. Drusilla and Agrippina were in no danger, but the atmosphere at court became tense and watchful. Caligula showed little overt hostility to anyone in particular until one night, at a banquet, he abruptly turned on Macro who had been offering advice on some petty matter.

'How dare you lecture me?' Caligula roared. 'How dare you set yourself up as my superior?'

'That is not true,' Agrippina intervened.

'Isn't it?' Caligula yelled.

The Praetorian Prefect leapt to his feet and made ready to leave.

'You won't get far!' Caligula shouted.

Two German auxiliaries, favourites of the Emperor, appeared in the doorway. Tall and blond-haired, they looked like twins and were nicknamed Castor and Pollux. Macro spun round, and glanced beseechingly at Agrippina. She could only stare sorrowfully back. We'd been invited to these banquets for days following the Emperor's recovery and until now nothing had happened. Caligula had lulled our suspicions until springing like a hunting panther.

'We should kill him now,' Agrippina whispered to me.

She moved further up the couch to elicit support from Drusilla but that empty-head was drunk and half asleep, her face pressed against the head-rest.

Macro tried reasoning with Caligula. 'I have only ever wanted to help . . .'

'Assassin!' Caligula screamed. 'You are under arrest! The charge is treason!'

The mercenaries seized Macro and dragged him from the room. I never saw him again: he was dead by the following morning. Macro's fall was the sign for a new bloodbath. Silenus, Caligula's former father-in-law, was arrested and openly accused in the Senate: his response was to cut his throat in front of all his colleagues. Gemellus, Tiberius's grandson, was released from house arrest, but then his fate followed the same pattern as Macro's. He was invited to a banquet, where Caligula shared his couch, and sniffed the young man's breath.

'What are you doing?' Caligula screamed. 'Taking antidotes for poison? Are you accusing me of trying to poison you? You, who prayed for my death!'

'I have not prayed for your death,' Gemellus replied. 'I take no antidote, it's cough medicine!'

Caligula refused to accept this. 'It's an antidote!' he insisted.

Gemellus, give him his due, realised his time had come. 'There is no antidote against Caesar,' he bravely retorted.

He was allowed to leave the banquet, but the following day Praetorians were sent to his house and forced him to open his veins.

Caligula's conduct became wilder and more outrageous. He attended the marriage of a noblewoman Orestilla, where he sat next to the bride and sent a note to the bridegroom, inscribed 'Don't make love to my wife!'

He ordered Orestilla to be taken to his own quarters and married her himself. A few months later he divorced the woman but ordered her never to make love to any man for as long as the Emperor lived. Sometimes his conduct was simply malicious. He made his uncle, Claudius, the constant butt of his jokes. Caligula would throw olive, fig and date stones at him and put slippers on his hands as he dozed in a wine-drenched sleep. Caligula would roar with laughter when the old man woke and tried to rub his face with his hands.

Agrippina ignored all this. She withdrew from court, more concerned that nothing would occur to upset the impending birth of her child. The boy was born in December, after a difficult delivery. The portents were good, though Agrippina kept them quiet. 'Now is not the time,' she whispered to me, 'to remind my mad brother that there's another Caesar in Rome.'

'What shall we do?' I urged.

'We must wait,' she replied. 'The same as we had to do with Tiberius on Capri . . .'

At first I admired my mistress's cunning and coolness, until two events abruptly changed this. In June the following year Drusilla suddenly died, and Caligula's grief was ostentatious, bloody and dangerous. She was granted a public funeral, and during the time of official mourning, it became a capital offence to laugh, bathe, or even dine with one's family. Caligula tried to console himself for the loss of his sister. He married a disreputable noblewoman, Lollia Paulina, who insisted on turning up at dinner parties drenched in jewels and pearls worth millions of sesterces. She actually made her slave carry the receipts around to show would-be admirers how much she was worth. Caligula soon tired of her and dear Lollia went the way of all the rest. Next he married Caesonia, a woman of high birth and low morals, who already had a number of children by other husbands. When I informed Agrippina of this, her rage was as surprising as it was fierce. She leapt off the couch, dropping all the accustomed poise of a noblewoman in retirement. She paced up and down her bedchamber, beating her fists against her thighs.

'He is mad but he can still beget!' she exclaimed. 'And never forget that Caligula is the son of Germanicus. Or might be,' she added in a half-whisper.

'I beg your pardon, Domina? What did you say?'

Agrippina looked over her shoulder at me, with that lopsided smile on her face. She went over and kicked the door shut.

'Have you ever really studied Caligula, Parmenon? Does he look like me? Or Drusilla? Or Julia? My mother bore him but that does not mean he is Germanicus's son.'

'You could lose your head for that,' I whispered back. 'And your son would disappear into a pit.'

I placed my hand on her shoulder – when we were in private she allowed such liberties.

'Are you going to kiss me, Parmenon? Make love to me?' she teased.

I never knew what would have happened if I'd tried. Perhaps it was her coldness which always stopped me. Agrippina regarded sex as a gladiator did a sword or shield, a weapon to be used.

'Or are you going to force me?' she grinned. 'Like Metellus did?'

'I am going to warn you,' I advised. 'Progeones is in this house: he would betray you at any time.'

'Nonsense! He's mine and always will be.'

'If he heard what you've just said,' I went on, 'he would sell the information to any of your enemies who would not hesitate to use it. The slightest hint that the Emperor is a bastard would bring about the cruellest punishments.'

Agrippina swallowed hard and broke free from my grip. She went over into a corner, crossing her arms like a young girl being scolded by her father.

'I've heard rumours,' she said. 'Even my mother once hinted at it. That could be why Caligula and poor Drusilla became lovers, since the blood-tie was not so strong.' She sighed. 'Now she's gone. I thought we could keep Caligula distracted with one woman or another but Caesonia is different: she's as fertile as a brood mare. Caligula is still a young man. In five or ten years Rome could have a nursery full of "Little Boots".' She rubbed her hands together. 'I am sure Caesonia will become pregnant, but Parmenon, we cannot allow her, her husband or any offspring to live.'

'If Caligula dies?' I asked. 'Do you think the Senate will accept your baby son as Emperor?'

Agrippina shook her head. 'He's of Germanicus's line but he's still too young. No, Uncle Claudius will do nicely for the moment.'

'Him!' I exclaimed. 'That doddering idiot!'

'He has the imperial blood, Parmenon. If the Senate accepted a madman like Caligula, they'd take a baboon from Africa.'

That was Agrippina's one great weakness. She would not listen and, once she decided to act, did so impetuously.

A stream of visitors began to call secretly at her house. Agrippina was sifting which ones would listen to her, who was sympathetic? Whom could she trust? Slowly her plan began to develop: Caligula's speedy assassination in Rome would be followed by letters to the legions on the frontiers. I watched helplessly. She would not be advised or warned.

There were three main plotters: Agrippina, her sister Julia and Drusilla's former husband Lepidus. Julia was involved because she was terrified of her brother. Lepidus, after Drusilla's death, had fallen from favour. Progeones and I became unwilling bystanders and spectators. I was used as a messenger. Often at night I'd slip along dark streets carrying cryptic messages to various houses. I would deliver these faithfully word for word, before taking an answer back to Agrippina.

It was a dangerous time! Caligula's madness worsened by the week. He turned up at the Senate and terrified everyone by saying how marvellous Tiberius had been, how wrong they all were to criticise him. This speech marked a renewed persecution. The prisons filled. Caligula liked to visit the torture chambers, eating and drinking whilst his victims experienced a slow, agonising death. Caligula would advise the executioners to go about their work slowly so that the victim would know he was dying. Agrippina, despite her plotting, still tried to restrain him. She sent begging letters but Caligula's only reply was:

'Let the people hate me as long as they fear me!'

Justice was sharp and cruel. Parents had to attend the execution of their own children. One father was forced to watch his son die and then invited to dinner immediately afterwards. Caligula joked and jested throughout the meal. The owner of a school of gladiators who had displeased him was beaten to death with chains. Caligula would only allow the corpse to be removed when the stench from the putrefied body became too great. Writers were burnt alive in the arena. A Roman knight was tossed to the beasts in the amphitheatre. He ran across the sand and begged Caligula for a pardon, claiming his innocence. Furious, Caligula ordered that his tongue should be removed before he was thrown back to the waiting lions. Other more hideous punishments were perpetrated. At one infamous banquet he had the hacked limbs and bowels of a senatorial victim stacked in a steamy heap on a table so all the guests could see. Caligula broke the brooding silence with a mad fit of laughter.

'Don't you realise?' he shrieked. 'I could have all your heads with one cut!'

No one was spared. He had Caesonia, his new wife, paraded naked before guests, accusing them of treason if they looked, and demanding whether his wife disgusted them if they turned away.

By the time the summer heat reached Rome, Caligula was tired of the city. He'd grown particularly concerned by a prophecy given to Tiberius that Caligula had no more chance of becoming Emperor than of riding over the Gulf of Naples on horseback. Caligula was determined to prove this wrong. He marched his troops down to the bay and ordered his engineers to build a bridge more than three miles long from Puteoli to Baiae. Merchant ships were anchored together in a double line and a road, modelled on the Appian Way, built across them. So many ships were commandeered that the corn imports from Egypt suffered. Caligula didn't care. He arranged for wayside taverns to be built on this makeshift road, together with resting places, even running water was supplied.

Caligula proudly proclaimed that even the God Neptune was frightened of him. The bridge was finished and Caligula had decided it was time to prove the prophecy wrong.

'You are coming with me, sister!' he yelled at the banquet held the night before. 'And you, Parmenon. You're my lucky mascot, Parmenon. Do you know that?' His cadaverous face broke into a wolfish grin. 'I have met him, you know,' he whispered to me, filling my cup to the brim so the wine splashed out over my hands.

'Who, Excellency?' I replied.

'Tiberius,' he whispered. 'He comes to my bed-chamber, drenched in blood. What a hideous sight!'

'Your Excellency, he didn't die of wounds.'

Caligula grinned, winked and tapped the side of his nose. 'You didn't see what I did to his corpse afterwards,' he replied. 'I did enjoy myself.'

And then he turned away to bestow slobbering kisses on Caesonia. Agrippina, on the couch before me, watched this red-haired, florid-faced woman intently. My mistress reminded me of a cobra about to strike. Once we were away from the banquet she turned to me.

'The bitch is pregnant!' she murmured. 'It's time we acted!'

The following day Agrippina and I joined Caligula

in a splendid chariot. The Emperor wore the breast-plate of Alexander the Great, ransacked from the Conqueror's tomb in Alexandria. He also insisted on wearing full armour, a purple cloak trimmed with gold and adorned with jewels from India, as well as a crown of oak leaves. He then made sacrifice to Neptune and rode across his makeshift road. Back-wards and forwards we went, both that day and the next, until I thought I would drop. Caligula rewarded his soldiers and invited all the onlookers onto the bridge.

The celebrations became frenetic. Many became so drunk and incapable, they fell off: corpses were washed up on the sands for weeks afterwards. Agrippina was furious, not so much with her brother's madness, more that he might have a possible heir.

When we returned to Rome, she made a decision. 'Caligula is to go to Germany. We must make sure he never arrives there.' She took a bracelet off her wrist. 'Give that to Lepidus. Tell him the die is cast!'

Chapter 9

'The smoke and wealth and noise of Rome'
Horace, *Odes*: III, 29

Mevania is a beauty spot a hundred miles north of
Rome. Agrippina chose it as the gathering place
for her fellow conspirators. A lovely setting to plot
mayhem and bloodshed. The villa was cool with
well-watered lawns, enclosed gardens, peristyle-
shaded walks. It was some distance from the
road, and Agrippina had it carefully guarded with
all approaches watched. Despite my protests, the
conspirators were invited and arrived one by one.
Progeones, of course. Lepidus with his long head
and shock of black dyed hair: a born conspirator
with his twisted smile and bitter, cynical eyes. His
weak, furrowed face mirrored unresolved grievances

171

and spite. Then came a brilliant orator, a small, dapper man with flickering eyes and a surprisingly deep voice, dumpy legs and a chest like a barrel. I had heard him speak in the courts: he was brilliant. Agrippina planned to use him to turn the Senate.

Uncle Claudius should have arrived but failed to do so. Instead his representative Seneca made his first appearance in my life. Seneca, a Spaniard, looked every inch the Roman patrician and philosopher. He was of medium height and well built, with a strong, broad face, aquiline nose, and snow-white hair carefully combed forward. Seneca looked like a pompous Platonist except for the shrewd cast to his mouth and those deep-set eyes, which viewed the world with cynical amusement. Seneca had no doubts about the rightness of Agrippina's cause. He reminded us all of Arrentius's last words, only this time he recast them: 'If life with Tiberius was bad enough, life with Caligula has been pure hell!'

Admittedly I was most uneasy. If you are going to form a conspiracy you must trust everyone involved. I knew little about these plotters. Time and again I broached the matter with Agrippina, but she acted as if she was possessed. She wasn't so concerned about Caligula, more with the child that Caesonia was expecting. One evening, at the end of December, all was ready. The conspirators, or their leaders, gathered in Agrippina's bedroom, a place of dark damascene cloths, jewelled cups, gold and silver statuettes, expensive furniture of oak, maple and terebinth, ivory-footed couches, stools and chairs made of tortoiseshell. Her large bed dominated the room. It was carved out of rare wood which reflected in its undulating grain a thousand different shades of colour, like that of the great peacock feathers adorning the wall above it.

Her son was not there. She had left him with trusted nurses in her house on the Via Sacre. We discussed how and when Caligula should die. Agrippina finally made a decision.

'Rome would be too dangerous,' she reasoned. 'And when Caligula reaches Germany, he'll be too well protected. I've invited him to visit me. We must do it here!'

'By poison?' Seneca asked.

Agrippina disagreed. She opened a leather bag and emptied three silver-embossed daggers out on the table.

'It will be done publicly enough,' she continued. 'And I will take responsibility.'

Agrippina had assumed the role of the democrat eager to save the republic from a tyrant. She laughed as if aware of her theatricality and looked at us from under dark, arched eyebrows.

'Who will strike the blow?'

'I will not,' I replied, getting to my feet. 'Nor will I take the oath.'

'Why not?' Agrippina asked.

I left and walked into the coolness of the garden. The murmur of voices rose from behind me, the sound of a door being firmly closed. I was in a sulk.

I hoped Agrippina would have followed me out but I was left to kick my heels.

At least an hour passed before she joined me. 'The others claim you can't be trusted,' she said, sitting down beside me.

'Well, say that I don't trust them.'

'What do you mean?'

Agrippina slipped her arm through mine and pulled herself closer. I smelt her delicious perfume, or was it a soap she used after bathing? Light, fragrant but still cloying to the nostrils.

'Oh, I trust them, I suppose,' I confessed. 'But I don't trust Caligula. He let you come here. He may be mad as the moon but he must suspect: someone in this villa is his spy.'

Agrippina refused to agree. Two days later Caligula arrived in a gorgeously decorated chariot pulled by four beautiful bays, their manes starred with special gems, breast-plates covered in sacred amulets. He had changed his role, now he saw himself as Charioteer of the Gods. Caligula himself stood upright like a victor about to prepare to receive the palm, helmet on his head, whip in hand, leggings of gold and red covering calf and thigh.

Of course, we all had to watch him drive up and down the gardens of the villa, creating chaos every time he turned. Lawns and flowerbeds disappeared, small, delicate walls were sent crashing under the spinning wheels. A group of Praetorians accompanied him and, of course, Castor and Pollux, his two German shadows. Caligula was frenetic with excitement. After a while he tired of the game, climbed down from the chariot, undressed in front of us and charged into the villa demanding a bath, his tunic and toga.

Agrippina entertained him late that evening. She tried to hide her own unease behind the pretence of a lavish banquet: hens made of wood containing eggs were brought in on platters, dormice rolled in honey and poppy seeds; hot sausages mixed with grilled damsons and seeds of pomegranate; wild pig, boiled carp and large jars of heavy Falernian. Caligula refused to eat unless Castor or Pollux tasted the dish first, whether it was a huge lobster, garnished with asparagus, or lampreys from the straits of Sicily. He even poked his dagger at the truffles and delicious mushrooms. After a while he threw the dagger onto the table and gazed around.

'I'm off to Germany,' he declared, and paused, head cocked to one side. At first I thought he was in one of his mad trances till I heard the clink of metal and the tramp of feet. I sprang to my feet, looked through a window and glimpsed pinpricks of torchlight: fresh troops were arriving. More torches appeared, and from outside came the sound of running feet. I heard a scream from the kitchen.

'I thought I'd supply the entertainment.'

Caligula swung his feet off the couch and stared evilly at his sister. Agrippina kept her poise. I felt my arm grasped. Castor had crept, as quiet as a cat, up beside me. He grunted and gestured with his hand that I re-take my seat.

'I'm off to Germany,' Caligula repeated, 'but, before I go, I must deal with traitors. Right, Progeones, tell your story!'

Our horrid little gargoyle sprang to his feet. Like an actor who has scrupulously learnt his lines, he confessed everything. Agrippina sat white-faced. Lepidus tried to rise but one of the German body-guard thrust him down. In the darkness behind the Emperor I heard a door open and the hiss of drawn swords as more of his bodyguard arrived. Once Progeones had finished, Caligula clapped, at first softly then louder and louder.

'That's the first part of the entertainment!'

Seneca began to cough, spluttering over something he had eaten.

'Don't spoil the entertainment!' Caligula shouted. 'Take the old fool away!'

Seneca was hustled out.

'Don't kill him!' Caligula shouted over his shoulder. 'I want to watch our philosopher die! See if he accepts death with the same equanimity as he faced life. Lepidus.' Caligula looked back at his guests. 'Lepidus,' he cooed.

The senator was seized and brought before the Emperor. Caligula swung his foot and cleared the table with his boot, sending dishes, cups and platters flying. Lepidus was forced to sit on the edge, with Castor and Pollux on either side. Caligula picked up a fork that had been used for the sucking pig. With one swift jab, he expertly dug out Lepidus's right eye. The man screamed and tried to rise but the guards held him fast.

'Do you see more clearly now?' Caligula leaned forward. 'You were married to my sister! You shared my bed! Garrotte him!'

Castor slipped the noose over Lepidus's shaking head. He took a small tube out of his belt and expertly turned it. We all had to sit and watch whilst Lepidus died with terrible, choking gasps. Occasionally, Caligula asked the German to stop so he could give the half-dead man a stern lecture on morality. The torture continued. A full nightmarish hour passed before Lepidus's corpse was allowed to fall slack onto the floor. His face had turned purple-black, and blood seeped from the hole where his eye had been.

Caligula raced round, shaking his fingers at the guests. He gestured with his fist at Afer the orator.

'You should have known better! You are going to answer for your treason in the Senate!'

Others were present, bankers and merchants who had been on the fringe of the conspiracy. The guests also included some innocent neighbours from surrounding villas. Caligula showed no mercy. One by one they were taken out to the garden and despatched by the waiting soldiers. Some were decapitated – Caligula shouting that one man's head should be pickled and brought back immediately

– others were strangled, and a few shackled and bundled into a cart for transport back to Rome.

Agrippina sat throughout the horror as immobile as a statue. Caligula turned on me and clicked his tongue, imitating Sejanus.

'I'll deal with you personally, Parmenon.'

He rose, gave Lepidus's corpse a vicious kick and led me out through the colonnades into the garden. That place of beautiful serenity had been transformed into a flesher's yard. Corpses lay about. A decapitated head had rolled to rest behind a seat. Pools of sticky blood glistened in the moonlight. Caligula ignored all this as, hand on my shoulder, he went across to sniff at a rosebud.

'Beautiful,' he murmured, closing his eyes. 'Such smells always takes me back to Capri and the old goat. Well, well, Parmenon, what a pretty mess, eh? What shall it be for you? Crucifixion? The garrotte? Or shall I stick your head on a pike?'

His face was solemn till he burst out laughing and punched me playfully in the stomach.

'I'm only joking,' he declared. 'You knew my spy was Progeones, didn't you?'

I nodded.

'And if he hadn't told me, you would have, wouldn't you?'

'Yes,' I lied.

'I can't kill you, Parmenon. You're my lucky mascot. But what –' his face turned ugly '– am I to do with that bitch of a sister?'

'Your Excellency.' I swallowed hard to prepare

the biggest lie in my life. 'Your Excellency, it's true she's a dangerous bitch but ... she is your sister and that of Drusilla.'

'True, true.' Caligula sat down on a garden wall and dropped his lower lip. 'By the way, where's that slut Julia? She's involved as well, isn't she?'

'Of course, your Excellency.'

'Now what were you saying about Agrippina?'

'She's a dangerous bitch, your Excellency, and she's also a blackmailer. She claims to have documents proving you are not Germanicus's son. If she dies,' I continued coolly, 'these are to be released to the Senate.'

Oh, it was a terrible gamble. Caligula was mad. He could have either exploded into rage or returned to the behaviour which had kept him safe on Capri. I wasn't disappointed. He positively cringed, fingers going to his mouth. I suspect Tiberius had often taunted him with the same jibe. He gnawed furiously at his nails.

'The filthy bitch!' he murmured. 'Is this true, Parmenon? I can have you tortured.'

'Torture me, Excellency, your lucky mascot. I tell the truth, you know I do. I think Tiberius told her. He had proof, didn't he? Some filth dug up by Sejanus?'

Caligula was not listening. He turned, speaking to that mysterious invisible presence beside him: a litany of curses and filthy epithets about Agrippina, his own mother, Tiberius and Sejanus.

He paused. 'What do you suggest, Parmenon?'

'Be careful, Excellency.' I knelt down on the ground before him. 'You are both Emperor and a God. Death is too quick. Separate her from her beloved son.'

Caligula gave a great sigh.

'Kill him instead, you mean?'

'No, no,' I hastened to add. 'Give her son to someone she hates.'

'I'll do that. And the bitch?'

'Exile her. Not too far away so she'll know what goes on in Rome.'

Caligula agreed. 'I'll have to talk to the Gods about this. But come, come, Parmenon, the punishment must be more than that.'

'Have her depicted as Lepidus's lover,' I continued.

'Good!' Caligula held his hand up. 'That's very good, Parmenon. I also want the names of all the other traitors involved in this plot, and something else.' He glared round at the corpse. 'When Mother returned to Rome she brought the ashes of my father,' – he emphasized the words, – '*my father* Germanicus, into Rome. Well, she can do the same.' He bawled for the captain of his guard. 'Take Lepidus's corpse!' he ordered. 'Have it burnt. I want the ashes poured into the cheapest vase you can find.'

The man hurried away and returned dragging Lepidus's corpse by the heels. Some of his companions brought out items of furniture and a makeshift funeral pyre was made, before it was drenched in oil and Lepidus's corpse tossed onto it. Caligula watched until the cadaver caught light.

'I can't stand the smell of burning flesh!' he pouted. 'It always makes me sick, whilst the sound of bubbling fat . . . Ugh!' He wafted a hand in front of his nose. 'Well, I'll go and look at the other prisoners.'

He walked away, then whirled round.

'Oh, Parmenon, I haven't forgotten you. You must follow your mistress into Rome and then join her in exile. You'll be allowed to return to the city three, no, four times a year, so the bitch can get all the news.'

Off he strode. To my right Lepidus's body was now engulfed in flames, black billowing smoke and a filthy stench. From the villa came the sound of screams and crashing, as Caligula's bodyguards helped themselves to the slave girls. I hurried back inside to find Agrippina still sat on the couch, white-faced, tense but ready for death. I told her quickly what I had said to Caligula. She listened hollow-eyed.

'Where there's life,' she whispered. 'There's hope.'

She stroked my cheek and then, if I hadn't caught her, would have crashed into a dead faint onto the floor.

Five days later Agrippina, bare-footed, dust strewn on her hair and clothed in a simple tunic, walked into Rome bearing a chipped urn containing Lepidus's ashes. She accepted her fate philosophically, more concerned about being deprived of her beloved Nero than any public humiliation. I was forced to walk behind, carrying a cushion bearing the three daggers Agrippina had bought for Caligula's murder. Praetorian guards forced a way through the jostling crowds assembled on the streets. I was aware of shouts, of strange pungent smells; spice, sulphur, the foul odours from the cesspits and sewers. The black ravens, flocking to the graveyards to pluck at those corpses not properly buried, seemed everywhere. A fire had been lit and its smoke billowed about. The slums disgorged their inhabitants who were only too eager to watch the spectacle of one of the great ones who'd fallen lower than themselves.

Yet there was no jeering, no catcalls, no abuse. People recalled Agrippina's father, how her mother had brought his ashes back to Rome in a similar but more honourable procession. The senators, the knights and the merchants were also wise enough to know that fortune's fickle wheel can be spun at the touch of a hand. Today Agrippina was in disgrace but tomorrow . . . who knows? Moreover, Caligula was hated and feared. Here was a woman who had dared to confront him. There was grudging respect and admiration. Indeed, by the time we had left the winding, narrow streets onto the Via Sacre leading to the Palatine, the atmosphere had imperceptibly changed. At the time I was only aware of that cushion which seemed to weigh as much as a rock, of the sweat pouring down me and of the tall, elegant figure of Agrippina, walking in front. She carried the urn with her head held high, gaze fixed before her, looking neither to the right nor the left. We climbed the Palatine hill, on which flowers and grass were strewn as if to protect her naked feet. The commander of Caligula's bodyguard, a Thracian, realising that this was not the disgrace Caligula had intended, urged her to move faster. If anything, Agrippina walked slower.

We reached the Forum. The intended humiliation had turned into a farce, with the Emperor the butt of the joke rather than Agrippina. The ashes were summarily snatched from her hand, the daggers taken off me as an offering to the Gods, and we were bundled away to some warehouse in the palace grounds. Once the door was closed behind us, Agrippina sat down, face in hands, and cried. I crouched beside her and put my arm round her shoulders.

'There's no need for tears' I comforted. 'There's no need.'

She took her hands away and glanced at me. She wasn't crying, she'd been laughing. She clutched my hand and squeezed it.

'Tomorrow's another day, Parmenon,' she whispered. 'I made a mistake, didn't I?'

I seized the opportunity to remind her of my warnings.

'I made one mistake,' she interrupted. 'Every one in that conspiracy had something to lose and all to gain, except for Progeones. I shall not make that mistake again.'

We stayed in prison for a week. Caligula swept

back into Rome. Seneca, surprisingly, wasn't punished. Someone had apparently informed Caligula that Seneca was going to die anyway, so the philosopher suffered no disgrace. The orator Afer was summoned before the Senate where Caligula delivered a fiery speech against him. Afer took his place on the rostrum and loudly proclaimed that he had no answer as he was more frightened of Caligula as an orator than he was of him as an Emperor. Caligula, the mad fool, was delighted and Afer was pardoned.

Agrippina heard all this; she sat clutching her hands in her lap. 'You'll forgive me, won't you, Parmenon?'

'For what, Domina?'

'I always thought there was more than one spy, and I wondered if the second one was you. Now I know that it must have been either Seneca or Afer.' She shrugged. 'Anyway, I would have lost my head if it hadn't been for your blackmail threat.'

The guards returned that evening. Under the cover of darkness, Agrippina and I were bundled onto a cart and taken secretly out of Rome to a warship at Ostia. It took a full day's sailing before we reached the island of Pontia, seventy miles off the coast of Naples. It was a pleasant enough place with woods and fields, a beautiful villa on the promontory and a small theatre nearby. The commander of the guard delivered Caligula's message.

'Remind my sister,' he had said, 'that I have daggers as well as islands.'

Agrippina heeded the advice. She behaved herself.

The greatest punishment was the absence of her beloved son who had been given into the care of Domitia Lepida, one of Caligula's favourite great aunts. If fortune's wheel was spun again, that was one woman marked down for destruction. Agrippina kept herself busy. She took up the study of botany, birds and wild life, and used the kiln to make pottery. She organised a set routine every day: we would rise early in the morning, and she would run down to the beach to swim and then return for a light meal. She would eagerly seek out any news from the mainland, write letters which were never sent and go out into the fields to collect specimens. If the weather turned harsh, she'd stay inside and work the kiln. She proved to have skilful hands and taught me how to paint the pots. Never once did she openly discuss Rome, Caligula or her son. Since most of the slaves and servants were spies, what conversations we did have took place at the dead of night when Agrippina was certain there was no one around.

I could have become her lover. Sometimes we shared more than a jug of wine, and would sit, hand in hand, or embrace.

One night I did grow amorous but she starkly pointed to a cobweb. 'Did you know, Parmenon, that the female spider eats her mate?'

She drew away. 'People like you, Parmenon, should have nothing to do with the likes of me. I have the same blood as Caligula. Everyone we touch dies violently. The Furies nest close to us.'

I heeded the warning. As the months passed, Agrippina was allowed more visitors and messengers from Rome, but they were only spies attempting to provoke some admission or treasonable remarks. They did bring news of her brother and his mad antics, hoping to provoke her.

Caligula had decided to launch an all-out war against the Germans. Eager to emulate his own father's triumphs, he assembled an enormous force of some quarter of a million troops, with a huge convoy of military equipment and food. The Emperor himself, however, travelled with a retinue of gladiators, actors and women. When he reached the Rhine he downgraded certain commanders and executed others on the grounds that they had conspired with his sister against him. Caligula then decided that he was the embodiment of Mars, but could find no one to fight him so he arranged for his German bodyguards to sneak across the Rhine and hide in the forest. One day, as the Emperor was finishing lunch, his scouts told him that the enemy were gathering. His bodyguard, pretending to be the enemy, launched a fictitious ambush. Caligula had them captured and brought back in chains. In honour of his triumph, Caligula had all the surrounding trees shorn of their branches and decorated the stumps with trophies. When the news reached Rome, the Senate pretended that Caesar had won a great triumph, and poor Uncle Claudius was sent north to congratulate the victorious Emperor. Caligula was furious that such a clumsy messenger had been sent and had his uncle pitched into the Rhine for his pains.

Eager for a fresh triumph, Caligula marched the army into Gaul, having decided to invade Britain. He assembled his forces along the sea coast in full battle order. Catapults and other engines of war were all primed. Caligula took to sea in a trireme, travelled a short distance and then returned to shore. He ordered the trumpeters to sound the charge. Caligula rode along the beach, instructing his soldiers to attack the sea and use their helmets and shields to pick up shells as plunder and spoils of their great victory against the God Neptune.

After this nonsense, he marched back to Rome. On the way he stopped at Lyons where he auctioned off all of Agrippina's property and possessions. He also organised a contest in Greek and Latin oratory in which the losers were forced to present the prizes to the winners as well as erase their own contributions, some with a sponge and the worst with their tongues. If they didn't like this they were given a choice of being beaten with rods or thrown into the nearby river.

Caligula continued his march on Rome, his carts full of seashells. He added a few captives and deserters from Gaul, making them grow their hair long and dyed. These unfortunates were taught a little German and were given barbarian names. Caligula was eager for his Triumph: the Senate and people of Rome had no choice but to accept this farcical turn of events.

Agrippina bore the loss of her property and possessions with equanimity. She listened to such news, nodded and then returned to her flower collection.

One visitor, however, brought secret messages. Cassius Chaerea, a tribune from the Praetorian Guard, had been sent by Caligula to search the island and ensure that Agrippina was observing the terms of her exile. I've never met a soldier who looked more like a woman. Agrippina conceded he was better looking than her: tall and graceful with a long, slim, olive face and dark expressive eyes. My mistress said he had lips and eyelashes which any girl would envy. Nevertheless, Cassius was a seasoned soldier and, from the beginning, it was obvious that his heart was not in his task. Agrippina studied him for a few days then summoned me to our usual meeting place on the cliff top.

'Cassius has brought me news from Rome. The Emperor's madness is now the talk on everyone's lips.'

'And your son?' I asked, trying to hide my jealousy. 'You persuaded Chaerea to talk about your son?'

Agrippina smiled and whistled under her breath. 'Are you jealous, Parmenon?'

'You dress your hair,' I replied. 'You put paint on your face and bathe your body in perfume. You wear the most elegant robes and always arrange for Cassius to sit near you when we eat. You are not trying to seduce him, are you?'

'Oh, I've already done that,' Agrippina murmured. 'Last night.'

I recalled Agrippina leaving the evening meal early, complaining she felt unwell, the usual sign that she wished to be left alone. Chaerea had retired an hour later.

'I didn't think you'd be so stupid!' I retorted.

'What's Cassius going to say?' Agrippina snapped. 'That he dared seduce the Emperor's disgraced sister? I know every mark on that beautiful body. More importantly, I have found a man who hates Caligula even more than I do. Do you think the army liked that stupid spectacle on the coast, escorting carts back into Rome full of seashells?'

'That doesn't make Chaerea a traitor,' I replied.

'Oh, Parmenon, think back to last night and the other times we've talked with Cassius. Every time I mention Caligula he blushes slightly. I discovered why: Caligula calls Cassius a girl. One of Chaerea's tasks is to ask the Emperor every day for the personal password.' Agrippina bit back her laughter. 'Caligula teases him with replies such as "Vagina", "Penis" or "Kiss Me Quick". Can you imagine the roars of laughter which greet this? Cassius also tells me that others hate Caligula just as much as he.' She tapped me on the hand. 'Now, for practical news. My husband Domitius has done us all a favour by dying of dropsy. I won't be a hypocrite – I didn't give his life a passing thought, so why should I mourn his death?'

'And your son?' I demanded.

'A bouncing boy with red curls. He's already ordering about the other children in the nursery.'

'And?' I demanded. 'There is something else?'

'Cassius has brought a pass. You can return to Rome for the winter. I think Caligula wants to find out how his sister is faring. When Cassius leaves, you are to go with him.'

'To plot, be caught and executed!' I exclaimed.

'No, listen.'

Agrippina gripped my wrist, a sign that she was going to impart something important. It always made me shiver, reminding me how Charicles used to take Tiberius's pulse.

'Caligula will die,' Agrippina insisted. 'And who is there left? Those doddering fools in the Senate may try and restore the Republic but the army won't allow that.'

'Your Uncle Claudius?' I replied.

'Precisely.' Agrippina squeezed my wrist even tighter. 'If Caligula dies suddenly, there'll be confusion. You and Cassius must ensure that Claudius is hailed as Emperor. He'll bring me back to Rome.'

Agrippina dropped my wrist. 'Whatever happens, Parmenon, you must ensure that, somehow, Claudius is brought forward. Naturally, in the chaos following Caligula's death, my son must be closely protected.' She got to her feet and pulled me up. 'By the way, I know you've got too tender a heart so Cassius will do this for me – ensure that Caligula's wife Caesonia and her little brat don't survive any longer than he does. Now, come! I am sure Cassius is already pining for me and we've got preparations to make.'

Chapter 10

'Chaos: an ill-formed and unordered Mass.'
Ovid, *Metamorphoses*: 1, 7

It was good to be back in Rome. Despite the winter, the taverns were crowded as usual. After the silence of Pontia, I enjoyed walking through the different quarters watching the barbers shave their customers in the middle of the street, the loud-mouthed hawkers selling their small boxes of sulphur matches and trinkets, the raucous cries of the sausage-sellers with their makeshift mobile ovens. Schoolmasters, ringed by their pupils in a small, dirty square, shouted themselves hoarse. Nearby, a money-changer sifted his coins in a metal grille whilst his assistant pounded with a shiny mallet on clipped and chipped coins. Conjurors and tricksters swarmed everywhere, competing with the beggars. The sheer frenetic bustle of their lives was a sharp contrast to the horrors of Caligula's court or Agrippina's seething anger as she plotted her return.

I lodged with Cassius Chaerea in the Praetorian barracks near the Viminial Gate. Of course, I had to be presented to the Emperor, and was obliged to attend one of his famous supper parties in Livia's old palace. Caligula was, as usual, lounging on a couch. He seemed taller and thinner, his face had assumed a skull-like look, hollow-eyed and sunken-cheeked. He was nearly bald except for an incongruous tuft of hair which rested on the nape of his neck. He looked me up and down. I was obliged to kneel and kiss his slippered foot.

'How is my darling sister?' he lisped. 'I often think of her.' He repeated his ominous threat, 'And, when you return, Parmenon, remind her I have daggers as well as islands!'

Chaerea had informed me that Caligula had banished many of his enemies and, on a mere whim, sent executioners to hunt them down and forced them to take their own lives. If they refused, they were cruelly butchered.

'Well, get up! Get up!' Caligula waved his hand airily. 'I have to retire.'

I took my place on the couches which were arranged in a horseshoe around the Emperor's which stood on a raised dais. The mood was one of sheer terror. No one dared eat without the Emperor's permission and everyone was petrified of catching his eye. The Emperor withdrew, and when he returned, he was dressed as a woman in a beautiful silk gown, with a veil over his balding head. He wore artificial green finger- and toenails. He didn't take a seat but clapped his hands and the musicians struck up the tune of a well-known Syracusan dance. The Gods be my witness, we had to sit and watch as the Emperor of Rome danced and cavorted as if he were a tumbler from Antioch. Of course, at the end, the applause was deafening. Caligula, still in his female clothes, returned to his couch, sharing it with an actor who was under strict instructions to treat the Emperor as if he was a woman.

I was forced to remain in court for the next few days. The Emperor lived in a world of his own. He often made public appearances in a woman's cloak covered with embroidery and precious stones. Or, in sharp contrast, he'd wear the famous military boots which gave him his nick-name. He had an artificial golden beard which he would fasten to his face and carry a thunder-bolt trident or serpentine staff as he pretended to be Jupiter or Apollo. On occasions he'd disport himself as Venus, which was truly dangerous: with his bony shoulders and spindly legs, it was difficult not to laugh out loud.

Caligula's only link with sanity seemed to be his love of chariot racing but even here his madness had eventually manifested itself. He fell in love with his own horse Incitatus and built him a marble stable with an ivory stall, purple blankets and jewelled harness. Before a race the entire neighbourhood around the imperial stable was put under armed guard, and sentence of death was passed on anyone who disturbed his horse. The charioteers were divided into different factions, with an intense rivalry between the 'Blues' and 'Greens'. Caligula supported the 'Greens'. Woe betide any charioteer from an opposing faction who threatened the Emperor's favourites – they could expect either themselves, or their horses, to be poisoned. No wonder Rome seethed with unrest.

At first I was left alone by the conspirators. Caligula had me watched but, as the New Year came and went, dismissed me as a nonentity; he was more interested in the games and festivities planned for the end of the month. I was left to my own devices. I went out to the Via Sacre and visited the baby Nero. He was, as Agrippina had described him, a bouncing, unruly, little boy with bulbous blue eyes and a shock of red-coppery hair. Even then he was a born actor. I had to sit with his guardians while the little fellow sang and danced. I don't believe in premonitions, yet, as I watched the child, I kept thinking of the monster on the Palatine. For the first time in my life, I quietly prayed that Agrippina had chosen the right course for her son. The aged aunt who looked after the boy was a cold, austere, old woman with a face like vinegar.

Never once, she proudly informed me, had she reminded the boy of his mother.

I smiled thinly and assured her that Agrippina would never forget such a remark. I also called on

Uncle Claudius in the library of the Senate house. His twisted face was unshaven, his tunic and toga soiled with dust and ink. He walked me up and down the rows of shelves, dragging his foot behind him, whilst delivering a lecture on the possible ancestors of the Divine Augustus. Round and round we went until I became dizzy. In a shadowy, dusty corner, he abruptly paused and sat down on a stool, mopping his face with the rag he kept up his sleeve.

'Are you part of it?' he asked. His eyes had lost that empty, vacuous look. His mouth was no longer slack, the jaw line seemed firmer, his voice free of any impediment. He spoke clearly and distinctly whilst those shrewd grey-green eyes studied me.

'So, you are Agrippina's man?' he asked.

'I am.'

He puckered his lower lip. 'And are you one of them?' he repeated.

'One of what, sir?' I asked.

'You know full well,' he teased. 'Caligula is going to die, isn't he? He's obscene. He's mad and his wickedness grows every day. At the moment, he's absorbed in his games but soon he'll lash out once more and his kin will feel his wrath. The signs are all there. The portents . . .'

'What portents, sir?'

Claudius sighed. 'The Capitol has been struck by lightning,' he explained. 'As has the Palatine here in Rome. Sulla the soothsayer sent a message to the Emperor to be careful.' Claudius's eyes narrowed. 'Caligula has been told to beware of a man called Cassius. But we don't need the Gods, do we, Parmenon, to tell us there's going to be a change?' He made a rude sound with his lips. 'Oh, don't worry, we can relax here. Spies find it very difficult to listen to conversations in a library, they can't openly eavesdrop; it's the best place to plot a coup. Come on, man, are you part of it or not?'

'Yes, sir, I am.'

Claudius rearranged his cloak round his shoulders.

'Now listen carefully, young man. Agrippina is directing matters.' He laughed at my surprise. 'Oh, didn't you know she's been writing to me? Don't be offended,' he soothed. 'Agrippina wouldn't tell you lest you were captured and tortured. She wouldn't use you as a messenger for the same reason. Caligula is to be killed and the best chance is as he leaves the games or the theatre. If we can separate him from his guards, the others will fulfil their task.' He tapped his sandalled foot on the floor like a schoolmaster giving instruction. 'Cassius Chaerea is a leading conspirator. Caligula still heaps insults on him: last night he made him kiss his little finger then waggled it in a most obscene manner. My only fear is that Chaerea may not be able to contain himself and strike before we are ready.'

'Will you be involved?' I taunted.

In answer Claudius got up and stood with his fingers to his lips as he examined scrolls on a shelf. He murmured to himself and plucked one down, greasy and stained with age.

'Do you know what this is, Parmenon? It's an

account of Julius Caesar's assassination. All those involved in his murder died violently themselves. I will not suffer a similar fate. I will act the frightened rabbit, and I suggest you do likewise. If, and when, the blow is struck, distance yourself. Ensure that the young Nero is safe and sound, and that I –' he smiled '– am discovered cowering in some apartment in the palace. If that's done, all will be well. The rest,' he spread his hands, 'is in the lap of the Gods. Now, I've got manuscripts to file and you've murder to plot.'

He rose and shuffled away. I suppose with someone like Agrippina you learn something new every day. I had always regarded Claudius as a fool, but Agrippina thought otherwise. She had learnt her lesson and, like Uncle Claudius, would not show her hand. Cassius Chaerea was different: his hatred for the Emperor was now a consuming passion. After nightfall, when free of the Emperor's spies, we met the other conspirators out in the gardens or shady groves where Cassius's men could defend us. Other tribunes of the Praetorian Guard were drawn in: Papinius, Asiaticus, Clovinus Rufus an ex-consul, as well as senators such as Balbus. The password was 'liberty' and the day of the murder was chosen: 24 January, the last day of the Palatine Games.

The conspirators chose their place well. A makeshift amphitheatre had been erected in the Emperor's palace, served by narrow galleries and passageways. The conspirators took oaths to either kill Caligula there or, if they failed, kill themselves. I became their shadow. The only person Agrippina had told me to take care of was Progeones, I had only glimpsed that awful little creature from afar. Progeones was now hated by everyone. He was regarded as Caligula's dagger man and constantly carried a list of those the Emperor wished to condemn.

On the morning of the twenty-fourth, Cassius arranged that I join the Emperor in the imperial box at the games. Caligula was in good form, shouting, gesticulating, throwing coins at the mob. He espied me, called me over and clapped me on the shoulder.

'I've had enough of your miserable face, Parmenon. It's back to Pontia for you. Tell my bitch of a sister that I have been thinking about her more often than I should.'

I kissed the Emperor's hand and withdrew. I glanced quickly at Progeones. He seemed nervous and ill at ease, and I wondered if he had a spy amongst the conspirators. Caligula then went to a makeshift altar and sacrificed a flamingo for good luck. When some of the blood splashed on his toga, he wiped it off and licked his fingers. He resumed his seat, now and again calling over a senator to kiss his slippered foot.

I glanced around. Chaerea, in full dress armour, tense as a bow string, stood next to the door clutching his sword. The strike had been planned for the end of the day, but the tension was already palpable. I left my seat and crossed to Chaerea.

'It must be done now,' I urged. 'Progeones suspects something.'

Chaerea shook his head, his pallid face soaked in sweat. I glanced down the tier of seats. Castor and Pollux and other members of the German bodyguard now ringed the Emperor. The morning drew on. The fighters in the amphitheatre were lacklustre. Caligula, bored, climbed over the balustrade and into the arena, accompanied by Castor and Pollux. The Emperor grabbed a sword and showed one gladiator how to fight. His opponent, overcome with fear, fell to his knees and begged for mercy. The Emperor neighed with laughter and drove his sword deep into the man's throat. Helped by his bodyguards, Caligula climbed back into the imperial box.

'I am hungry!' he shouted. 'I want something to eat!'

He turned round and his eyes met mine, a cool, sane look. I've always wondered if Caligula knew he was going to die that day.

'Parmenon!' he shouted. 'Join me. I have fresh messages for my sister.'

He shoved his guards aside and climbed the steps towards me. Castor and Pollux followed. For a while confusion reigned, as senators leapt up and wondered whether they should accompany the Emperor or not. Caligula took me by the arm and pushed me out. Chaerea and the others clustered by the doorway. There were a number of underground entrances, some for the crowd, others for the Emperor and his important guests. Caligula went towards one of the latter, and I seized my opportunity.

'No, your Excellency, it is safer down here.'

Caligula didn't object. He turned quickly and we went down a narrow passageway towards a pool of light. Footsteps echoed behind us. The Emperor thought it was his bodyguard: in fact it was Chaerea and the rest.

I heard shouts in German. The Emperor, alarmed, peered back through the gloom.

'What is this?' he exclaimed.

Chaerea's sword was already drawn. I pushed the Emperor away from me. Caligula staggered back, his eyes rounded with terror. He lifted his hand to fend off the blow but Chaerea was too swift, and he sliced the Emperor between neck and shoulder. As the Emperor collapsed to his knees, a second blow slashed his jaw. Caligula gave a cry and collapsed on one side. The rest joined in, a melee of screams and shouts, daggers and swords rising and falling. The alarm had been raised, and the German body-guard, led by Thracian officers, thronged down the passageway, shields up, swords out. In the confusion they had first chosen the wrong way. I glanced down. Caligula was dead, his corpse saturated in blood. Some of the conspirators chose to defend themselves as the Germans closed in. I decided to flee and was soon out in the sunlight, running back towards the city.

Rumours of the attack and the Emperor's death had gone before me. The Palatine was all confusion, some people running towards the scene of the murder, others, with more sense, trying to put as much distance between them and the murder as possible. I stopped in the shadow of a statue to catch my breath. I wiped off the sweat and made sure there were no bloodstains on my clothing. If Agrippina was correct there would now be a bloodbath but the coup had been successful. Today Caligula learnt, too late, that he wasn't a God.

Of course, the expected blood-letting followed. The German guards and their Thracian officers went on a senseless rampage. They took the heads of some of the conspirators and placed them as victory trophies on the altar of Augustus. They, in turn, were cut down by the Praetorians who hurried in from the camp. Chaerea escaped, though he spent time desecrating Caligula's corpse, ripping his dagger through Caligula's genitals.

Caligula's friend, the Jewish king Herod Agrippa, intervened as the bloody fray drifted away from the Emperor's corpse. Herod took the corpse to the Lamia Gardens on the Esquiline where he tried to arrange a funeral pyre. The confusion was so great that he gave up and interred the half-burnt corpse in a shallow grave. No one was able to protect Caligula's wife, who threw herself on the outstretched sword of one of the tribunes, who had come for her. They then took her child Priscilla by the heel and dashed her brains against the wall.

Meanwhile the Senate, that group of old hypocrites, clustered like a gaggle of frightened geese, not in the Senate house but in the temple of Jupiter, to which they had also brought the city treasure.

Protected by guards, they started the usual debate about restoring the Republic. It was a vain hope: both the army and the mob had far more to gain from supporting whoever was to be the next Emperor.

I had bribed certain guards to look after the young Nero and now went searching for Claudius, who, in the general chaos everyone had ignored. Looting had broken out in the palace, where slaves, soldiers and servants were helping themselves. I searched the library but found it empty. I then recalled where his mother's chamber had been and discovered Claudius hiding behind a curtain.

'Everything is going to plan,' I assured him. 'Agrippina's son is safe but you have to assert yourself.'

Claudius was almost wetting himself with fright. It took two cups of wine before he stopped shaking. I grabbed him by the hand and bundled him down the steps.

A group of Praetorian officers were waiting, and greeted the old man as if he was a God incarnate. Claudius was immediately put into a litter and, protected by soldiers, taken down to the Praetorian camp outside the city gates. Once he was there, Claudius started to regain his nerve. In a clash of gleaming swords, their cloaks billowing out, the Praetorian Guard hailed Claudius as Emperor and Caesar. He stood shaking on the purple-draped rostrum but accepted their salutes and oaths of fealty. Slowly but surely the word spread. Clerks, secretaries, civil servants, and even a few senators joined Claudius.

The Senate tried to negotiate, whilst Claudius prevaricated, dodging and swerving like an old fox. He pointed out that the army had already hailed him as Emperor. He had promised them a donative and he hoped the Senate would see sense and recognise him. They had no choice: Rome accepted him as Emperor. Two weeks later Claudius invited my mistress back to Rome. He treated her honourably, restored her possessions and, after executing those who had murdered Caligula, studiously ignored any reference to her or me.

Agrippina was delighted to see her son again. She was now twenty-five years of age. The different crises had created furrows in her olive-skinned face and silvery lines in the night-black hair but her eyes were still bright and vivacious. When she saw Nero, however, the years fell away. She picked him up and danced. For days afterwards, she wouldn't let him out of her sight. She studied every inch of his little body and questioned him closely about what he liked, his favourite toys. At first he was shy and coy with her, but eventually they became inseparable. Domitia Lepida who looked after him during her exile was totally ignored. Agrippina would have liked to have torn her eyes out but Lepida was the mother of Messalina, that copper-haired, round-faced beauty who had the good fortune to be married to Claudius the Emperor.

Agrippina very rarely mentioned Messalina's name, yet, I could tell, they were the deadliest enemies from the start. One day, shortly after her return,

Agrippina asked me to comb her hair. She sat on a small stool in front of a silver sheen mirror. Young Nero sat at her feet, thumb in mouth, watching her with wide eyes.

'I have learnt my lesson, Parmenon,' Agrippina declared, studying her reflection closely.

'In what way, Domina?'

'To survive.' She leaned down and rustled Nero's hair. 'And to wait.'

'For what, Domina?'

'Is the door closed?' she asked.

'You know it is, Mistress. You've chosen this room carefully, just like the one where we first met.'

'I'll tell you what I've planned,' she murmured, so matter of fact you'd think she was choosing an ointment or a pot of paint for her face. 'One day Nero will become Emperor, won't you, my little child?' She smiled beatifically at her son as he sat at her feet. 'And I shall become Empress.'

I dropped the brush.

'And you, Parmenon,' she continued, 'must not be so clumsy.'

'And how will you achieve all this?' I asked. 'Ask Claudius to divorce Messalina and marry you?'

Agrippina pulled a face.

'Messalina has already given birth to one child, a girl Octavia.' I continued warningly.

'So?' She shrugged one shoulder. 'I doubt if she is Claudius's child.' She bit her lip. 'I mustn't say that again.'

I gave her hair one hard brush and stood back. She caught my gaze in the mirror.

'What is it, Parmenon?' she whispered.

'Haven't you heard the news, Domina?'

She spun round on the stool. When she lost her temper, Agrippina's face changed; it seemed to grow longer, harder, her high cheekbones more pronounced, the sensuous lips a mere pink, thin line. She could read my thoughts.

'What is it, Parmenon?' she demanded again.

'Mama, Mama, what's the matter?' Nero jumped up and clutched at her leg.

Agrippina put an arm round his shoulder.

'Hush, little one,' she soothed. 'I'll take you into the garden. I've bought some new fish. Parmenon has something to tell me, haven't you?'

My throat had gone dry. I had never seen Agrippina look so furious.

'Rumours, Domina, mere gossip. That's what you pay me to collect, isn't it?'

'I don't pay you anything,' she whispered hoarsely. 'You are mine, Parmenon, body and soul. I can see it in your eyes: Messalina is expecting another child, isn't she?'

I agreed. 'Her women are talking about her courses having stopped for two months in succession. They will take oaths that Claudius is the father. Messalina has already consulted the midwives and the auguries. She has been promised a fine boy.'

Agrippina didn't move.

'Did you hear me, Domina?'

She hugged Nero closer. 'Get out!' she ordered.

She had bitten the corner of her lips so savagely that a trickle of blood ran down her chin. 'Get out and leave me alone!'

For the next few days I never saw Agrippina. She remained closeted in her apartment, sending to the kitchen for food for both herself and her son. Other people came and went: the legion of spies she had in the city; merchants; traders; tinkers; the occasional soldier from the Praetorian Guard. I knew it was best to leave her alone. I was also aware of visitors arriving late at night, of horsemen, soldiers in the garden below, pinpricks of light in the darkness, the rumbling wheels of a cart.

Eventually the crisis passed. Agrippina invited me back to her chamber, where she was sitting on the same stool. Her long, black hair was thrust behind her but her face bore no paint. She looked older, more severe.

'I want you to brush my hair, Parmenon,' she declared, 'for the last time.'

My heart sank. I thought I was to be dismissed.

'Brush it, feel it, smell its perfume. Go on!'

I picked up the brush from the ivory basket and obeyed. I held her hair to my face.

'So,' she said as if there had been no interruption in our conversation. 'Messalina is expecting a brat?' She sighed. 'More obstacles eh, Parmenon? Someone else in the arena. I shall tell you what we'll do!'

'Yes, Domina.'

'We'll keep quiet and we'll wait.'

I brushed Domina's hair. It was the last time for many years.

From that day Agrippina transformed herself: she wore her hair tightly caught up as if she was a Roman matron. Her stola and dress would have been more appropriate for the fashion of the Republic than for the ostentatious finery of Claudius's court. Her face went largely unpainted and rarely did I see jewellery around her throat or fingers. She also hired a tutor, that little turd Anicetus, who educated her in the history of Rome and the intricacies and subtleties of the Julio-Claudian family. I was fascinated. I had never seen such an actress. She was no longer the young, passionate, tempestuous Agrippina but a severe Roman matron. Her dinner parties became so conservative and boring I often fell asleep. Sometimes, rarely, she'd catch my eye and wink quickly. She invited her sister Julia more and more to her banquet evenings and afterwards they would stroll, arm-in-arm, around the gardens. Julia was very much like Drusilla: dark with a lush, sensuous body, provocative eye-catching gestures, and a twinkling laugh, but she was vapid and empty-headed. She soon fell under Agrippina's sway, to whom she brought the gossip of the court and all the scandals of the city. Agrippina would sit, listen and nod wisely.

One evening Domina invited the Emperor Claudius to dine. Power, I suppose, changes people: Claudius could act the fool but he had soon proved himself to be shrewd and as ruthless as any of his predecessors –

opposition both at home and abroad had been cruelly crushed. Agrippina welcomed him as her revered kinsman and led both Claudius and Messalina to the couch of honour. If Agrippina looked dowdy, Messalina was as brilliant as the sun in the heavens. She was not very tall but perfectly formed; just the way she walked made men's heads turn. She had a round, doll-like face, a petite nose and full-lipped mouth, with strange dark-blue eyes offset by her red-gold hair. She wore more jewellery on one wrist than Agrippina had in her treasure coffers. She loved to dress herself in white. As she walked into the dining chamber, the light caught the jewellery at her throat and ears and she shimmered like some goddess appearing to mortals.

Agrippina courted her and tried to indulge her every whim. Claudius swallowed the bait whole, but Messalina suspected what Agrippina was plotting. Throughout the meal she drank little but listened with a sneer on her pretty face as Agrippina flattered Claudius and impressed him with her knowledge of Rome, its legends and customs. Claudius listened open-mouthed in admiration, until eventually he fell asleep as he always did. Messalina leaned across. She reminded me of how Helen of Troy must have looked: beautiful, treacherous and very, very dangerous.

'I thank you,' she lisped. 'For the food, the wine, the company.' She waved her hand airily in the direction of the musicians. 'And I do admire your knowledge of Roman history.' The smile faded from her lips. 'If it's true,' she continued, 'that Claudius is descended from Aeneas of Troy and if my midwives are correct, it would seem that Aeneas is going to have another descendant. Doesn't that please you, Agrippina?'

'I'm ecstatic for you,' my mistress cooed. 'Please accept my sincere congratulations. I can assure you,' Agrippina popped a grape in her mouth, 'both you and your children are never far from my thoughts.'

'And you and yours,' Messalina retorted, 'are never out of mine.'

On such a note the banquet ended. Claudius, drunkenly murmuring about the Auguries, was helped to his litter. Agrippina and Messalina kissed, looking more like gladiators saluting each other in the arena, and the imperial party left in a blare of trumpets and a line of spluttering torches. Agrippina clapped her hands and pronounced herself satisfied.

'Be careful,' I warned.

'Oh, I'm going to be, Parmenon,' she whispered. 'I am going to be very, very careful. I sincerely hope Messalina is as well. Now, was the music appropriate? Do you think Claudius was impressed by my knowledge of Roman history?'

'Rome has no finer actress,' I applauded.

She slapped me on the hand. 'Well, they've gone,' she continued, 'and I've got business to do. It's going to be a busy night for us, Parmenon.'

She went out, and when she returned, two burly, shadowy figures entered behind her. My heart skipped a beat: their outlines were familiar. I glimpsed thick hair falling down to the shoulders and bearded faces. Castor and Pollux stepped into the pool of torchlight.

'By all the Gods!' I exclaimed.

Both Germans glanced at me, those icy-blue eyes studying my face carefully.

'You've got nothing to fear,' Agrippina assured me. 'These men took an oath of allegiance to my brother, and now he's dead, they owe it to me.'

Agrippina stepped forward and looked at each from head to toe. They were now dressed in simple tunics, no longer the red and white of the Emperor's personal guard. Silver torcs circled their necks, copper bracelets were round their wrists. They still looked very dangerous in their marching boots, with broad daggers hanging from the belts across their shoulders.

'They have taken an oath of allegiance,' Agrippina declared, 'and we have shared bread and salt. They are my shadows, protection for me and my son.'

Chapter 11

'He goes along the shadowy path from which, they say, no one returns'

Catullus, *Carmina*: 3

Agrippina made the two Germans take a similar oath of loyalty to myself, a macabre ceremony carried out by torch and candlelight. The two Germans ate bread and salt and swore their loyalty by earth, sea and sky. When this makeshift ceremony was over, Agrippina ordered me to follow her down into the cellars of the house; a place I seldom visited, with its warren of galleries and passageways. Agrippina led us to a heavy reinforced door at the end of a corridor. Castor opened it and stepped inside. I sensed someone else was there; there was a moan, a clink of chain. Torches were lit and I gazed upon

Progeones, manacled to the wall. Agrippina's torturers had taken his eyes out, leaving nothing but black, bloody sockets.

'Here he is,' Agrippina mocked. 'The man who carried Caligula's execution list and had the temerity to betray me.' She leaned closer and whispered in the man's battered ear. 'Well, Progeones, do you want to die?'

He groaned and nodded. He didn't know who I was, having lost all sense of reality. A man in such pain looks forward only to death.

Agrippina studied his face once more then left. She never mentioned him again but I discovered later that the Germans took him out into the countryside and buried him alive.

The horrors of that night were not yet over. Agrippina had the rest of her retinue summoned. We shared a litter and, preceded by torch-bearers, were taken along winding roads and alleyways to the Lamian Gardens on the Esquiline. It was a haunting, forbidding place, bathed only in the light of a pale moon. Agrippina didn't say anything as she led us across the lawns to the edge of a secluded cypress grove. Here, the Germans, who were usually frightened of nothing, refused to go any further. Their fear and panic spread to the rest of the retinue. Agrippina berated them but they just stared back and refused to take a step further. She snatched a torch, cursed in exasperation and led me on.

The glade was circular, as if man-made, fringed by the dark cypress trees, totally deserted except for a few rocks piled in the middle. Agrippina paused at these. I do not have a fanciful imagination but the longer I stood there, the heavier weighed the silence: oppressive, no sound at all, no night bird, no rustling in the grass, not even the slightest breeze stirred those trees. It was as if we were studying a mural or a painting. Agrippina was pale-faced, her hand shaking so much I had to take the torch. I followed her gaze. A mist, or what looked like a mist, snaked out from the trees, creeping across the grass. When it reached the rocks it began to rise. I experienced a nameless terror, a panic as if someone was quietly menacing me with unseen horrors. Agrippina began to speak. She was invoking protection against the powers of darkness. I pressed her shoulder, and found it ice-cold. A sound came from the mist, like a rustling on the breeze, before a harsh guttural voice spoke.

May the Gods be my witness: my heart chilled, my bowels and my stomach curdled with fear. Caligula! The dead Emperor's ghost had risen from his grave. He was standing behind me whispering in my ear, those same awful sounds he had made when talking to himself. The glade assumed a horror all of its own. A shadow seemed to race across yet there was little light from the moon, and our torches spluttered weakly. A place of hideous terror.

'This is Caligula's grave, isn't it?' I asked.

'It is,' Agrippina answered. 'The stories are all over Rome, of how this place is haunted by demons.' She glanced at me, eyes beseeching. 'He comes to me, Parmenon, in the dark watches of the night. I see

his blood-spattered face and he begs me for burial.'
She paused. 'I have tried to arrange it but no one will
help me.'

I summoned my courage and did what she asked.
Hoes and mattocks lay about, dropped by slaves
who'd attempted the task only to flee. I removed the
rocks and dug at the soft soil beneath. I soon disin-
terred the corpse, which was wrapped in soiled, dirty
sheets. Partly cremated, the fire had at least cleansed
and purified the remains. The face was indistinct,
obliterated by dark scorch marks, although it was
easy to recognise the shape of the head and that
monstrous tuft of hair on the nape of the neck
which had not been touched. Agrippina's bodyguard
recovered their courage and, urged on, they collected
dry kindling. I hardly looked at what I carried but
laid it on the ground and helped the others build the
makeshift funeral pyre, before placing the corpse on
top. Agrippina murmured a few prayers and coated
both cadaver and wood with the contents of an
amphora of oil. A torch was brought and then all
that remained of Caligula, friend of the Gods, was
consumed by fire.

Agrippina never mentioned her brother's funeral
again. She returned to our house and continued the
role of the noble recluse. She settled down to the life
of a peace-loving matron, totally devoted to her son,
ever ready to entertain the Emperor with lectures,
masques and declamations, most of them connected
with Rome's history. She and Messalina watched
each other like sparring leopards. If the Emperor

couldn't come, Agrippina entertained his freedmen, Narcissus and Pallas, powerful officials in charge of the treasury, the courts and access to the Emperor.

I accompanied her everywhere. Agrippina never referred to the Emperor, the court or contemporary politics, even when Claudius began the usual purge of the Senate and settled grudges with those who had insulted and belittled him over the years.

In the February following his accession, Messalina gave birth to a puny boy who was promptly named Britannicus. Agrippina played the kind kinswoman, sending gifts to both parents as well as to the child. She hid her rage and resentment well. She stalked Messalina like a feral cat would its prey, but never once did she show her claws. Instead, she fought her battles through her sister Julia who, with her beauty and wild, wanton ways, had soon become the toast of elegant Roman society.

Agrippina quietly urged Julia on. She introduced her sister to the one man whose mind Agrippina admired: our noble Spanish philosopher and financier, Annaeus Seneca. I never really found out why Agrippina admired that man so much.

'It might have been he who betrayed us to Caligula, remember?' I warned.

Agrippina shook her head. 'That traitor's still alive!'

'What? Afer the orator?'

'That traitor is still alive!' she repeated, eyes widening.

She was, of course, referring to old Claudius.

She pressed a finger against my lips. 'In time, Parmenon, in time all debts are settled!'

I was still concerned about Seneca. He'd returned from exile, more cunning and vindictive than ever. He was also an arrant hypocrite. He wrote treatises on youth and on old age and composed eloquent reflections on man's destiny. He preached poverty and austerity, and yet he relished the comforts of high society. He claimed to despise wealth but was as shrewd an investor as any banker.

Agrippina discussed philosophical matters with him, sharpening her mind, preparing herself for further debates with Claudius. She also made no attempt to disguise her ambition for Seneca to become her beloved Nero's tutor. Agrippina played a clever, subtle game, or thought she did. She wined and dined Seneca, laughed at his witticisms, flattered his overweening ego but refused any dalliance. Instead, Julia her sister was discreetly put forward as the philosopher's possible mistress. They became regular visitors to the court, the favoured guests who had to be invited to any important banquet or supper party.

'I know what you are doing,' I challenged Agrippina one evening after the couple had left.

'Do you, Parmenon?' she replied. 'I love my sister.'

'No, you don't. You love only one person, Domina – your son.'

She refused to hold my gaze but walked back to a side table and poured a goblet of wine.

'Have you heard the rumours?' I asked.

'Oh, don't tell me that Messalina's pregnant again!'

'No, Domina, Messalina is watching you.'

'And?'

'Be careful, you can provoke her too far!'

Agrippina refused to heed the warning. She continued to entertain and flatter Claudius as well as encourage her sister to become the leading light of Roman society. Messalina decided enough was enough and struck. One night I was awoken by the sound of crashing and screaming and the clash of swords. I left my bedchamber, a sheet wrapped round me, and fled down the passageways and galleries. The rest of the household had already been disturbed. The sounds were coming from the far end of the house where Agrippina and her son had their bedchamber. Both were safe but Castor and Pollux paid for their brave defence of their mistress and her son with their lives. Castor was already dead, with a terrible gaping wound to his neck. Pollux, who had fought on single-handedly against the intruders, was a mess of blood and gore from head to toe. Before the intruders had fled, he had taken a thrust to the stomach. When I reached them, Agrippina was already bending over him, listening to his harsh, guttural whispers. Agrippina got to her feet, whispered to a servant who stepped forward and quickly cut the German's throat. I had both corpses removed and sent out armed retainers to search for the intruders. They followed the trail of blood to the wall but returned empty-handed.

Agrippina was beside herself with fury. She moved her frightened son to another heavily guarded chamber and met me in her writing office. She reminded me of a raging lioness, pacing up and down, furious at the attack on her son. Only gradually did I get the details from her. She and Nero retired late, and as usual Castor and Pollux stood guard over both chambers. She had suspected nothing until woken by cries and the clash of swords. The Germans had apparently drawn the bolts on the outside of each door, a shrewd move as it prevented Agrippina or her son panicking – if they'd tried to flee their chambers, they would have run straight on to the swords of the assassins. Both Germans had fought bravely until the rest of the house had been aroused and the attackers fled, dragging their dead and wounded comrades with them.

'How many?' I asked.

Agrippina stopped her pacing and gestured with her hands.

'Pollux told me there were at least ten, all masked and hooded.' She continued, 'Before he asked me to put him out of his agony, Pollux claimed at least half of them were either killed or wounded.'

'It will be passed off as housebreaking,' I replied. 'A gang of thieves trying their luck.'

'Housebreakers don't move in groups of ten,' Agrippina snapped. 'And they don't like cold steel. These men knew where to come and what they were after: Nero and myself.'

'Messalina?' I asked.

'That bitch,' Agrippina agreed. 'Only someone wealthy could hire so many men, and give such precise instructions on what to do.'

'You are safe,' I replied. 'Your son is unharmed. You can appeal to the Emperor.' I spoke flatteringly.

Agrippina dismissed my words with a flick of her fingers. 'I must think. I must plot!' she declared and she was gone.

Agrippina was given little choice to do either. Messalina struck again, ruthlessly and to the point. The household slept late that morning until it was roused by messengers, informing Agrippina that both her sister Julia and the philosopher Seneca had been arrested for adultery, public lewdness, conspiracy and possible treason. If I hadn't stopped her, Agrippina would have left immediately for the Palatine.

'There's nothing you can do,' I urged.

Agrippina was fighting hard to control her temper. She had dismissed the stewards and the others waiting for her to carry out the funeral rites of the two Germans.

'See to the funeral pyres,' I urged. 'Pack your bags and then clear your house. We'll load the carts and leave Rome.'

Agrippina leaned forward, gripping the sides of the table as if the house was shaking.

'Leave?' she whispered. 'Like some beaten dog?'

'What can you do?' I retorted. 'Trot along and see Uncle Claudius? Tell him that his beloved wife tried to kill your son? You know what Claudius is like, he'll dither about asking for evidence and Messalina will pounce. She'll rope you in with your sister! Two of a kind, she'll cry.' I clutched her arm. 'Or you can even be more stupid: go to the Emperor and defend your sister, tell Claudius that Julia is innocent of any charge. Do that,' I warned, 'and, by the end of the month, you and Nero will be no more.'

At first, Agrippina wouldn't listen and let loose the most terrible rage. She strode up and down, knocking goblets, vases, statuettes onto the floor, slashing at cushions with a small knife, kicking over stools. At last her rage subsided, and she slumped onto a couch, face in her hands.

'I'm thinking, Parmenon. Before you start boring me with your advice, I'm thinking.' She took away her hands. 'We'll give the Germans honourable burial, and meanwhile tell my steward and chamberlains to pack, and load the carts. We'll be gone from Rome within the day. I'll send a message to Claudius protesting my innocence and saying how shocked I am by my sister's actions.'

I smiled in agreement. Agrippina turned her head and glanced sideways at me.

'But, one day, Parmenon, I'll return!'

'One day,' I repeated.

Agrippina pointed to the door. 'Leave me. Let no one come in.'

Agrippina kept to her word, except in one small detail: we stayed in Rome a further day to hear the verdict passed against Julia and Seneca. Both were exiled: Seneca, with all his stomach and liver troubles, to Corsica; Julia, that beautiful butterfly, was despatched to Pontia. Messalina showed her little mercy – within weeks the island was visited by Praetorian guards and soon afterwards we heard of Julia's death.

Agrippina retreated to her villa at Antium with its flowery grottoes and shady colonnaded walks. She returned to her studies, corresponded with friends and entertained. She taught Nero how to swim and fish. She gave up pottery but took an active interest in gardening, in particular the development of certain poisons. She tested and preserved these before developing antidotes. She hired physicians, leeches and apothecaries, who would comment on the properties of certain substances and plants. Agrippina was a keen student. At the same time, she was careful not to be seen as posing a threat to anyone in Rome.

'It's not enough,' she declared one morning, 'for me to hide here, Parmenon. Messalina must be distracted. She must think I'm safe, comfortable and well away from the court.' She picked up a hand mirror and studied her olive-skinned face. 'I'm twenty-six years of age,' she stated. 'Do you know, Parmenon, it's time I married. Oh no, not to a prince of the blood or a victorious general. I have chosen my man: he's very rich, very witty and will keep me amused.'

The lucky, or unlucky, man, depending on your perspective, was Passienus Crispus, a constant visitor to Agrippina's villa and a former friend of her brother Caligula. In his heyday, Passienus had been a great orator with a sharp wit. He was also very wealthy, owning property at Tusculum, in Rome and elsewhere. A small, balding man, Passienus's tart observations on life caused merriment without provoking hostility. An old dowager of Rome once alleged he'd accused her of buying old shoes.

'I didn't say you bought them,' Passienus replied. 'I said you sold them.'

The remark caused bellows of laughter throughout the city and the dowager dared not show her face for months. Even Tiberius and Caligula met their match with this court jester; they took no offence when Passienus said of them: 'Never did such a good slave have such a bad master!'

Caligula used to love teasing him. One day he questioned Passenius on the orator's romantic liaison with his beloved sister Drusilla.

'Have you slept with her?' Caligula demanded.

Anybody else would have fainted away. To have said 'No' could be taken as an insult to her beauty; to say 'Yes' could be construed as treason. Passienus, however, just hitched his toga up and calmly replied, 'Not yet, your Excellency.'

Caligula hooted with laughter, and pounded Passienus on the back. He kept repeating the remark to himself for days, a constant source of chuckling amusement. Passienus had always been Agrippina's friend, lending her money, attending her banquets, one of the few men who could genuinely make her laugh. In his role as court jester, I suspect, he had secretly used his influence and wealth to advance Agrippina's cause in Rome. Messalina would see him as no threat. Agrippina and Passienus were allowed to settle down into quiet, boring nuptial bliss.

Passienus was overwhelmed, flattered to be a kinsman, a member of the imperial family. Agrippina wove her web around him. Once, under the influence of wine, Passienus cheerfully admitted to me that Agrippina was a marvellous lover: energetic and enthusiastic in bed sports. I told him to keep such opinions to himself. He was a likeable, cheerful rogue, thirty years Agrippina's senior, and he soon settled into his role as her companion and protector. She used him as she used every man. Passienus had a finger in many pies and he had the wealth to finance an army of informers. Nonetheless, Agrippina kept well away from Rome, staying at Antium or travelling north to Tusculum. She never spoke to me of her relationship with Passienus. She was absorbed with Nero as well as listening carefully to whatever news Passienus brought from the city.

Within four years of the marriage, Passienus began to suffer the effects of dropsy. I happened to remind her that her first husband, Domitius, had suffered from the same ailment.

'It's quite common,' Agrippina evenly replied, 'in men of that age group, of a certain social class. I am doing all I can to help.'

Passienus became a shadow of his former self, more subdued and withdrawn, as if concentrating on a problem to which the solution constantly evaded him. More and more Agrippina took over their affairs. I noticed that Passienus had little love for Nero and the boy responded in kind.

Nero was developing into a sturdy, copper-headed dumpling, with thick lips, a podgy nose and striking blue eyes, which he would constantly screw up as if short-sighted. A clever boy who learnt his lessons quickly, Nero was also a consummate actor. He loved singing or dancing, and composing his own poetry and every visitor to his mother's household was always entertained by Nero's childish songs, poems or performance in some play. He was a creditable athlete, graceful at running and swimming, and with no fear of horses. Acting, however, was his great passion – that and his mother. Perhaps their separation in his early years had created an insatiable hunger for her presence. He clung to her and she responded, allowing him to share her bed as protection against his constant nightmares. Even when Passienus joined her, Nero slept on a couch in the same room. One morning I heard Passienus arguing with Agrippina about it – he never protested again.

As Nero grew older, I became more interested in the little monster. I would often find him crouching by Agrippina's door, listening or peering through the keyhole. The servants and slaves gave him the run of the villa, treating him with fawning adoration. Of course there were also whispers and gossip about their relationship. One maid made the mistake of telling others that she had seen Nero wearing his mother's clothes. Within a day she disappeared and was never seen again.

Passienus avoided the boy as much as he could. I once heard him refer to Nero as 'that little horror' but generally he had the sense to keep such sentiments to himself. I didn't like Nero's cloying sweetness, the mock adoration in those chilling blue eyes as he questioned me, particularly about his mother and the activities of Uncle Caligula. I tried to answer as tactfully as possible. Nero had a sharp mind and keen wit, and would pester me until he was satisfied.

Agrippina still used me to send messages into the city.

'You are nondescript, Parmenon,' she declared. 'You can enter rooms and stand silently without being noticed. You are a born spy.'

I baulked at the insult but she threw her arms round my neck and kissed me on the lips. 'Not my spy,' she murmured. 'More my shadow.'

I never knew exactly what I took into Rome, letters hidden away in a flask of wine, coded messages which only the recipient could understand. I would collect the gossip and the scandal, scooping it up like a fisherman would a catch in his net, and bring it all back to Agrippina. I told her how the Lamian Gardens were still haunted by Caligula's ghost, whilst the same eerie phenomenon had been experienced in the place where he'd been assassinated. Nero overhead this, absorbing every detail avidly. Of course, he questioned me closely later and made me repeat all the ghastly stories.

On one beautiful afternoon at Tusculum, a slave reported that one of the hanging cages in the garden had been forced and the songbird was missing. Usually, a chamberlain or steward would have dealt with such a matter but they were all enjoying a wine-soaked siesta. I decided to take care of the problem myself. I inspected the cage, became intrigued and went deeper into the garden, where I heard a childish voice chanting in the bushes. I quietly moved these apart, to see Nero kneeling inside. His body shielded a small rock, a makeshift altar on which the songbird had been sacrificed. The bird had been slit from throat to crotch, its innards spilt out in a bloody mess. Nero had dipped his fingers into the blood and daubed his face as if he was a priest.

'What are you doing?' I demanded.

'I am performing a sacrifice.'

'For what?'

'For nothing, silly!' Nero retorted. 'I'm sacrificing to Uncle Caligula. When he comes to me, I talk to him.'

Despite the sunlight and the warmth, my skin crawled and my hands turned clammy. It wasn't just the sacrifice, the destruction of a beautiful bird, but those clear blue eyes looking at me so earnestly and Nero's aimless chatter, so reminiscent of Caligula.

'Uncle is a God,' Nero pressed the point. 'And I am his nephew. It is right to make pious sacrifice.'

He was only eight years old but he talked and

looked like a seasoned conspirator. I started to withdraw but he sprang to his feet. He grasped my wrist, digging his nails deeply into my skin.

'It's our secret, isn't it, Parmenon? Just between you and me. You won't tell Mother?'

'I won't tell Mother,' I promised.

'That's good,' the little horror replied. 'It's not the first time I've done this you know, Parmenon. Uncle tells me everything. He sends his regards.' His face creased into a smile. 'Now you may go and I'll finish the rite.'

I never did tell Agrippina: I was too frightened to do so. In her eyes, Nero could do no wrong. In those heady, conspiratorial days, as Agrippina spun her web, no one was safe. Much as she loved me, much as she needed me, I, too, could become an offering on the altar to her adorable son.

Six years in all passed, slipping away like a dream. Sometimes I tried to live my own life: I'd meet a pretty face, I'd invest a little money. I was planning to buy my own farm but remorselessly Agrippina drew me back. I had no choice; I danced like a moth round the alluring flame. Agrippina used me more and more as her messenger to Rome.

'Concentrate on Claudius,' she warned, 'and that glorious bitch of his.'

I did so. There were plenty of people ready to tell their tales. Claudius had won some respect, being more restrained and less bloodthirsty than his predecessor. However, his growing eccentricity was a constant theme at dinner conversations. Claudius liked the old ways and he fancied himself as a great judge or lawyer. He would often sit in the courts to hear and arbitrate on cases. Sometimes he proved himself a tyrant, at other times he'd allow the lawyers to insult him. One little Greek, frustrated by Claudius's refusal to give him a fair hearing, hurled a wax tablet across the court, striking Claudius on the face.

'As for you!' the Greek screamed. 'You are not Caesar, you're just a silly, old man!'

Claudius dabbed at the cut, and allowed the Greek to have his say and leave without being punished. At other times Claudius would become involved in the day-to-day lives of his subjects. He began a campaign against ostentation, which he initiated by buying a beautiful silver chariot and having it smashed to pieces in front of a crowd of onlookers. Or he would issue edicts such as: 'Yew juice is a sovereign remedy against snake bite', or, 'breaking wind at table is not a breach of etiquette'. I think the latter was to excuse his own lack of personal hygiene.

Claudius loved to stage games and pronounced that any gladiator who pretended not to fight well would have his throat cut. Sometimes he would bandy words with the mob or even with the gladiators themselves. On one occasion, during the draining of the Fucine Lake, Claudius decided to stage a mock naval battle. It was the usual nonsense: two triremes, each manned by a team of gladiators, would crash together and the crowd would be treated to a sea battle. Just before the games began the gladiators, as was customary, paraded in front of the imperial box and gave the ritual salute.

'Hail, Caesar! We, who are about to die, salute you!'

'Or not die, as the case may be!' Claudius retorted.

The gladiators thought he was pardoning them, granting them life, so they put down their weapons and refused to fight. The crowd was treated to the spectacle of their Emperor having to climb into the arena and bribe both sides to continue.

Agrippina was most interested in Claudius's relationship with Messalina. She listened avidly to the tales of her rival's amorous exploits whilst Claudius was growing more and more puritanical. He banned prostitutes from Rome. When he discovered that the husband of his elder daughter, Antonia, was more interested in pretty boys, Claudius sent soldiers to his house: they caught the miscreant in bed with one of his lovers and promptly stabbed both to death.

Nevertheless, I warned Agrippina that Messalina's influence over Claudius did not appear to be waning. She was ruthless and sly in exploiting her husband's fears and growing superstition. One day as Claudius entered her court, a litigant came running up and begged for an audience.

'Your Excellency,' he fawned. 'Take care this day, for I dreamt you were assassinated.'

Claudius, of course, was full of concern and begged the man to describe the would-be assassin: the cunning litigant turned and pointed to his rival waiting in the court. Claudius was taken in by this nonsense and the poor victim was immediately hustled away and executed on a fictitious charge of treason. Messalina was equally successful in using the same method to despatch a senator she hated. One morning Narcissus, the powerful freedman, burst into the Emperor's bedchamber. Sweaty and stricken, he threw himself on his knees and told the Emperor of his dream in which Messalina's hated senator had forced his way into the palace and stabbed Claudius to death.

'I have dreamt a similar dream,' Messalina divulged.

Claudius heard them out, not yet fully believing, until a chamberlain promptly arrived to say that the very same senator – whom of course Messalina had secretly invited to the palace – had tried to force his way into the imperial chambers. It was confirmation enough for Claudius: orders were issued and, by noon, the senator concerned was forced to take his own life.

Agrippina listened to this story and asked me to repeat it several times.

'A clever ruse,' she murmured. 'A very clever ruse. If only poor Passienus was better, I'd travel to Rome myself to see what was happening.'

Poor Passienus was by now in a terrible way. His mind was wandering and, for some strange reason, he had fallen in love with a beech tree in his garden at Tusculum. He would embrace the trunk and kiss it, ordering his slaves to water the tree only with the finest wine from his cellars. He would sit and talk to it and sleep in its shade, and, late one afternoon, he died there. Agrippina mourned dutifully, and then had the body cremated and buried in the family tomb on the Appian Way. Once the funeral was over, Agrippina announced it was time for her to return to Rome.

Chapter 12

'What times! What manners!'
Cicero, *In Catilinam*: I, i

Agrippina used Passienus's wealth to set up in luxury in her house on the Via Sacra. Once again she was visited by the powerful and the mighty Claudius himself came, to eat and drink, and listen owl-eyed to Agrippina's lectures on Roman history. He would fall asleep, mouth open, and a slave would come and tickle his throat to get rid of the excess food and wine. Once this was achieved, two Nubian slaves lifted him up and carried him back to his litter.

Oh, Agrippina was still plotting. I sometimes ask myself why I stayed with her but . . . I loved the woman! In spite of all her wrongdoing and, yes, her killings, I admired her courage, and the fact that, once she had given her heart, she loved without compromise or constraint. She reminded me of a beautiful eagle, wings back, plunging down to the earth; once she had chosen her quarry, only death itself could stop her. During those early months after her return to Rome, Agrippina, like an eagle, perched on a branch, high above the scheming politics of the court, watching, waiting for her opportunity.

Claudius was undoubtedly tiring of Messalina's strident ways, her jealousy, her fury when her will was blocked. So Agrippina prepared to make her first move. The secular games were being held in Rome, and Nero was invited to take part whilst Agrippina joined Claudius in the imperial box. Messalina and her coterie were also there, and Agrippina watched them avidly, fascinated by Messalina's open flaunting of her favourites. One of these, Vitellius, Governor of Palestine, was even allowed to carry one of Messalina's slippers next to his heart as a token of his undying love for her. We all settled down, and watched Nero, aged eleven, and Britannicus, aged nine, lead the procession into the arena. Both boys, their hair dressed in decorative garlands, carried long, sharp javelins, a bow and quiver over their backs and around their necks chains of gold. When Nero came forward and saluted the Emperor, he was greeted by thunderous, rapturous applause, a sharp contrast to the courteous cheers and polite hand claps that greeted Britannicus: Domina had hired a special claque and they did a brilliant job. Messalina turned in her chair and glared at Agrippina, who smiled icily back, her message clear: Agrippina, daughter of Germanicus, had returned to Rome and her war with Messalina had only just begun. Afterwards I advised caution, but as usual Agrippina just ignored me.

'What can the bitch do?' she taunted. 'Attack me? Attack the grandson of Germanicus? Rome would not tolerate it. It's time we went to work, Parmenon.'

The invitations to Claudius and his freedmen Narcissus and Pallas increased, but at these evenings Agrippina began to look anxious and troubled, refusing to tell Claudius the reason. At last she produced Styges, an Egyptian soothsayer, a mountebank who could convince even prudent men that he had the gift of seeing the future. At first Agrippina pretended to be reluctant to let her self-styled seer inform the Emperor of what he had divined. Only when Claudius cleared the chamber and took the most solemn oaths, did Styges reveal that he had dreamed the husband of Messalina was in great danger.

'Not Messalina herself?' Claudius asked.

'No, Excellency, her husband.'

'But, but . . .' Claudius stammered. 'What can be done? What shall I do?'

Agrippina reminded Claudius of the oath he had taken not to tell anyone of the seer's prophecy. The Emperor, now hooked like the fish he was, asked Agrippina for advice.

'At the moment the danger is some time off,' Domina replied. 'But, Excellency, you must plan how to deal with it. If Messalina . . .' She let her words hang in the air.

'If Messalina what?' Claudius demanded.

'If Messalina could be encouraged to take another husband, just for a while . . .'

Claudius blinked and glanced at me. 'Wh– wha– what do you think, Parmenon?'

I stared at my mistress, who was acting to the full her role as concerned Roman matron. She held my gaze, and I glimpsed the laughter in her eyes.

'The most important thing, your Excellency,' I insisted, 'is the health and safety of your sacred person. That's why you must keep this warning to yourself. If it became public knowledge . . .'

Claudius bit his lip.

'Think of it this way, your Excellency,' I continued, 'danger threatens on all sides, but that is part of your sacred duty. Didn't the divine Caesar, the noble Augustus, and all the great heroes of Rome have to face danger?'

Claudius nodded. Oh, in many ways he was such a great fool!

'What Domina Agrippina wishes to ensure,' I explained smoothly, 'is that there is protection between you and that danger.'

Claudius poked me sharply in the chest. 'You could become Messalina's husband for a while, but no bed sport, mind you.' He threw his head back and bellowed with laughter at the look of consternation on my face.

'I was only joking,' he wheezed. 'Messalina would

never have anything to do with someone who was not only of inferior rank but ugly with it!'

I smiled in acknowledgement of his wit.

Once the Emperor had gone, Agrippina made me share her couch. She embraced and kissed me on the lips and licked my ear.

'Clever boy, Parmenon,' she whispered. 'We have the rod, we have the line, the fish is near. All we need to do is choose the bait.'

Agrippina now dug deep into her treasury and started to throw the most lavish of parties. Invitations were extended to every member of the high society of Rome although Claudius and Messalina were quietly ignored. Agrippina's chefs became the toast of the city, serving dishes such as ostrich brains and peas mixed with gold, or lentils on a bed of precious stones, so the guests were both well-fed and well-rewarded. Plump chickens, sows' udders, sucking pig, hot boiled goose, stuffed hare, venison, bream and the tastiest oysters fresh from the dredge were all on offer. Troupes of poets, musicians, dancers and entertainers were hired. Agrippina was the most charming of hostesses, flirting and dallying with all the most eligible bachelors until she found her prey: Gaius Silius, probably the handsomest man I have ever met. He had the looks, body and deportment of a Greek god, with a brain as thick and as dead as a statue. Agrippina acted the role of the infatuated maiden, lavishing attention and gifts on him, and pretending to be distraught when he was absent. Their affair became the talk of Rome and attracted the attention of Messalina, who had her own plans for young Silius. A romantic tug of war took place which was won by Messalina. She and the young bachelor became utterly infatuated with each other, united not only in lust but a desire to mock and shame Agrippina in the eyes of others.

The lavish banquets ceased and Agrippina became more reclusive. Claudius and his freedmen were now invited to little private supper parties where Agrippina and the Emperor could converse closely together. Claudius was full of anger about his wife's conduct, but Agrippina quietly reminded Claudius of Styges's prophecy, gently coaxing Claudius to let the adulterous pair have their heads. The Emperor submitted and, when Messalina's infatuation with Silius only deepened, Claudius's powerful ministers, Narcissus and Pallas, entered the game.

Claudius was persuaded to go to Ostia to make sacrifice, and whilst he was away, Agrippina moved into the imperial quarters as the guest of Pallas. At last Agrippina was able to drop her mask and invited Narcissus, Pallas and myself to a secret meeting.

'This is truly ridiculous,' Agrippina began. 'The Emperor, my Uncle Claudius, is being made a cuckold, a public laughing stock.'

Of course, she made no reference to her own involvement in this affair or the way she'd persuaded Claudius to turn a blind eye to what the rest of Rome was talking of. Pallas and Narcissus needed little encouragement: they were tired of Messalina, fearful of her terrible rages. If the opportunity presented itself, they were both prepared to strike speedily and ruthlessly.

'I have heard rumours,' Agrippina said. 'That Messalina and Silius intend to marry.'

Narcissus and Pallas cried out in disbelief.

'It is true,' Agrippina insisted. 'They are going to hold their own Bacchanalian festival and celebrate a marriage both unlawful and impious.'

After intense discussion, it was agreed that, if such a ceremony took place, Claudius should immediately confront his wife. Messengers were sent speeding off to Ostia, beseeching Claudius to return, and Agrippina and the freedmen met him in the Praetorian camp outside the city. They produced witnesses who described in every detail Messalina's affair with Silius, their proposed bigamous marriage and a litany of previous infidelities. Claudius, trembling, at first panicked.

'Am I still Emperor?' he demanded of Narcissus and Agrippina. 'Will Silius become Emperor in my place?'

Agrippina calmed him down and advised him precisely what to do.

The information Agrippina had gathered about Messalina's activities, proved to be astonishingly accurate. Messalina and Silius, their brains turned by arrogance and lust, performed a marriage ceremony in the palace grounds, acting out the rituals of a grape harvest. Messalina and her female friends were garbed in animal skins, as if they were Maenads, whilst Silius and his cronies were dressed as satyrs. Frenzied in their drunkenness, they threw all constraints aside: men and women made love to each other in the shade of trees in wine-induced orgies, three or four men taking one woman, their performance watched and cheered by the others. Agrippina's spies reported back to the Praetorian camp, and, by late afternoon, Claudius had recovered both his wit and his courage.

Helped on by Agrippina, rumours of the Bacchanalian orgy, with particular emphasis on Messalina's conduct, spread amongst the guards. Outraged tribunes demanded an audience with the Emperor, insisting that the illicit celebrations be stopped and the participants ruthlessly punished. Claudius, hectored by Agrippina, quietly agreed. Soldiers were despatched into the palace grounds, bringing the revelry to an abrupt end as both Satyrs and Maenads fled for their lives.

The guards hunted the revellers through the trees and into the streets. Some were executed immediately, others were loaded with chains and taken off to prison. As the wine and opiates wore off, Messalina panicked and fled to the house of the Chief Vestal Virgin, begging her to plead with the Emperor. The priestess refused. The Empress of Rome, the beautiful Messalina, still dressed as a Maenad with fading garlands round her neck, was reduced to running from one end of the city to the other, vainly imploring former friends for help. No sympathy was shown and she tried to leave Rome in a cart used for removing garden rocks.

At the Praetorian camp Claudius was wavering. Agrippina whispered hoarsely to me that if the Emperor changed his mind we would all have to flee from Messalina's undoubted fury. She conferred quickly with Narcissus and Pallas but was openly alarmed when a guards officer announced that the Empress had appeared at the camp gates, an arm round each of her children, Britannicus and Octavia. The guards let her in and Messalina threw herself on the Emperor's mercy. I lurked in a corner of the imperial pavilion and saw that Messalina was using all her beauty, charm and eloquence to gain a hearing.

The Chief Vestal Virgin arrived, pricked by conscience, to argue that a wife should not be executed unheard. Narcissus and Pallas intervened, rudely telling the Vestal to return to her religious duties. The old woman, frightened, mumbled an apology and withdrew. Narcissus now attacked Messalina, saying she was unfit to be a mother and ordering Britannicus and Octavia to be taken away from her. He crouched and whispered in the Emperor's ear that Messalina had effectively divorced him by her impious marriage to Silius. Then, his voice rising, he started on a long list of Messalina's former lovers. Claudius could do nothing but cry, shake his head and moan loudly.

Messalina shouted at Narcissus to produce proof. The Emperor glanced expectantly at the freedman who was unable to answer until Agrippina decisively intervened. She hastily wrote a short note and passed it to me. I read it quickly then handed it to Narcissus. His podgy face, red with embarrassment, eased into a smile, and he bent down again and whispered in the Emperor's ear. Agrippina had given him all the proof he would need.

'We will go to Silius's house,' Claudius declared, lurching to his feet. 'And seek the necessary evidence.'

Once we'd arrived at Silius's house, Narcissus, prompted by Agrippina's note, pointed out all the items from the imperial palace, gifts from the Empress to her lover, that were crammed into every available corner. Claudius was a greedy, acquisitive man, and when he saw the statuettes, vases, precious cloths and other items brought out and laid at his feet, he issued orders for the arrest of Silius and all his companions and returned to the camp. Once there a hasty platform was erected and the captives brought in. Unluckily for Messalina, they did not challenge the accusations but simply asked for a speedy death. One by one they were hustled from the platform to be decapitated by guards. They all died bravely except the actor Mnester, who begged for his life.

'Others,' he whined, 'have sinned for money or ambition; I was simply compelled to.'

'Are we to stand here and listen to this rubbish?' Narcissus barked. He pointed to the execution grounds now strewn with bleeding, decapitated corpses. 'Others have died, why spare an actor?'

And Mnester went under the sword.

Once the executions were finished, Claudius

insisted on being taken back to the palace, where he ate and drank and grew maudlin over Messalina.

'I'll see her tomorrow,' he declared tearfully. 'I'll listen to her explanation.' He became more and more befuddled, his anger cooling, his lust for Messalina resurfacing.

Pallas reported to Agrippina that Claudius had started to refer to Messalina as 'that poor woman'.

'She cannot live till morning,' Agrippina declared. 'Where is she now?'

'She has fled to the gardens of Lucullus.'

'Then let her die there. Parmenon,' Agrippina ordered. 'Go and see her. Tell her the Emperor's heart has not changed. Pallas, she must be dead by nightfall.'

Reluctantly I left. No, that's a lie, I wasn't reluctant: if Messalina survived, she'd claw her way back into Claudius's affections and both my head and that of my mistress would roll. Whether I liked it or not I was in the amphitheatre facing a fight to the death. Our opponent was down and I could almost hear the roar of the crowd, '*Hoc Habet*! *Hoc Habet*! Let her have it!'

Messalina was sheltering in an olive grove, prostrate on the ground, with her mother kneeling beside her. The former Empress glanced up hopefully, but when she saw me her lip curled.

'So, Agrippina's shadow has arrived,' she mocked.

I knelt down beside her. Even at this moment, Messalina was incredibly beautiful: the gorgeous ringlets framing her exquisitely shaped face, those strange eyes that seemed to shift in colour, lips like a full red rose and skin as white as the purest milk. She was still dressed in her Bacchanalian costume, her body coated with the most expensive perfume, her face streaked black where the tears had spread the kohl.

'What have you come for?' she whispered, sitting up.

'You know why he's here!' her mother snapped.

This tall, grey-haired, severe woman had little love for her daughter, but at least she had the courage to attend her during her last hours.

'What's your name?' Messalina smiled through her tears. 'Parmenon, isn't it? Tell me one thing, Parmenon, is Domina Agrippina in the palace?'

'She is!'

'My mistake,' she sighed. 'I should have taken her head years ago. It's finished, isn't it, Parmenon?'

'It is,' I replied. 'All that remains is an honourable death.'

'Not here,' Messalina declared.

She grasped my hand, got to her feet and pointed to a small garden pavilion deep in the trees. Gripping my arm she hurried across, her mother following. Inside, the pavilion smelt of damp wood and leaves, but she must have been there before as a lamp was burning, cushions and blankets were strewn on the floor, and a roll of parchment and a tray of pens and ink lay on a table. Messalina ordered her mother to close the door and pull the bolts across; even as she did so, we heard the tramp of feet followed by a pounding on the door. Messalina crouched on the floor, drawing the blankets around her, whimpering like a puppy. I felt sorry for her at that moment but I had no hope to offer her. The door was forced, and a Praetorian officer with one of Pallas's henchmen, Evodus, stepped into the darkened room.

'So, there you are, you bitch!' Evodus bawled. 'You haven't even the guts to take your own life!'

The officer peered through the gloom, recognised me and nodded. Evodus was now indulging in a litany of abuse, as the officer stood staring down at the Empress. Messalina lifted a dagger, and pressed the tip against her throat, then against her breast, but couldn't drive it in. The officer took a step forward. Messalina's head went down and she sobbed.

'Quickly!' her mother murmured. 'For pity's sake, do it quickly!'

The officer took another step forward. 'Excellency,' he whispered.

Messalina looked up hopefully. The officer was well trained and his sword leapt from the scabbard. In one quick thrust he plunged it into her neck. Messalina's mouth opened and shut, her hand clawing at the blood pumping from the gaping wound. She whispered something and slumped on her side. Evodus cackled with glee, until the officer pressed the edge of his glistening-red sword against his throat.

'Shut up, you bastard! Just shut up!' He nodded at me and Messalina's mother, re-sheathed his sword and joined the cohort outside.

I was with him when he reported Messalina's

death to the Emperor. Claudius, deep in his cups, nodded and barked for more wine.

Years later, when everything had turned to dust, and Agrippina and I were preparing to flee to Antium, I broached the subject of Messalina's fall.

'Never once,' I said, 'after your rival's death did you refer to her. You never gloated. You never rejoiced. It was as if she never existed.'

'She was an opponent,' Agrippina replied. 'She died and that was the end of the matter.'

'How did you achieve it?' I asked. 'How did a woman like Messalina lose her senses and involve herself in such stupidity?'

'Have you ever watched a pastry cook, Parmenon, prepare one of those marvellous delicacies: strawberries mixed with cream, all hidden in layers of pastry?' She wetted her lips. 'That's what I baked for Messalina and she gave me every assistance.' Agrippina motioned with her hand as if to indicate layers. 'She was wanton and spoilt. She offended the freedmen. She threatened. She believed she could do what she wanted. She hated me and was determined to take Silius at any cost. The more Claudius tolerated her wantonness, the greater grew her fury, until she lost all reason.' She shrugged. 'After that, it was simply a matter of waiting.'

'As you did?' I asked.

'Oh yes.'

'And the rest?' I asked. 'Your marriage to the Emperor?'

'The groundwork had all been laid,' she sighed. 'Claudius was a goat, but as well as his mistresses he wanted a wife who was the opposite of Messalina. He believed that I was quiet and studious and, of course, I had the blood of Augustus in my veins.' She laughed mockingly.

'But you were his niece?'

'Oh, you remember how we managed to overcome that little problem, Parmenon, firstly, I had old Vitellius, who was only too willing to advance my cause with the Senate and with the Emperor.'

'Bribed already by you?'

'Of course, as was the Senate and the Praetorian Guard. Although some people spoke out against the marriage – I remember one soothsayer describing it as a "wicked marriage bed, a torch for mourning" – Claudius and I had our way. I thought he would be too old for bed sport but I'll give the old goat his due, he kept me as busy as I did him. The rest?' She paused. 'Well, perhaps, I did overdo it. I became the Emperor's wife, and received the title of Augusta. My image was stamped on coins, and when I went through the streets, lictors carrying the fasces preceded my litter. I listened to the debates in the Senate, received the flattery of the standard-bearers.' She smiled. 'Marvellous times, eh, Parmenon?'

'And what of the opposition?' I asked.

'Come, come, Parmenon. There was no bloodbath. You must admit I was quite restrained.'

'Except in the case of Lollia Paulina.'

'Oh yes.' She tapped her sandalled foot. 'I had to

watch her. Claudius developed a passion for her; he liked to make love to her when she wore all her jewellery, especially those pearls she kept close to her skin so as to retain their purity. Within a year of our marriage, Claudius was inviting her to banquets, but she was stupid enough to start consulting fortune-tellers on how long my marriage would last. She should have kept her nose out of my business. I had her accused of treason. One night I dressed in my own jewels and pearls and gave Claudius a night of delight. The following morning Lollia Paulina was exiled.'

'But that wasn't enough?' I insisted.

'I had to make sure,' she replied. 'Yes, after I sent a guard to decapitate her, I wanted to make sure she was dead, so they brought her head back to Rome in a bucket of brine. I kept the head as a memorial before giving it over for burial. Were you shocked, Parmenon? Of course you were,' she mocked. 'Once she was gone!'

'You made some mistakes.'

'Oh, yes I did. You're thinking of Seneca, our Spanish Socrates? What does Petronius say about him? "As big a humbug as he is a philosopher"!'

'Why did you bring him back from exile?' I asked.

'I wanted my son to have the best: a true classical education. He did deserve that, didn't he, Parmenon?'

Oh yes, Nero deserved the best! The person to have benefited most from the fall of Messalina was Nero. Agrippina had seized power, but not to glory in it. She had only one purpose: to ensure the accession of her son. Nero was adopted as Claudius's heir. He was declared the 'Prince of Youth' and shown every honour, both in public and private. He was given his own household, and Seneca became his tutor. Everywhere he went Nero was hailed as if he was Caesar already, a god-designate. His only rival was Messalina's son but Britannicus was weak and sickly, and Agrippina soon dealt with him. One by one his friends and protectors were removed and replaced with Agrippina's spies, and he was edged out onto the limits of court life. I only met the boy on a few occasions; he was smiling-eyed but weak-faced, and I always felt sorry for him. Nero, on the other hand, chilled me. He loved the adulation and delighted in the role his mother had created for him.

To strengthen her son's position even more, Agrippina decided Nero should marry Claudius's young daughter Octavia, although she was already betrothed to a nobleman, Lucius Silanus. Agrippina began a campaign against him, accusing him, of all things, of incest with his sister. Lucius cut his throat and Nero and Octavia were betrothed; the fact that they were second cousins proved little obstacle.

Just after his fourteenth birthday, Nero received the 'Toga Virilis', the mark of manhood, as Agrippina was in a hurry for her son to grow up. She asked me to attend on him, which I did reluctantly as I would have preferred to keep well away from him. Whenever I was in his presence I was always reminded of Caligula, though Nero looked nothing like his hollow-eyed uncle. By that time Nero's hair had a strong tinge of auburn, almost copper-red, and was dressed in thick masses of curls around his forehead and the nape of his neck. He had blunt, heavy features and protruding eyes. His near-sighted pale-blue eyes and heavy eyelids gave him a dreamy, innocent look, which he used as a mask to portray himself as the noble young prince, the studious scholar, the Caesar in waiting. Now and again this mask would drop, as it did on the day of his toga ceremony.

Before leaving the palace, Nero consecrated the gown of his boyhood to the House of Gods, and placed at their feet the golden chain every boy wears as a charm during their childhood. Afterwards he was escorted solemnly to the temple of Jupiter amidst the waiting, clamouring crowds. Nero loved every minute of it. He stopped at the crossroads where the priestesses of Bacchus, their heads crowned with ivy, gave him small fried cakes dipped in honey, a symbol of his new manhood. From the temple Nero was escorted to the amphitheatre, where free corn had been distributed to the mob and silver to the troops. Nero, wearing triumphal dress, was hailed and adored, and sat beaming at his worshippers, licking his lips as his eyes leered at the women. He touched my wrist and leaned over.

'Do you know, Parmenon,' he laughed. 'Seneca says I must be offered all temptations so that I can be trained to master my passions!'

His remark created ripples of laughter around us.

Nero's eyes held mine, and his smile faded; even then he was plotting how he could escape Agrippina's influence. I reported this to my mistress but she refused to believe it.

'He's only testing the water,' she replied.

'Was it wise to hire Seneca?' I asked. 'Remember what the old humbug said; "If you preach austerity to a young man, eventually it makes him want to savour the opposite".'

'Seneca is doing a good job,' Agrippina replied absent-mindedly. 'My son is being schooled well, so when the Emperor dies, may the Gods forbid, Nero will be Caesar.'

Of course, in power everything has its own reaction. For four years Agrippina was given the run of Rome, removing opposition, managing the Senate, bribing the guards, keeping the freedmen in her camp. Opponents such as Lollia Paulina were given short shrift but Agrippina had no blood lust, preferring instead to influence people, to ease the way, to open doors through guile. Through Pallas she could organise the Senate and eventually the Praetorian Guard. Whoever controlled that crack regiment had a strong power base: they would be the ones to hail the new Emperor and take care of any opposition. Agrippina had already distributed largesse and, of course, as the daughter of the great Germanicus, the troops held her in high regard. Agrippina made sure that such adoration remained constant and eventually persuaded Claudius to appoint her nominee, the thickset, capable and loyal Sextus Burrus, as

Commander of the Praetorian Guard. He was an administrator rather than a campaigner but a man Agrippina thought she could fully control.

Only one obstacle remained: the freedman Narcissus. Although he had joined Agrippina in bringing down Messalina, he had soon realised he'd merely replaced one Empress with an even more powerful one. Narcissus withdrew from Agrippina's circle, studying her tactics carefully. He did not oppose Agrippina or Nero openly but instead, reminded Claudius constantly of the 'sweet days' he had enjoyed with Messalina, and emphasised the rights and duties of poor Britannicus. Claudius had quickly tired of each of his wives and Agrippina was no exception. Once Narcissus realised he was sowing on fertile ground, his campaign gained pace. Britannicus was invited back to court, fawned on and favoured, and Agrippina knew that she would have to strike quickly.

Chapter 13

'It is part of human nature to hate those whom you have injured'

Tacitus, *Agricola*: 42

'What am I to do with Claudius?'

In the spring of the fourteenth year of Claudius's reign, Agrippina was openly showing her discontent. She was thirty-nine years of age but looked much younger, despite the occasional white hair or faint lines on her olive-skinned face. Power and influence can create eternal youth, or at least the illusion of it. During those years of power, Agrippina had very rarely consulted me: Nero was the beginning and end of her life, and Agrippina suspected I did not share the same, unquestioning adoration of her son. She would hear nothing even slightly derogative about the young man that I secretly called 'The Monster'. Nero was a superlative actor in front of those who mattered, but allowed his mask to slip with me. He would sidle up to me and make the occasional salacious remark about a senator's wife or tell me in vivid detail what he would like to do to some person who had inadvertently offended him. He was an apt pupil of Seneca; the old, yellowing-skinned hypocrite had a tongue coated in acid and all the compassion of a striking viper.

'What am I going to do about Claudius?' Agrippina repeated.

We were seated in one of the gardens outside the palace, a sinister place that had once been used as a paupers' burial ground. The outlines of the death-pits were still visible. During the time of Augustus its use as a cemetery was abandoned and it had been lawned over. Seventy years of lying fallow had benefited the rich soil, in which almost every bush and flower known to the empire bloomed. The heavy scent of flowers was almost overbearing but few birds flew or nested there. Many claimed it was a place of darkness, and the many palace sorcerors and soothsayers would often go grubbing amongst the abandoned graves for bones and herbs to make their magical potions.

'Are you listening, Parmenon?'

'I always listen, oh, August one,' I retorted.

'Don't be sarcastic.' Agrippina pinched my arm. 'You are getting old, Parmenon.' She tousled my hair. 'There's a good deal of silver here, but even more in the bank, eh? Do you ever think of leaving me, Parmenon?'

I pointed to a butterfly resting on a flower.

'I'm like that, Excellency. I would love to fly but I am always drawn back.'

Agrippina leaned down and tightened the thong of her silver-gilt sandal, before dabbing at the sweat on her neck.

'You've heard the rumours?'

'I've heard Lepida is dead.'

'Yes, the mother of the wild whore.' Agrippina stared up at the sky. 'She had to go, Parmenon. Blood will out. I killed her daughter and, in time, Lepida would have struck back at me or Nero.'

'They say the guards threw her into boiling water before the executioner took her head.'

'I didn't ask for that,' Agrippina replied.

'Nor did Narcissus, Domina, and he's the real problem, isn't he? Whispering his poison into Claudius's ears, openly courting young Britannicus?'

Agrippina was half listening: her mood had changed as her rage began to boil.

I know she had heard the reports. Claudius himself was now inviting Britannicus to supper parties, begging his forgiveness, toasting him with his goblet, saying he would show the people a proper prince. The Emperor was appearing more and more at the Senate House to plead that both Nero and Britannicus should be treated fairly. More dangerous were rumours that Claudius was threatening to change his will. His relationship with Agrippina had soured, and he was fond of repeating the witticism that it was his destiny to suffer the wickedness of wives, and to punish them.

'You are going to attack, aren't you?' I asked.

'Next week it will be May,' Agrippina replied. 'I tell you, Parmenon.' She looked over her shoulder satisfied that the guards were in position. 'If I do not move now, this time next year none of us might be here. I don't fancy another long period of exile. Are you with me, Parmenon?'

'That's a stupid question, Domina. If you fall we all fall with you.'

'You could retire,' she smiled. 'Buy a villa or farm out in Campania. Marry some pleasant girl, have children, raise a son.'

'A son like Nero, Domina?'

'You have it all wrong.'

She rose, patted me on the shoulder and walked away.

I didn't have it wrong but Agrippina was intent on proving herself right. She moved slowly, carefully, distancing herself from the Emperor. She began to act like a recluse but took me more and more into her confidence. I once saw a wolf in the arena, which, although famished and dangerous, only attacked when it was sure which of his intended victims was the weakest. Agrippina was the same. She perched above Claudius's court and watched carefully. Pallas was her man, body and soul, and she thought the same of Burrus and Seneca; but Narcissus was now her enemy. She studied them carefully one by one, weighing their worth, all the time refusing to rise to Claudius's baiting.

It was late summer before she was finally ready to strike.

I was told to stay up late one night and act as door-keeper, whilst the slaves and servants were dismissed to their quarters. Agrippina was evidently expecting a visitor, but in fact, it turned out to be two. I recognised one immediately: the fat-faced, small-eyed, balding court physician Xenephon. The other was a diminutive, pale-faced, red-haired woman with strange green eyes and heavily painted lips. She was dressed in tawdry finery except for the pearls around her neck which were genuine enough. She was Locusta, the descendant of a long line of famous poisoners. After Locusta had been seen and dismissed, Xenephon was treated to the pleasures of both board and bed. Agrippina had discovered that the Emperor had secretly changed his will. He'd also confided to this treacherous physician how tired he was of Agrippina's ambitions. Now that both Xenephon and Locusta were in Agrippina's net, they would find it impossible to extricate themselves.

Ominous portents appeared in the city: rumours of a flaming comet; showers of blood in the forum; a lightning strike at the Praetorian camp; a swarm of bees settled on the Palatine. Doors to the temple of Jupiter opened and closed of their own accord. The birth of a hermaphrodite was reported, as well as a pig born with the claws of a hawk. It was the usual farrago of nonsense. Some were natural phenomena, others sprang from Agrippina's fertile imagination. Claudius became frightened, withdrawing more and more into the palace, but Agrippina followed like a hunting leopard. I had no idea how and when the attack would begin but, from Agrippina's air of subdued tension, I sensed that if she had her way, Claudius would never welcome another new year.

On the night of 12 October, Agrippina invited her husband to a supper party in one of the palace banqueting halls. Claudius arrived with the four women who had become his constant companions: a blonde Syrian; a huge negress with purple lips; a slim Jewess whom Claudius loved to have pinch and slap him; and finally, a bronze-skinned Egyptian. The sole task of these women was the sexual gratification of the Emperor, a welcome relief for Agrippina as it distracted his attention from her. On that particular evening Agrippina was charm personified. Nothing was too good for her husband. An artificial ceiling had been created above the banqueting hall, which opened to shower full-blown roses and perfumed water on Claudius and his small coterie of guests. A troupe of Ephesian dancers mimed the marriage of Psyche and Cupid to the sound of flutes and pipes. Once this was finished, the imperial taster Helotus brought in the hors d'oeuvres, a bowl of deliciously cooked mushrooms, Claudius's favourite dish. I was standing behind Agrippina's couch as Helotus tasted the mushrooms. Agrippina nibbled at the side of the dish and smilingly invited Claudius to partake of the bigger ones. Claudius ate them with relish and asked for more.

'Where is Narcissus?' Claudius raised his head. 'He should be here. He loves mushrooms.'

'He's gone to the baths at Sinuessa,' Xenephon said. 'He's suffering the symptoms of early dropsy.'

Xenephon caught Agrippina's eyes, smiled and glanced away. The removal of Narcissus was essential to Agrippina's plans. More mushrooms were brought, but Agrippina became anxious when Claudius, helped by his escort, eased himself off the couch to go outside to purge his stomach and then on to the latrines to empty his bowels. When the old glutton returned hale and hearty, Agrippina's agitation grew. I could detect the signs: the movement of her head as if to ease a crick in her neck, the quick false smile. I leant over to whisper 'Relax,' when Claudius squirmed on the couch, clawing at his stomach. He half raised himself but fell back with a groan; his face had turned livid, his big tongue lolled out, he shivered, and his teeth chattered. Xenephon sprang up and came over.

'Oh, Divine One!' he exclaimed. 'What is the matter?'

The rest of the guests fell silent.

'Quick! Quick!' Xenephon gestured at Agrippina. 'The Emperor has eaten something which has upset his stomach. It's best if he purges himself.'

A silver bowl and a peacock feather, its tip soaked in perfumed oil, were brought. Xenephon, helped by Agrippina, thrust this into Claudius's mouth, attempting to tickle his throat and make him vomit. Claudius was immediately sick and, wiping his mouth, pronounced that he felt better; but within minutes the cramps had returned.

'The Divine One must rest.'

Agrippina got to her feet, gesturing at the slaves to lift the Emperor from his couch. With me and Xenephon trailing behind, Agrippina and her husband retreated into their private apartments. Once the Emperor was laid on the bed, the slaves dismissed and the doors locked, Agrippina turned on Xenephon.

'You said the poisoned mushrooms would be enough.' She glared, totally ignoring her husband's groans and retching on the bed.

Xenephon, trembling with fright, spread his hands. 'Excellency, he must have taken antidotes, otherwise what was on the tip of that feather alone would have been enough to kill him outright.'

Agrippina glanced at me. 'Look, Parmenon. This is like the death of Tiberius all over again.' She pointed to the bed. 'If Claudius recovers, we will all die.'

She began to organise the palace guards, and no one was allowed into the chamber. For the next two days Agrippina allowed false messages to be disseminated, stating that the Emperor was recovering from a stomach ailment and all would be well. Seneca and Burrus were brought into the plot. A hand-picked cohort of the Praetorian Guard took up residence in the courtyard. Agrippina never left her husband's side and for two whole days that old body, rotten with gluttony and excess, tried to fight the effects of the poison. Sometimes Claudius would attempt to rise but the cramps kept him prostrate. Agrippina scrupulously banished all food and drink from the chamber so as to dispel any suspicions that the Emperor was being poisoned. Instead she just waited for the full effects of that first poisonous meal to wreak its effect.

The Emperor, his body wracked by vomiting, retching and violent diarrhoea, gradually weakened. He lost all sense of feeling, muttered about the cold and, on the morning of the second day, finally slipped into death.

Xenophon checked the corpse scrupulously, whilst Britannicus and Octavia were brought to an ante-chamber and kept there under close guard. Seneca and Nero were summoned to prepare the speech the heir would give to both the Praetorian Guard and the Senate. By mid-morning Agrippina was ready, and the palace doors were thrown open. Nero, with Seneca on one side and Burrus on the other, emerged onto the steps of the courtyard whilst Agrippina's claque amongst the waiting crowd began the whisper, 'Claudius is dead! Claudius is dead!'

The Praetorian Guard was also prepared: standards were lifted in salute, trumpets brayed, swords beat against shields and the roar of the soldiers drowned the whispers of the crowd, 'Long live Nero! Emperor and Caesar!'

My first intimation that Agrippina was not fully in charge of the plot, emerged during Claudius's funeral. A gilded tabernacle, shaped as a small replica of the temple of Jupiter, was set up in the Forum, containing a bed carved out of ivory and covered with cloth of purple and gold. The dead Claudius lay inside, propped up at the head of the bed, his eyes closed, his face heavily made up as an exhibition to the crowd that the Emperor had not died violently but from some 'sickness of the stomach'.

Nero stood by the tabernacle and delivered the funeral speech. When he reached the part describing Claudius as, 'Moderate in his desires, master of all passions, neglecting his personal happiness for the greatness of Rome', the muffled laughter of the crowd was widespread. Claudius was known as glutton, an old reprobate. Through Seneca's sarcasm, Nero was openly ridiculing his predecessor. A similar speech was delivered to the Senate and, within a few days, Seneca's satire appeared on the streets, 'The Metamorphisis of the Pumpkin', a sly, vicious attack on the attempts to deify Claudius.

'Listen to this!' I said to Agrippina as I read Seneca's pamphlet. '"The Emperor's soul went out of his body with a clap of thunder from his favourite organ, and he cried: 'Oh Heavens, I think I've messed myself'".'

'Claudius deserves to be mocked,' Agrippina replied. 'He was a glutton, a man of excess.'

'That's not the point,' I retorted. 'If Nero is encouraged to mock the office he now holds, he mocks you as well.'

'My son doesn't mean to do that,' Agrippina replied,

eyes shining. 'Have you heard the password that was given to the troops?' She clapped her hands. '"Best of mothers"!'

She wouldn't hear any more. I disagreed, but the damage was done. Seneca had not only taught Nero Rhetoric, but had also instilled in him a mocking attitude to authority and to all that had gone before: although Agrippina couldn't see it, that included the 'best of mothers'.

Oh, Agrippina was accorded every honour. She continued to listen to the Senate debates, sitting on a chair behind the veil. When she processed round the city, Praetorian Guards protected her palanquin; the title of 'Augusta' was used more and more; her image appeared on statues and coins. She had an apartment in the palace and Nero visited her every day. Under such fawning love Agrippina blossomed, and the years seemed to slip away from her. She believed she had nothing to fear: Burrus was in charge of the Praetorian Guard; Seneca was now First Minister; Pallas was in charge of the Treasury. The Senate had been purged of any enemies whilst the crowd and the army not only hailed her as mother of their young, handsome, charming Emperor but as the daughter of the great Germanicus. Ah well, politics are like the seasons: the changes are imperceptible until you suddenly realise that you have passed from the mellowness of Autumn to the chill of Winter.

Narcissus returned to Rome a broken man but still a very wealthy one. Agrippina ignored him, but Seneca, for old times sake, dined and wined him; he also encouraged that old wily fox to have one last throw before the game was over. Narcissus kept in the background, claiming ill health, and to all appearances he looked a broken man. Narcissus responded to Nero's solicitude by agreeing to pay for the games held in honour of Nero's accession.

I remember that day well. It was a beautiful spring morning and all of Rome was on holiday. Nero and his mother processed down to the amphitheatre near the Forum with all the panoply of power. Beautiful young slaves dressed as satyrs or fauns surrounded their gold-tasselled litter. Senators walked behind in brilliant white togas. Crack cohorts of the Praetorian Guard, in full dress armour, went before. Agrippina, of course, shared the Emperor's litter, and I walked beside them, holding a curtain back as Nero saluted the crowd with a miniature statue of the goddess Victory carved out of pure gold and studded with precious gems. Nero regarded it as a good luck charm and took it everywhere. He was also sporting an emerald eye-glass and, every so often, would scrutinise the crowd through this before raising a languid hand to acknowledge their salutations. Agrippina wore a wreath of gold and carried a silver staff surmounted by a golden eagle with wings outstretched. She was hailed as 'Empress' and 'Augusta'. She reminded me of a bride on her wedding day. The streets were strewn with flowers; canopies, stretching from one upper storey to another, showered down rose petals, and carpets and tapestries hung from the windows. At every crossroads white-garbed acolytes from the temples burnt perfumed incense in golden pots.

At the amphitheatre, guarded by lines of Praetorian Guards, Nero escorted his mother through the main entrance and up into the imperial box. The mob was already waiting, clad in their browns and greens, munching melon seeds and shouting at the water-bearers for stoups of refreshment. The day was warm and the awnings had been pulled across. To protect the mob a huge fence had been erected around the arena, on which elephant tusks were hung at intervals from which thick nets draped. The mob took this as a sign that not only would wild beasts be part of the spectacle but the games would be bloody and dangerous. The sand in the amphitheatre had been ground from a special stone, and in the sunlight it shone like golden snow. The imperial box smelt of the most fragrant perfume through which the breeze wafted the smell of stale sweat, onions, raw wine and that strange, eerie odour of imminent bloodshed.

Nero and his mother, hand-in-hand, walked to the edge of the box, its front draped in purple and gold cloths. The crowd rose as one man and roared its salutation. Nero lifted his hand, and the cheering grew even more deafening. As Nero and Agrippina took their seats, throne-like chairs raised well above the rest, Nero signalled and down the alleyways trooped imperial slaves carrying barrels filled with gifts: necklaces and brooches, food and free tickets for future events. These were thrown into the air and Nero laughed to watch the crowd scrambling to grab as much as they could, pointing to where the crush was great. I later learnt that ten people had been killed in the stampede.

Once Nero was settled, the magistrates, principal senators, leading Vestal Virgins, courtiers and their ladies garbed in silk and adorned with jewels, entered the box. These were followed by Nero's special guests for the day who included the imperial physician, Xenephon of Cos, and the poisoner Locusta, both looking nervous and ill at ease. I knew that Agrippina hadn't invited them, but Seneca, seated at the Emperor's left, looked round specially as if he wanted to ensure that they were present. When Nero was distracted, deep in conversation with a Senator, I managed to catch Agrippina's eye and indicate the two arrivals to her. Agrippina, her black hair hidden by a silver coronet to which a veil was attached, looked a little concerned but dismissed the new arrivals.

'Why should Xenephon not be present?' she whispered. 'Although I admit I did pay Locusta to leave Rome and not return.'

She could say no more. An official had entered the arena and threw a roll of scarlet cloth up into the air. It spread out like a spurt of blood before floating down on the smooth raked sand. Trumpets brayed, the crowd roared its approval and the games began.

First came the usual blood-letting, an hors d'oeuvre to whet the appetite before the main meal was served. A group of condemned criminals, lashed to 'T'-shaped crosses on mobile platforms, were wheeled into the amphitheatre. All were women, naked, their chins resting on the cross beams and their arms lashed beside them, leaving them free to move their hands. They reminded me of pinioned birds. The crowd pelted them with whatever they could lay their hands on, and soon the gold-silver sand was filthy. From the cross, in front of each victim, hung a dirty, cracked cup, the symbol of a convicted poisoner. I moved in my seat. Seneca turned to glance sideways at Nero and I caught the smirk on his face. Again the trumpets brayed. Wild, starving animals smoked from their cages, she-bears and tigresses, burst into the arena. For a while all was confusion, as a tigress attacked a bear and the most hideous, bloody struggle ensued. The condemned criminals, terrified of what was about to happen, screamed for mercy, drawing the attention of the animals to themselves. The tigress, having severely mauled the bear, turned and sprang at one victim, attacking her from the back, biting deep into her neck. The rest immediately joined in. I knew that the spectacle of poisoners, all of them women gathered from the prisons of Italy, being attacked by she-animals would jog memories and soon scandalous comparisons would be drawn. I recognised the vengeful hand of Narcissus proclaiming that this was how Rome dealt with poisoners. Agrippina appeared unperturbed, more interested in the report she had brought with her, studying the rolls of documents, as if she was in the imperial chancery rather than at a bloody spectacle.

I disappeared into one of the passageways for a while, until the roar of the crowd told me the wild animals had completed their task. By the time I returned to the box, the bloody remains of what was left on each platform had been wheeled away. Slaves, wearing grotesque masks, were clearing the offal. Fresh sand was strewn and raked, as Nero and the imperial party were served refreshments of iced wine and cold fruits. After this, the second session began, and a flock of Moroccan peacocks were released into the amphitheatre. A master archer, using curved tipped arrows, let loose at them, taking off each head with one well-aimed arrow. The decapitated birds, blood spurting, would continue to run for a while to the approval and pleasure of the mob. At last the whole flock were dead, and the archer approached the imperial box to receive his reward. Narcissus must have paid his claques well, as from every corner of the amphitheatre the cry rose up, 'Save the feathers! Save the feathers! Use them at dinner time!'

I glanced across to see that Xenephon looked worried and Locusta had put her head down. Agrippina, however, was laughing and clapping her hands. She was sharp enough to realise the story was already round Rome and it would be better to appear unconcerned. She clapped her hands and the crowd imitated her. Seneca rather than Narcissus seemed to be in charge, and I saw him make a cutting movement with his hand. The trumpets brayed and another pantomime, of monkeys dressed as Amazons, either riding or perched in chariots pulled by goats, entered the arena. Nero roared with laughter, put one arm round his mother's shoulder and pointed out what he thought was particularly funny. Seneca sat slumped in his chair. Again I realised, what the crowds would be whispering once the games were over: Claudius had been regarded as an old goat, and the monkeys were supposed to be the coterie of women who surrounded him, which included Agrippina.

Once the monkeys and goats had left the arena, it was time for the real games to begin. The fight was to be between the retiarii, net men, and Thracians. The gladiators filed into the arena and saluted the Emperor. It was only when the fight began that the mob realised these were not ordinary gladiators, but women. At first the crowd took this with humour but when the women proved to be poor fighters, the joke turned sour, and the crowd pelted them with rotten fruit. The lanistae came into the arena to lash at the fighters and ensure a proper combat. The odds in such fights were heavily weighed in favour of the nets: another powerful reminder of Claudius who had hated this imbalance. By the late afternoon the games were finished, and the mob, fickle as ever, saluted Nero and his mother. It might be considered that Narcissus had achieved his revenge, but the day's events were not yet finished.

Nero took his guest up to the Palatine Palace where the dining hall had been specially transformed. A broad, golden awning shaped in the form of a mushroom hung down from the ceiling, and mushrooms fashioned out of silver and peacock feathers decorated the wall. The same motif was found on the tables, where knives, spoons and tooth picks were all embellished with the same theme. The guests took their seats, and were served with honey wine. The allusions continued as the meal continued. First came roast kid, served with slices of pumpkin, Seneca's nickname for Claudius, in his bitter satire, which was a punning reference to his gaseous stomach and unfortunate habit of breaking wind at table. Then came fruits from the island of Cos, the birthplace of the physician Xenephon, which were served by the four women who had accompanied Claudius to his last meal. Roast peacock was brought in by slaves disguised as silver skeletons and finally, of course, came dish after dish of mushrooms served in a wide variety of sauces.

'Mushrooms are the food of the Gods!' Nero exclaimed, raising his goblet to his mother.

She toasted him back, so immersed in her son's glory and favour, that she failed to appreciate the barbed witticisms and pointed reminders of how her husband had been helped into the Hall of the Gods. The high point of all this punning farce was a huge concoction of red confectionery, shaped in the form of a man's buttocks, penis and testicles. This was served on a great silver platter taken round the guests by four Nubians, before being placed in the centre of the table. The buttocks were smacked by a female slave and the chef had arranged the confectionery so that it squeaked as if emitting a fart. The guests, their bellies soaked in wine, roared their applause. They watched gleefully as another female slave began to stroke the penis until it split, spouting out thick, white cream all over her. She was then summoned by different guests who scooped it from her skin with spoons or even their tongues. After the meal, a troupe of actors presented a burlesque scene of an old man, nicknamed the Pumpkin, who was frightened of mushrooms and peacock feathers. Everyone laughed, including Agrippina. Seneca was lounging on his couch, next to his personal guests, an old banking friend called Serenus and a beautiful young woman with a dark, oval face, pouting red lips, and hair arranged in black ringlets. I caught my breath and stared again, ignoring the pantomime and shouts of laughter.

'Who's that?' I asked a chamberlain.

'Why, sir, that's Acte, one of Rome's most beautiful women. Serenus is a very lucky man.'

I studied the girl carefully. She was dressed in green and white, and jewellery of the same colours adorned her neck, ear lobes and wrists. Despite the wine, I felt coldly sober. It was as if I had gone back some twenty-five years in time. Acte was beautiful, and had a powerful presence but the more I stared and saw that Nero was doing the same, the more that young woman reminded me of Agrippina as she had been when I first met her.

Chapter 14

'Who gains?'
Cicero, *Pro Milone*, 12

'Did you attend the games?'

Pallas looked anxious, his eyes red-rimmed and ringed with shadows. He'd invited me into the treasury, and we sat in a small chamber near the imperial counting house, with its door locked, bolted and guarded. I knew by the fact that Pallas had invited me down there, that he must be upset and very wary, since he normally tended to acknowledge my presence only with a smile or a nod, considering me little more than Agrippina's minion.

'And is it true what happened?'

He picked up a wine jug, its lid carved in the form

of a beautiful mermaid, and filled my Agamemnon goblet.

'Well, is it true?' he insisted. 'One insult after another?'

'The whole day was given over to it: goats, pumpkins, peacock feathers, mushrooms.'

'But the crowd didn't understand the significance?'

'They will eventually,' I retorted.

Pallas sighed noisily. 'Doesn't Agrippina realise what is happening?' he wailed. 'Seneca, that clever bugger, might be mocking Claudius but he is also mocking her. He's proclaiming to the world that Agrippina killed her husband. With sarcasm as his weapon,' he continued, 'he's nibbling away at Agrippina's position like a dog at a juicy bone. Soon he'll reach the marrow.' He paused. 'And what is Locusta doing back in Rome?'

'Agrippina didn't mind,' I replied. 'I have made enquiries and it seems that Nero himself ordered her return to Rome.'

'Oh, he would!' Pallas laughed sourly. 'And how can Agrippina object? "You can't have that woman in Rome",' Pallas mimicked Agrippina, '"I used her to poison the Emperor".' He fished amongst the scrolls on the desk and held one up. 'There's more. Nero hardly knew his father, and certainly never regretted his loss, but now our Emperor is suddenly all tender and dewy-eyed over his father's memory. He's planning to ask the Senate to pay the drunken, dropsical, dead Domitius special honours. I wouldn't be surprised if some town or city, even Rome itself, isn't forced to raise a subscription to

have a beautifully carved statue of Nero's degenerate father gracing some podium or the portico of a
temple.' Pallas let the scroll fall back on the table.
'Nero doesn't give a dog's breath about his father,
but Agrippina is going to find out that he doesn't
give a fig about anything: that old humbug Seneca
has encouraged our Emperor into a course of action
which he knows will offend Agrippina.'

Pallas picked up a thin parchment knife. He used
it as a gladiator would a sword.

'It's prick, prick, scratch, scratch.'

'But it won't work,' I retorted. 'Agrippina is convinced of Nero's love, his undying adoration and
loyalty, so if he mocks Claudius's memory, honours
his dead father and employs the service of a well-
known poisoner, how does that affect her position?'

I was being deliberately naive. I knew the answer
even before Pallas replied.

He kicked the stool back and leapt to his feet, his
podgy hands flailing the air. 'Parmenon, Parmenon.
You survived Tiberius, Caligula and Claudius: you
know this is only the beginning. Seneca has yet to
sink his teeth deeper into the bone. Now tell me,
what has been Agrippina's greatest achievement?'

'You know that,' I replied. 'She managed to ensure
that Nero became Emperor and Britannicus was dis-
inherited. And, before you repeat yourself, Pallas, I
know Seneca is now mocking us.'

'But have you asked yourself why?'

'Of course. He's trying to drive a wedge between
Agrippina and her son.'

'Good, and what else?'

'He's trying to disassociate his pupil, our golden Nero, from the murder of the pathetic man who appointed him his heir.'

'Good!' Pallas agreed like a teacher.

'At the same time,' I added, 'Seneca is quietly reminding Nero that he owes the throne to his mother and if one Emperor can be murdered . . .'

'Exactly!' Pallas agreed, sipping from his goblet. 'They are,' he searched for words, 'they are trying to separate son from mother. Nero is the new Emperor, the golden boy of prophecy.' He waved his hands. 'Agrippina belongs to the past. She's achieved her task, and should now retire. The next step will be to provoke Nero, who is an adolescent boy after all – Emperor or not – into full-scale rebellion against his overbearing mother. I'll tell you a story: two days ago Agrippina brought Nero here, into the Chamber of Silver. Apparently he had given a generous sum of money to a friend. Agrippina, to make him realise its value, made me place the same amount in front of him on this table. Nero lolled in my chair as the slaves emptied out the bags of gold, examined it carefully, and then scoffed, "If I had known it was so little I would have doubled it." He got to his feet and walked out, leaving Agrippina bemused.'

'The impetuosity of youth,' I commented. 'More important are Seneca's reasons for this attack.'

'Your guess is as good as mine,' Pallas replied. 'Seneca is sarcastic and bitter.' He held up a hand. 'He's been exiled twice now by the imperial family.

He loathed Corsica and its inhabitants, and despised their customs, their food and their drink. He regularly wrote begging letters to Caligula asking to have the exile lifted.'

'And now he blames Agrippina for that?'

'Yes, I think he hates the Augusta, and holds both her and her family responsible for his misery, so he's going to settle his grudge once and for all. Seneca also likes wealth and power, and Agrippina has opened the door to both for him. Seneca, the former exile and philosopher, now has the chance to control both an Emperor and an empire, and he wants to do it by himself. He'd love to kiss Agrippina goodbye. So whilst Nero acts the angry, young man, Seneca will continue to plot. What do you think his next step will be, Parmenon?'

I recalled Agrippina and her young son sitting in the gardens at Antium or her estates in Tusculum.

'Nero is Agrippina's Achilles heel,' I replied. 'She will make the same mistake that all mothers do. A mother's love is limitless and unconditional, her loyalty is undying; like all mothers, she expects her son to reciprocate.' I paused. 'Seneca has demonstrated that Agrippina can be criticised with impunity. He's depicted her as a greater fool even than Claudius, whilst also reminding Nero that she cleared his path to the throne. The next step Seneca will take is to start asking Nero if it is truly he that rules, or his mother? It will be easy to turn that young man's head.'

'And then what?' Pallas demanded.

'Seneca will go for the throat. He's studied his young student very closely, and really it's a matter of logic, isn't it, Pallas? If Nero can be dominated by one woman, his mother, then why not another . . . ?'

'Acte?'

'Acte,' I agreed. 'She's wealthy, civilised, courteous, extremely beautiful and alluring. She bears more than a passing resemblance to a young Agrippina. Seneca has chosen well. What do you know of her?'

'Some say she's a courtesan,' Pallas replied. 'Others claim she lives a chaste life, which will appeal to our Emperor. Apparently Seneca brought her into Rome and persuaded his friend Serenus to set her up in a house in a fashionable district. The young woman has been paraded before Nero like a prize mare. If rumour is to be believed, Nero's interest in her is growing by the day.'

'But all Emperors have favourites,' I replied. 'Nero is only seventeen, it will just be a passing infatuation.'

'Oh, it will pass all right,' Pallas agreed. 'But Nero's youth is his very weakness: he's determined to show his mother that she's no longer the most important woman in his life; that he loves Acte, or someone else, more than he does Agrippina.'

I could see where Pallas was leading. Agrippina was truly vulnerable. She adored her son and, for the first time ever, would experience the pangs of jealousy.

'Now we come to the purpose of this meeting.' Pallas picked up a stack of coins and tossed them from hand to hand. 'If Agrippina can be persuaded to keep her temper, to ignore Seneca's provocation, to maintain a still tongue . . .'

'All will be well,' I finished.

'All will be well. If Agrippina attacks, however . . .' He threw the coins on the table. 'Then the game is lost.'

I left the treasury with Pallas's warnings ringing in my ears. On that same day I begged for an interview with Agrippina and warned her exactly what Seneca was plotting. She laughed at my worries but promised to heed my advice, although I could see it was already too late. When I mentioned Acte, red spots of anger appeared high in her cheeks and her eyes narrowed. The damage was already done.

'You could try and remove Seneca?' I suggested.

'Impossible.' She shook her head. 'If I have made one mistake in life, Parmenon—' She smiled. 'What am I saying? I've made many – Seneca must rank as my greatest. I'll heed what you say.'

She brought the interview to an end and was already at the door when she called my name.

'Tell me, Parmenon, do you think Narcissus was mocking me with those games, that banquet?'

'I don't think so, Domina, I know. He may be a wounded animal but Narcissus is still dangerous.'

Agrippina kept her head down. 'Wounded you say? Thank you, Parmenon.'

A few days later Narcissus was taken ill on a journey. He had barely left the city when the slaves heard moans and thrashing coming from the litter. They pulled back the curtain, to discover Narcissus hardly breathing, his skin clammy and cold, complaining of pains throughout his body. They hurried him back to Rome but it was too late, and Narcissus died, strangely enough close to Messalina's tomb. Seneca sent Praetorians to his house, to search for papers and certain letters, but to his fury all they found were charred fragments: Narcissus, or someone else, had taken great pains to destroy any incriminating documents.

Narcissus's funeral rites were barely over when Nero despatched a letter to Pallas thanking him for his hard work at the treasury, and pointing out that, as the burdens of state must be affecting Pallas's health, it was time he retired. Pallas had no choice but to agree. He left in style with an escort of German guards, the personal retinue of Agrippina, walking before him, as he sat enthroned in a litter. Eight Abyssinians carried it shoulder high whilst his servants and friends, slaves and household retainers trooped behind in a solemn procession. Nero watched him go, standing on the top step of the treasury. He waved goodbye, waggling his fingers as if Pallas was a fellow pupil leaving a school.

'Take care!' the Emperor cooed.

In one quick stroke Seneca had removed Agrippina's most powerful and loyal ally. He returned to the attack. Acte appeared more and more in the Emperor's retinue, and Nero singled her out for pleasant, private conversations, and quiet supper parties – just the two of them – followed by night walks in the gardens. He showered her with costly gifts, and granted her a suite of apartments in the imperial palace. Nero stopped visiting his mother as often as she wished, and even worse, when Nero wanted to be alone with Acte, Agrippina was shown the door.

Agrippina became like a woman obsessed. Unable to sleep, she neglected affairs of state, and spent most of her waking hours railing at Acte and her son's ingratitude.

'What am I to do, Parmenon?' she cried.

'Nothing,' I replied. 'Domina,' I fell on my knees before her, 'Acte is not Narcissus, an enemy to be removed. Let your son have his way. Leave Rome for a while.'

It was the only time Agrippina ever struck me in anger. She refused to listen and instead ordered me from of her presence. I waited in the antechamber, hoping she would regret her actions. Suddenly the door to her chamber flew open and Agrippina swept out, her maids running behind her. She walked like a general down the galleries and corridors, to where Nero was drinking with a small party of friends. Bursting in, she openly confronted her son.

'See,' she shouted, pointing at Acte lying on a couch next to Nero, 'what a spectacle my son offers to Rome! Nero the Emperor!' she sneered. 'Like a doting, old man lying at the feet of a former slave: a woman who can be bought to give a man an hour of pleasure!'

Agrippina stood in the doorway, as I and the other

servants huddled behind her. She was beyond all reason.

'Look at her!' Agrippina shouted. 'She's nothing more than a painted whore but the Emperor of Rome has made her his official mistress. Is it for this that I made you Emperor, the legitimate heir of Claudius?' She turned on Seneca who was lying on the couch to Nero's left. 'I thought I was choosing a tutor, the wisest man in the whole Empire, but in truth, I picked a fool. His student, my son, fornicates with a freedwoman whilst Octavia, his proper wife, is neglected and repelled and I, Germanicus's daughter, am insulted and ignored!'

She stopped, shoulders heaving. She put a hand out and leaned against the lintel. Nero's guests stared in disbelief, a frozen tableau in some play. Acte kept her head down, and Seneca looked astonished, his eyes screwed up in mock hurt. Nero had the measure of his mother. He picked up that emerald eye-glass and examined her closely.

'Why, Mother? What is the matter? Have you been drinking? As you know, I invited you here this evening but you said you were unable to come.' He shifted his gaze. 'Is that you, Parmenon? Take my mother back to her apartments. She's overcome with exertion.' He let the eye-glass drop on its silver chain and waved his hand. 'Now, leave!'

Agrippina withdrew. I tried to seize her by the arm, but she shook me off. Behind the closing doors I heard muffled conversation and the sound of laughter. Agrippina walked slowly back to her chamber.

She dismissed the maids and spent the rest of that night pacing up and down, pondering her next move.

The following day Nero added insult to injury: he opened the storerooms of the palace where the jewels and ornaments were kept, and chose from the treasure an exquisite headdress and pendant which he sent as gifts to his mother. I was with Agrippina when they arrived. She had been trying to calm her rage by dictating letters to stewards and bailiffs on her estates outside Rome. When the servants presented the gifts, she knocked them out of their hands.

'Tell my son,' she hissed, 'that everything he possesses actually belongs to me! He is only sending me what is already mine!'

I attempted to reason with Agrippina but she was possessed by anger. All she was conscious of was her waning influence over her son and the hated presence of Acte. Nero now decided to twist the cord a little tighter, telling her that in view of his love for Acte he might divorce Octavia and marry his new love, abdicate as Emperor and retire to Rhodes to live as a private citizen. The barbs struck home: he was rejecting Agrippina and everything she had worked for.

Agrippina brooded and refused to tell me what she was planning. Her next confrontation with Nero, during one of Nero's eternal banquets, struck terror in my heart. Agrippina was given the place of honour, though Nero spent most of his time whispering to Acte, showing her every mark of public affection.

The guests were all aware of Agrippina drinking a little too fast as she glared at her son: it was like waiting for a violent storm to strike on a beautiful summer's day. Nero turned to fill his mother's cup and she let it drop to the floor, the precious goblet smashing to smithereens.

'Why, Mother,' Nero drawled. 'What is the matter?'

Agrippina swung her legs from the couch, got to her feet and stood over him. 'Why, son, have you forgotten?' She gestured down the hall to where Britannicus sat with his friends. 'He is no longer a child,' she snapped. 'He is Claudius's true son, the real heir to the throne.' Her voice rose. 'The throne that you stole with my help – your mother whom you now insult. All Rome shall learn of all this! The army will choose!'

It was ridiculous scene. After Agrippina withdrew, for the first time in my life I pushed her through the antechamber into her own private writing office, where she stood like a little girl ready to be chastised. I could not forget Nero's face at that banquet, those popping blue eyes, the effeminate curls and pouting lips.

'Domina,' I shouted, 'you've signed our death warrants and that of Britannicus. You've challenged your own son!'

Agrippina did not break down in tears. She sat on a stool clutching the fringes of her robes, staring at the wall. In that moment her greatest weakness was exposed: this wasn't about the empire or power, about who controlled the court and army, this was a mother who truly believed her son had publicly spurned her. She'd lashed out, uttering the first thing that came into her mind. I sighed and knelt beside her.

'Domina, listen!' I urged. 'Would it be so bad if your son abdicated and took you with him to Antium to live as private citizens . . . ?'

Her eyes crinkled in amusement.

'Why, Parmenon, you are quite a philosopher. You are right: all my life I dreamt of being the Augusta, a new Livia, mistress of an empire. I have achieved that but now I've lost my son, haven't I, Parmenon?'

'It can be rectified, Domina.'

I've told many lies in my life, but that was my greatest. Nero was no longer her son. He was what the empire had made him: a monster. Or had his father been right? Was there something in the blood, some evil taint? Did Nero have the same penchant for wickedness as Caligula and Tiberius? Of course he did!

He did not dare touch Agrippina but, like a panther, he turned on Britannicus. The young man was invited to another banquet, where, hoping to make fun of him, Nero asked to hear one of his poems. Britannicus performed so brilliantly that even Nero's claque, a group of professional hand-clappers who wore their hair bushy and went under the name of 'The Bees', were impressed. Nero took a vile revenge: he attacked Britannicus and buggered him, heaping humiliation upon him. Caligula's ghost had returned.

Nero spent more time with his foppish courtiers, consulting Seneca or Burrus if he wanted advice, whilst Agrippina stayed in her own apartments, where most of her household, apart from Acerronia and Creperius, were Seneca's spies. The hangers-on and time-servers soon sniffed the breeze and realised what was coming. Agrippina was still physically safe but Britannicus, a mere shadow of his former self, had to be dealt with. He started to suffer from epileptic seizures, during which his face would turn blue, his neck would swell convulsively and he'd froth at the mouth. Britannicus one could see was marked down for death. I pleaded with Agrippina and she tried to do what she could, sending antidotes for Britannicus, warning him to watch what he ate and drank. But Nero brought Locusta the poisoner back into the palace and put her under the direct charge of one of Burrus's lieutenants, the tribune Julius Pollio. All the court suspected what was happening. A poison was given to Britannicus but the dosage was too small, and after stomach pains he soon recovered. Nero was so annoyed that he beat Locusta with his own hands until she promised something that 'would act like lightning'. The poison she concocted was served to a pig and within seconds it had dropped down dead.

A sumptuous supper party was arranged, to which all of the court were invited, including Agrippina and me. The theme was Persian and the rooms and couches were decorated with exquisite Persian tapestries, whilst we were served with delicious dishes from that country. A special soup was brewed for Britannicus to avoid upsetting his delicate stomach, but finding it too hot he returned it and asked for some cold water to be added. The poison must have been added then. In less than a minute, Britannicus lurched off his couch, with his hands clutching at his throat, only to fall lifeless to the floor.

'Do not trouble yourselves,' Nero drawled to the guests. 'My brother Britannicus is subject to fits.'

Two Nubians carried Britannicus's body from the dining hall and the banquet continued. Agrippina and I managed to slip away and discovered Britannicus's corpse sprawled on a couch in an adjoining room. Embalmers were already smearing it with creams and cosmetics to hide the livid, dark spots appearing all over the skin. Within hours the body was sheeted, taken out to a makeshift funeral pyre and consumed by flames.

Agrippina returned to her chamber, her face as pale as that of a ghost. She sat at her writing desk, hastily scrawled a note on a wax tablet and told me to send Creperius with it to a house in the Jewish quarter across the Tiber. Once this was done I returned to the chamber.

'What is this nonsense?' I demanded. 'Do you really need to consult a soothsayer to learn what the future holds?'

Agrippina refused to listen. Creperius returned and said that Joah the Israelite would meet her immediately. Agrippina ordered a plain litter to be brought to the side door of her private apartments, and Acerronia and I were ordered to escort her. The bearers, all trusted slaves, took her at a soft-footed run down through the alleyways of the Palatine and across the bridge into the Jewish quarter. Joah's house was unpretentious, flanked on one side by a cookshop, and on the other by a small warehouse. Joah was tall and lean with a gaunt face, cascading white hair and a moustache and beard of the same colour. He had large, deep-set eyes and the sort of magical presence which appealed to his select clientele of wealthy, Roman women. He opened the door before I even knocked.

'Tell the Augusta to come in.' He looked at me closely. 'And you and her waiting woman. You can be trusted, Parmenon, can't you?'

I don't know whether he truly had magical powers or was just shrewd enough to know that I worked closely with Agrippina.

The room he ushered us into was dark and lit by flickering oil lamps. 'I have the answer to what you are going to ask,' he declared, closing the door behind us. The magician strode across and placed a hand on Agrippina's shoulder.

'Lie down on the floor!' he urged. 'Parmenon, Acerronia, stand in the corner. Do not react to what happens.'

Agrippina pulled off her headdress and lay down. Immediately strange shrieks and cries seemed to echo from the earthbeaten floor, and the air became thick with the odour of pungent sharp spices. The light seemed to grow, showing great spider webs that glimmered on the floor and crept over Agrippina's prostrate body. Only then did I glimpse the altar half way down the room. Joah drew what looked like a white, gleaming circle round Agrippina's body. The light became as intense as that of the corona of the sun during an eclipse. I had to shield my eyes even as I marvelled at the magician's trickery. How he created that illusion, I have never understood. He ordered Agrippina to hold a small sheaf of corn in her left hand and, with her right, to count out thirteen grains of corn. As Agrippina obeyed, Joah scooped these up and put them in a small copper cup which he poured into a silver bowl and filled with water.

'Drink!' he urged Agrippina.

She later told me that the grains of corn sparkled like diamonds whilst the water seemed to fire her blood. She lay back again, as Joah made signs over her face and the phenomena disappeared. We were just in an ill-lit, dank room with the mother of the Emperor of Rome lying on a dirty floor. Joah helped Agrippina to her feet and kissed her fingers.

'Well?' Agrippina demanded.

'It is finished,' Joah murmured, stepping back. 'Another woman will take your place.'

'Acte?' Agrippina spat out.

Joah shook his head. 'No, another woman!'

We left that magician's house and returned to the Palatine, where Agrippina brooded for days. Joah was either a true prophet or possibly just a very shrewd observer of court affairs. The open opposition, behind which I could detect Seneca's hand, began with murmurs and whispers. Court cases were begun against her and the Emperor railed that his palace was becoming a meeting place for her litigants. He visited his mother less and less and eventually it was tactfully suggested that Agrippina should leave the palace and move to a nearby house. She had no choice but to obey. Although she was allowed to take her possessions, the guards were withdrawn: she was no longer a member of the imperial circle.

Nero seemed intent on demonstrating to his mother the depths of his decadence. He organised an elaborate, mock naval engagement on an artificial lake of salt water but the display got out of hand and many of the sailors were killed: Nero declared himself disgusted with such bloodshed. He next staged a ballet of the Minotaur legend with an actor disguised as a bull actually mounting another playing the role of Pasiphaë. The crowd were treated to the sight of the bull copulating with the hind quarters of a hollow heifer. At night Nero, disguised in a cap or a wig, prowled the streets and the taverns looking for mischief. Occasionally he'd visit the theatre in a sedan chair to watch the quarrels amongst the pantomime actors, joining in when they came to blows and fought it out with stones and broken benches. His feasts started at noon and would last till dawn, with an occasional break for swimming in warm baths or, if it was summer, snow-cooled waters. On one occasion he floated down the Tiber to

Ostia and arranged for a row of temporary brothels to be erected along the shore in which married women, pretending to be inn-keepers, solicited him for custom. He never wore the same clothes twice and would stake thousands of gold pieces on the throw of a dice. He always insisted on being accompanied by a lavishly garbed retinue, and even the mules of his pack train were shod with silver.

Agrippina tried to hide herself away from all this but Nero kept up the insults. He would send her mushrooms, calling them 'the Food of Gods and Goats' and taunted her by granting Locusta a house in Rome as well as country estates. He despatched lawyers and their clerks to stand under her window, disturbing her with jeers and cat-calls. Mysterious gifts of food arrived, some of them blatantly poisoned.

I tired of this nonsense and opened my treasure chests to hire bodyguards, who drove away the litigants and ensured that any gifts brought to the house were immediately destroyed. Agrippina's hair began to turn grey, and her face became gaunt as she lost weight. Nero had perfected his sadistic teasing of her. He would visit Agrippina in a profuse show of solicitude and concern, and build up her hopes, as he sat at her feet, wide-eyed, listening to her advice. Then he would jump to his feet, crowing with laughter, and leave, mimicking what she had said.

Agrippina, now full of guilt over Britannicus's death, also tried to comfort the young Octavia, who was in a parlous state: her face was ashen and, in spite of her youth, she was losing clumps of hair from worry. Terrified of what had happened to Britannicus, she refused to leave her chamber, and would fret herself sick if her nurse, an old family retainer, left her sight.

Agrippina tried to fight back but Nero's cruelty became even more barbed. I was in the Forum when I first heard rumours that Nero had been seduced by his own mother. On investigating these stories, I discovered that Nero had paid his servants to ransack the brothels of Rome until they found a woman who looked remarkably like Agrippina. Nero then had the woman dressed in his mother's clothes, and would sit closeted with her in his litter. When he emerged, people could tell from the stains on his tunic and his air of dishevelment that, as one wit put it, 'he'd not been discussing the problem of Parthia!'. I tried to protect Domina but Nero ensured such rumours reached her, and in despair she took to her bed, refusing food and drink.

I called on the services of every physician and quack in Rome, but they examined her and walked away, shaking their heads. Nero's game became more intense, and he sent the woman masquerading as his mother to the house. I intervened and courteously turned her away. It was a chilling experience: she was the image of Agrippina until she opened her mouth and spoke, displaying her blackened teeth. At last I decided to sue for terms. For days I kicked my heels outside Seneca's office until that wily, old Spaniard granted me an audience. He studied me with black, hooded eyes, a faint smile on his lips.

'Your mistress will know peace, Parmenon, once she leaves both the Emperor and Rome alone.'

'Exile?' I asked.

'When she leaves Nero and the Empire alone,' he said, flicking his hand as a sign of dismissal.

By the end of the week, despite her feeble protests, Acerronia and I put Agrippina in a litter. We packed whatever possessions we could and took the road to Antium. Perhaps I should have waited for Nero was soon distracted from his cruel games against his mother, not by Acte, but by the new love of his life, the beautiful, exquisite Poppea. By that time, however, we were out of Rome. Agrippina began to recover even before we reached Antium, curious about where we were going and mocking what little retinue the Emperor of Rome's mother possessed.

So we came to Antium, and enjoyed soft summer days, good food and delicious wines, and Agrippina took a new lover, Callienus, a Greek actor. We became accustomed to spending more and more of our afternoons together in the garden, reminiscing about the past and wondering about the future. Even then Agrippina was still convinced that her son's love was only dormant, not dead. Because of that, she accepted Nero's invitation to Baiae and that last, splendid feast. Because of her deep unconditional love for her monster of a son, she took ship across the Bay of Naples at night and was almost drowned by his minions. In the end, because of her all-consuming love, she and I sheltered in a dark, cold villa and waited for her beloved son to finish the task he had begun.

Chapter 15

'With you I would love to live,
With you I'd willingly die'
Horace, '*Odes*' III. 9. 24.

Whilst we sat and reminisced, Nero and his cronies
put their heads together. I later found out exactly
what had happened: after all, I was the man who
assisted both Burrus and Seneca to end their lives.
Oh yes, Agrippina was pushed into eternal night but
I became the nemesis of those who had plotted her
downfall.

After his mother left on the bireme, Nero was as
happy as a lark on a spring morning. He closeted
himself in his private dining chamber at Baiae, his
minions around him. He was already preparing the
funeral speech, in which he would praise Agrippina's

virtues and berate Neptune for taking the 'best of mothers' from him. He lounged on his couch whilst Anicetus sniffed at a garland of flowers. As the evening wore on, Nero became more restless, until at last a messenger arrived, the freedman Agerinus, who, although a member of our household, was a born informant. He'd been picked up by the trireme, and although suspicious, was still not sure whether the accident was genuine or arranged. He threw himself at Nero's feet, blurting out, 'The Empress, your beloved mother, has had an accident! The boat sank but the Gods of sea and sky were with her, and she swam to safety. She sends word for you not to be anxious.'

Of course, Agerinus had invented the last part, protecting Nero as well as himself. He could hardly have burst in and shouted, 'The accident you arranged for your bitch of a mother went wrong and she's now safe!'

Nero promptly dismissed him. As soon as Agerinus was out of the room, the little monster had an anxiety attack. He paced up and down, half swooning with fear, and threw himself down onto his couch.

'Oh Gods!' he bawled. 'Mother has survived. She will arm her slaves, seek the Praetorian Guard's protection and demand to speak to the Senate. What can I do to save myself?' He turned to Burrus and Seneca. 'What can I do? Help me!'

This precious pair simply stared back at him. Nero was correct: if it had been against anyone but her son, Agrippina would have marched on Rome, and the Praetorian Guard would certainly have been aghast at any attack on the daughter of their beloved Germanicus. I am sure their minds teemed with the knowledge that, if there were a coup, they would fall with Nero. Much as they might have wished to see the back of him, who could be the next Emperor? Thanks to Tiberius, Caligula, Claudius and Nero, with a little help from Agrippina, there were no successors left in the Claudian line. What if the troops hailed Agrippina as Empress or allowed her to choose the next Emperor for the Senate to confirm? There were other considerations: as a soldier, Burrus might not have liked the odds stacked against him. Seneca, although a hypocrite, was a well-known philosopher – how could the First Minister of Rome advise his Emperor to murder 'the best of mothers'?

Nero sobbed on the couch, and lifted his tearful face. 'Burrus, can't you order your troops to strike?'

'They will not do it,' the Praetorian tribune replied. 'They love your Excellency but they also love your mother.' He waved a hand contemptuously at Anicetus who was still sniffing the flowers. 'He started this, so let him finish it!'

As Burrus and Seneca withdrew, Anicetus threw the garland on the floor, got to his feet, stretched and said lazily, 'Caesar, you go to bed, and dream happily. I have work to do.'

He then summoned two of his lieutenants, naval officers Hercules and Oberitius, as well as a group of tough marines. They took the fleetest horses in the stables and rode around the bay to Agrippina's villa.

As I said, I discovered all this later. Since our escape, I'd been listening to Agrippina's reminscences, and begging her to flee. But Agrippina knew it was the end. She just sat by the brazier sipping her wine. As the news of the accident and her escape had spread, people had flocked to the villa. Once they'd discovered it was not the accident they'd first thought, they soon disappeared. The maids and servants also slipped away into the night. As Agrippina heard their fading footsteps, she glanced at me and smiled.

'Won't you go too?'

'I will stay, Domina.'

'He will not harm me.'

I closed my eyes at the foolishness of it all. She had just escaped a drowning arranged by her son and, within hours of reaching safety, she'd started to excuse him.

'Let us remember, Parmenon?' she continued. Her eyes had a dreamy, far-away look and she'd go back down the years, laughing and joking about all people we had known: Claudius and his strange edicts about breaking wind at table; Tiberius's ears; Passienus embracing his favourite tree. She was still talking when I heard the sound of galloping horses, and shouts from the courtyard. I sprang to my feet and, picking up a sword, put myself between the door and Agrippina. Anicetus, followed by his two lieutenants, burst the lock open and swaggered in. All three must have drunk heavily before they'd left Baiae, I could smell the wine on their breath.

Agrippina got to her feet and gently pushed me out of the way.

'Why, gentlemen, good evening, or should I say good morning? If you have come to visit me, you can report that I am recovered. But if you don't mean me well and come as assassins, I know my son is not responsible – he would never order his mother's death.'

She paused at fresh sounds of further horsemen on the road outside. She nodded at me, and I went to the door, down the empty passageway and into a small paved courtyard. In the light of torches fixed in the wall, I glimpsed a clump of red-gold curls: Nero was there with his German mercenaries. I know that he had not come to save his mother. He swaggered across, a small wine cup in his hand.

'Why, Parmenon, good evening.'

I sank to my knees before him and he patted my head.

'Are you grieving already, Parmenon?'

I knew the reason for his visit even as I heard shouts from inside the house. Nero shrank away, as I leapt to my feet and hurried back down the passageway. The door had been closed but I kicked it open. Anicetus and his two lieutenants had now pushed Agrippina back onto the small pallet bed. She was half sitting, her black hair loosened and framing her face. She glanced quickly past them at me: it was her farewell, a slight smile containing all her bravery, and her beauty in those lustrous eyes. One of the lieutenants, I think it was Oberitius, pushed

her further back, and before I could intervene, he
brought down the flat of his sword, dealing her an
ugly blow to the head. Hercules drew his dagger,
as Agrippina, the blood coursing down her face,
pushed herself back against the wall. She looked
once more past them as if she knew that her son
was nearby, hiding in the shadows. She took her
gown by the neck and ripped it open, thrusting her
body forward.

'I am Agrippina!' she shouted, eyes blazing. 'Daughter of Germanicus, sister of Caligula, mother of
Nero! Yes, mother of Nero!' She clutched her stomach. 'If you must strike, then strike here!'

Hercules hesitated.

'Strike at my womb!' Agrippina shouted.

His blade went down, thrusting in up to the hilt.
Agrippina arched forward, eyes closed, mouth open.
She collapsed to the floor. I crept within the doorway
and stood in the shadows. I couldn't stop trembling.
I felt as if a cold wind had wrapped itself around
me, numbing my mind and heart. Agrippina's body
sprawled on the floor, as the three assassins stepped
back, looked fearfully at each other. There was a
sound of footsteps and Nero's shadow crossed the
threshold. He grinned sideways at me and I saw
Caligula's face. Two devils in one! Nero stretched
his hand out, fingers twisted into a claw, which he
pressed into my face pushing my head further back
into the corner.

'Is she dead?' His voice was coarse and deep. 'Is
my mother dead?'

He walked across and pulled over the corpse. Squatting down, he stared curiously at the face.

'Give me some wine!'

Anicetus filled a goblet, which was the one Agrippina had used. Nero slurped from it, as he stretched out his hand and touched the pool of blood. He stared and, grabbing his mother's torn dress, rent it even further. He minutely examined the corpse, noting each bruise and lesion.

'She was beautiful,' he murmured. 'Wasn't she, Anicetus? Look at her breasts, her neck?'

The silence in the room grew oppressive. Nero got to his feet.

'Parmenon, are you still there?' He looked up at the ceiling. 'And what of Mother? Do you feel her, Anicetus? Her ghost? They make a precious pair, don't they? Uncle Caligula and her.'

Nero began to hop strangely from foot to foot. He went to the window, looked out at the fading moon and quickly withdrew, flattening his back against the wall.

'She's in the garden!' he whispered. 'Anicetus, get me . . . get me some black broad beans!'

Anicetus stood rooted to the spot.

'Get them!' Nero urged.

Anicetus hurried to the door, glancing fearfully at me. A short while later he returned and thrust a handful of beans into Nero's hand. The monster stood, head tilted back, and put the beans into his mouth, some dropping out to clatter on the floor. Nero took his sandals off and did a strange barefoot dance, snapping his fingers, a popular exercise to frighten away ghosts. He left, running out into the garden where a small fountain bubbled. Three times he washed his hands in the icy water and came back, snapping his fingers and throwing over his shoulders the black beans he'd stuffed into his mouth. He paused gasping, muttering strange words, spells he had learnt. All the time I stayed still, until the left side of my face grew numb and I began to rub it. I wanted to flee but I couldn't. All I could see was that madman and Agrippina's corpse stiffening on the floor, the widening pool of blood mixing with her long black hair.

'Excellency.' Anicetus stepped forward and grasped Nero's shoulder.

'What is it?' the monster gasped.

'You are to be congratulated,' Anicetus soothed, 'on being rescued from a treasonable conspiracy against your life.'

'Am I?' Nero asked anxiously. The monster was still half drunk.

Anicetus pointed to Agrippina. 'She was responsible; her threats were well known.'

Nero staggered to a stool and sat down.

'And her accomplice?' he asked anxiously.

Anicetus turned his head, smiling at me through the darkness. 'Why, Caesar, he stands just within the doorway. He should be brought back to Rome. I am sure Tigellinus would be delighted to put him to the question.'

Anicetus walked towards me. He didn't even flinch

as his sandals slapped through Agrippina's blood. He stretched out his sword and thrust the tip into the soft part of my throat.

'The eyes and ears of Agrippina,' he whispered. 'What are you going to do, Parmenon? Beg for your life? Hercules! Oberitius!' He called out to his two lieutenants. 'Bind his hands!'

The two ruffians came forward. I became aware of warmth, of hands touching me, of what had happened, of the yawning emptiness. I would never talk to Agrippina again. I would never shout at her, smile at her, tell her she was wrong. Above all, those eyes of hers would never again catch mine, smiling and winking. Oh, I know all about her cruelties, her depravity ... but I loved Agrippina. The sheer emptiness of a life without her shattered my soul. I lashed out, longing to grasp a sword and plunge it in deep. I was aware of footsteps in the corridor outside, and one of the Germans came to enquire what was going on. Anicetus bawled at him to stay away and guard the gates. I was pummelled and kicked, my arms seized, my wrists lashed and bound together. I was forced to kneel, while Hercules seized my hair, yanking my head forward. I heard the hiss of a sword drawn by Oberitius. Looking to the left, I glimpsed his sandalled feet apart, legs tense. He was bringing the sword back for the killing blow.

'Caesar!' Anicetus's voice was low and soothing. 'We should execute him now, and take his head back to Rome as further proof. Or, as I have said, Tigellinus could put him to the question. Once

Parmenon has confessed the details of how he and his mistress plotted your overthrow, we could make it public and read it out to the Senate, the Praetorian Guard, the provinces and the army.'

I tasted blood in my mouth. Lifting my head, I stared at that figure sitting in the chair still muttering to himself. I thought of Tiberius's cruel face, Caligula's mad eyes and Claudius's twisted mouth opening and shutting like that of an ugly carp. I didn't really care whether I died now or was taken back to Rome. I'd confess to nothing.

'Caesar!' Anicetus demanded. 'I await your orders!'

I heard the stool scrape back, as Nero got to his feet and made his way over.

'Well, well, well!' he breathed. He patted me on the head. 'What are you doing down there, Parmenon? Get him up! Get him up!'

I was hustled to my feet. Nero pushed his face a few inches from mine, his eyes lazy, his mouth half open. The monster was smiling at me.

'What do you think of Anicetus's plan?' he whispered. 'Come on, Parmenon, tell him what's wrong with it. You might win your life.'

'If you kill me,' I declared, my mind suddenly sharp and keen. I needed to live – for revenge. 'If you kill me,' I repeated, 'and take my head back to Rome, the people will laugh, and the Senate will mock.'

'Good!' Nero murmured. He tweaked my nose playfully.

Anicetus tried to object but Nero held up his hand. 'Go on, Parmenon,' he urged. 'Why will they laugh?'

'They'll say it wasn't much of a conspiracy, Your Excellency.' I replied. 'Just one woman living in exile and her manservant. You can scarcely call my head that of a Parthian king or the commander of one of your legions on the Rhine.'

'Very good!' Nero wagged a finger in my face. 'You see, Parmenon.'

I tried not to flinch at the stale wine on his breath.

'You've been around for some time, haven't you? You've danced with Tiberius, Uncle Claudius, Uncle Caligula, not to mention Sejanus and Macro.' His face suddenly turned ugly. 'If we are going to have a plot,' he shouted at Anicetus. 'Then it has to be a proper plot! Gods!' He threw his hand up dramatically. 'Can you imagine what they'd say?' He mimicked Seneca's voice. 'And the lieutenant in this conspiracy was Parmenon! Who's that, everyone will ask.'

Nero walked up and down like an actor on the stage. If Caligula had been mad, Nero was truly insane. He had built his own reality. To him everything was an act. I am sure he had forgotten about his mother's corpse stiffening in her own blood.

'And if we took you back to Rome?' He came back and stood before me.

'I wouldn't confess,' I replied. 'Tigellinus can play with my ears, my tongue, my balls or the soles of my feet.'

Nero threw his head back and laughed.

'Precisely! You see, Anicetus, the lesson you have

learnt.' He turned back and tapped me on the cheek. 'What is that, Parmenon?'

'Say as little as possible, Excellency.'

'Say as little as possible,' Nero repeated dreamily. 'Cut his bonds!' he ordered.

Anicetus reluctantly agreed. Nero grasped me by the shoulder and took me out into the courtyard.

'I am giving you your life, Parmenon. Do you remember that day in the garden long ago when I was sacrificing the bird to Caligula? You never did tell Mother, did you? See how your Emperor rewards you?' He pushed me away and stood back. 'And you're my link with Mother. I can't slice through the umbilical cord completely. You'll say as little as possible, won't you?' He smiled sheepishly. 'Of course you will, because you're like me, Parmenon, aren't you?' He drew closer. 'You were in the audience at the beginning of this play and you want to see it through to the end, don't you?'

He turned and talked as if into the darkness, chattering like a child. I suppose I could have killed him then, but I could think of nothing but Agrippina's corpse.

'You take care of her, Parmenon,' Nero declared as if he could read my mind. 'You take care of "the best of mothers".'

He walked to the fountain and washed his hands again. He came back and dried them on my tunic, kissed me on each cheek as if I were a favourite uncle, and walked off into the darkness.

The villa fell silent. Nero, his minions, the marines and the Praetorians departed but I knew spies had been left to watch and see what might happen. I picked up Agrippina's corpse as gently as a mother would cradle a child. Despite the blows to her head and the awful rent to her stomach, her face was peaceful and composed, although already the limbs were cold and stiffening. I feared further degradation, the monster changing his mind and coming back to take her head. Nero was insane: those who are both evil and mad have no sense of what is real. They live in a world of their own dreams and phantasms. Did I feel grief? Well, of course I did! An eerie grief, a profound, enduring sense of loss. My world had died with Agrippina. I stared into her face, kissed the half-open lips and took her out into the courtyard. I laid her on the wet flagstones and went back into the house, to which some of the braver servants and slaves had returned. Wide-eyed, with white, haggard faces, they moved like ghosts, helping me to collect kindling. I took Agrippina's favourite couch, which was covered in purple and a cloth of the same colour edged in gold. I laid the corpse on it, climbing up the kindling to look once more on her face. I had two coins bearing her imprint, which I used to close her staring eyes. I brushed her hair the way she liked it so that it lay on either side of her face, not piled up like some Roman matron. Wild flowers she'd collected and pressed were placed in her hand. The villa was ransacked for her favourite ornaments and some of the pots she'd made in the kiln.

I stacked all these round the corpse. I said a prayer to some unknown God, to the lightening sky or the breeze. I sprinkled incense and poured oil, and then I covered her face and climbed down. With a torch in one hand and a sword in the other, watched by slaves, some of whom may well have been in the monster's pay, I saluted and hailed her name: 'Agrippina, daughter of Germanicus, Imperatrix and Augusta!' I lit the funeral pyre. The kindling roared, as the flames leapt up to the sky. The shrouded form disappeared in a sheet of blood-red fire and billowing smoke. I do not know how long I stood there watching, as the flames died and a light rain fell. I was aware of dawn, the sun rising, but still I refused to leave. I stood there until late afternoon. One of the servants brought me wine and something to eat.

'Go on!' she urged. 'You must keep up your strength.'

A Praetorian came galloping through the gates, young and sharp-featured under the ornate plumed helmet. He paused, his horse's hooves skittering on the cobbles before, yanking at the reins, he left as quickly as he had arrived. I collected the ashes in a funeral vase and buried them near Misenum on the promontory overlooking the bay. Julius Caesar had once owned a villa nearby. It had been one of Domina's favourite spots for a picnic, where she'd sit, staring out at the sea and sky.

Afterwards I returned to Rome to watch and wait. I was left alone: there was no bill of indictment, no harassment by the secret police or the monster's agents. It was as if I had never existed. Sometimes

I received invitations to suppers at the Palatine and, occasionally, I attended. Now and again I would catch Nero watching me with those bulbous blue eyes in that fat, purpling face. He'd smile weakly and I'd smile back.

'Nero can't sleep at night,' someone told me. 'He has hideous dreams. He refuses to go back to Baiae: he claims he can hear the funeral flutes and pipes blowing from the headlands.'

I didn't care. I haunted Rome like a prowling wolf, through the quiet districts where the nouveau riche had built their elegant mansions and laid out perfume-filled gardens. I rubbed shoulders with white-robed Arabs, Germans in their strange coats and trousers, Greek and Spanish slaves in their scarlet and gold liveries. I listened to their strange chatter and watched the aristocrats lolling in their litters. I was in the Forum in the early morning when the beautiful statues were bathed in the golden glow of the rising sun. Sometimes I'd sit at the foot of the statue of the She-Wolf, the great symbol of Rome, where an old Arab sold sulphur matches. I sniffed the odour of ripe fruit from the market and the cloying whiff of the perfumed ladies. In the afternoon I'd wander amongst the bookstalls. All the time I listened for news and scandal.

I was in the city when the monster burnt it, and the wind sent the flames roaring over the Palatine till they scorched the great Babylonian steps on the right flank of the river. Tigellinus encouraged Nero to compose a poem on the fire of Rome. Nero was stupid, or insane, enough to agree. When people pointed the finger of accusation, Tigellinus blamed that eccentric bunch of Jews known as Christians. Condemned as the perpetrators of the inferno, they were cloaked in animal skins, soaked in oil and used as human torches in the great gardens. Further arrests were made and Christians were forced to run round the amphitheatre pursued by ravenous animals. The crowds loved it. Nero boasted that he'd rebuild Rome, but all he managed was his Golden Palace, with its revolving roof depicting the sun and the moon and the main stars of the heavens. Nero would invite people to supper, bombard them with scented roses and force them to watch the revolving ceiling. They'd stagger out giddy and sick, especially if they had drunk too much Falernian.

Nero publicly proclaimed himself a great artist, poet and, above all, singer. He travelled from place to place staging performances, at which the theatres would be sealed and locked till he'd finished. One person even killed himself trying to climb the wall to escape. Women would give birth and still the monster would burble on.

Conspiracies, of course, flourished as thick as weeds in a stagnant pool. I watched as those who had hounded Domina to death met a similar fate. Burrus claimed he had a tumour in his throat. He was attended by Nero's personal physician who gave him relief from the pain by despatching him to Hades. I held his hand as he died and told him about the horrors waiting for him. Seneca, the old fox, twisted and turned, but Nero eventually had enough of him. He died as he had lived, spouting humbug. A centurion was sent to order him to open his veins. The blood came so slowly when Seneca did this that he was forced to slash the veins in his ankles, as well as his wrists. Whilst the blood seeped out into the hot water, Seneca, that old fraud, babbled on as if he was Socrates. He even asked for hemlock! He had an eye for history, did Seneca. Yet he died as he'd lived, totally blind to the truth. When the tribunes brought the summons of death, I managed to sidle in amongst his acquaintances and clients, and when the fatal moment came, I slyly drew alongside him to whisper in his ear that Agrippina would be waiting for him on that far, dark shore.

What of Tigellinus and Locusta? Nero didn't kill them, but others did. I watched Locusta being paraded through Rome before she was strangled, and, catching her eye, I made the sign, the well-known curse for someone about to enter the underworld. Others died just as violently. Poppea, who had replaced Acte in Nero's affections, became pregnant and Nero kicked both mother and her unborn child to death in a fit of rage. Little Octavia had already been banished and invited to open her veins. The poor girl was so terrified that the blood didn't flow so they drowned her in boiling water. Nero had wanted to divorce her so he could marry plump Poppea, and tried her on trumped-up charges of adultery.

'Who with?' Octavia cried.

Nero cast about for a name and came up with that of his old friend Anicetus.

'Confess you slept with Octavia!' Nero insisted. 'Or I'll put you on trial for murdering my mother!'

Anicetus confessed and was given comfortable retirement in Sardinia; which is where I caught up with him. He was washing his clothes in a vat of greasy water when I cut his throat. I had spent six months of my life hunting him down. All the others went into the darkness, some quietly, some cursing.

Nero went from bad to worse. He became a new Caligula, his depravity and cruelty shocked all. He plundered the treasury and made the imperial throne a laughingstock. In the provinces the discontent spilled over until Vindex, Governor of Spain, rose in rebellion and marched with his troops on Rome. It was the opportunity I had been waiting for. As Nero panicked, I joined his household, bringing false comfort and promises. Nero had changed. His face was coarser, vein-streaked, his neck fat and thickset, his stomach bulging out in a sack-like paunch. To the very end he didn't believe what was happening. He grasped my hand, tears brimming his eyes.

'I'm glad you've come, Parmenon,' he whispered. 'At a time like this, I need my friends and allies.'

He was totally forgetful of that dark, wind-swept evening in Agrippina's villa. Portents started to appear all over Rome. I did give these a little help and tied a bag to one of his statues with the phrase: 'TRULY HE DESERVED THIS': a menacing reminder of Agrippina's murder. The bag was a symbol of the ancient punishment for a matricide: to be sewn into a sack with a cook, a goat, a viper and an ape and thrown into the sea. Such auguries unnerved Nero. He dragged me into his bedchamber which looked unclean and badly swept.

'Last night,' he whispered, 'I dreamt I was steering a ship when the rudder was forced from my hand. Octavia's ghost came over the side and tried to drag me into the water. Above her head was a swarm of huge winged ants! They picked me up and carried me to the Mausoleum of Augustus, where the doors were flung open and a voice boomed, "COME IN NERO, WE'VE BEEN WAITING!".' His fingers went to his lips. 'What shall I do, Parmenon, what shall I do? If only Mother was here!'

The others gathered around him, his freedman Phaeon, his secretary Epaphroditus, Acte faithful as ever, and his new love, a young Greek called Sporus, the spitting image of the dead Poppea. According to rumour, a surgeon had turned Sporus into a woman.

They were of little help and could only advise flight, but Nero still dallied.

'Must I really flee?' he whined. 'Must the master of the world escape like a thief in the night, his nose hidden in his mantle?'

That evening, 8 June, fresh letters arrived at the palace stating that yet more legions had renounced their allegiance to him. In a furious burst of temper, Nero broke his two favourite cups, the Homer goblets. A special poison was sent to him in a golden casket. I urged him to go to the Servilian Gardens to meet certain Praetorians although I knew what their response would be. They taunted him with being frighened of death and turned away.

We returned to the palace to find that the golden casket of poison had been stolen and that, apart from the faithful few, his household and guards had fled. Nero became hysterical. He ran on to the palace steps, screaming that he would throw himself into the Tiber but the only response was a mocking laugh from the darkness. At last he calmed down, and it was agreed we'd flee to Phaeon's villa, about four miles to the north-east of the city. Nero, clad in a sorry tunic, with a dirty old cloak thrown over his face, joined us in the stables. We galloped through the night, under a dark sky clouded by a threatening thunderstorm. On one occasion we passed a group of Praetorians, and Nero let his cowl slip and someone glimpsed his face. Soon we were out in the countryside where low hills were honeycombed with quarries and carpeted with grass and gorse. We turned our horses loose and forced our way through briars and brambles towards Phaeon's deserted villa. Phaeon tried to persuade him to shelter in a cave but Nero, gibbering with fright, refused. Eventually we reached the villa, where Nero sheltered in a cellar on a dirty wine-soaked pallet. Phaeon brought some crusts of bread, and the Emperor of Rome chewed on these, talking to himself, wondering what to do.

Morning came and the day dragged on. I sat by Nero, watching his fleshy face gibber with fright, the sweat mingling with tears. May the Gods be my witness, I had no compassion for him. He droned on that, since he was such a great artist, perhaps the people would forgive him and allow him to retire and spend his years composing poetry and singing. Such hopes were soon dashed. A messenger arrived from Rome, bringing news that sentence of death had been passed on Nero. He was to be stripped, his neck fastened to a wooden fork and be beaten to death. Nero immediately grabbed the daggers he had brought with him. He pricked his neck and chest but lacked the courage to thrust deep. He begged Sporus to show him first how to die. When that effeminate monster refused, Nero beat him till he fled in terror. Time and again Nero got up and prowled round the cellar muttering, 'It is not seemly. Nero! Rouse yourself! Rouse yourself!' He turned to us.

'Bring water and wood!' he begged. 'Prepare for my burial.'

He still believed he was in a play, acting out a part. Matters were brought to a head by the sound of horsemen outside; shouts, the jingle of harness and the clash of armour. Nero crouched in a corner of the cellar, one of the daggers at his throat.

'Help me!' he croaked.

I crawled across; his hand was trembling.

'Faithful Parmenon,' he whispered. 'Why have you stayed with me?'

'Because your mother asked me to.'

His eyes widened, his mouth opened to scream for the others congregated in the doorway at the other end of the cellar. I grabbed his wrist and forced the dagger into his throat. The sharp pointed edge cut deep. As blood bubbled out from both wound and mouth, he leaned forward, coughing, his eyes popping hideously. I could hear the shouts of the approaching Praetorians. Nero tried to touch me, his body trembling.

'What—' he muttered.

'What?' I asked.

'What a great artist perishes in me . . .'

'Aye, Nero, and what a great monster,' I replied.

His eyes were already glazing over in death, as Phaeon and the others held back the soldiers. I slipped down a narrow passageway, which led out to an old wine cellar, its roof long gone. I climbed the walls and in the distance I could see the soldiers crowding round their horses. I hid for a while then fled. Behind me, the last of the great Julio-Claudian family had died like a rat in that dirty cellar.

I allowed others such as his secretary to take the honour and credit of having persuaded Nero to die and thus save Rome and its Senate from a humiliating trial. I stayed out of Rome for months, watching as the generals fought over the empire. Galba, Otho, Vitellius: all reigned for a short while before they joined Nero in death, leaving the empire to that cunning, old fox Vespasian and his two darling sons Titus and Domitian. The stage had been cleared. Tiberius, Claudius, Agrippina, Caligula, Nero, and all their hangers-on, were gone like leaves in autumn: dry and dead, nothing but whirling memories. I bought a small farm near Misenum, to be close to Domina's grave. I erected a proper tablet, laid flowers. I also married a local girl, who was soft and kind, more interested in the seasons, the sky, the soil and the sea than the harsh lust for power. She became a follower of the Christos and tried to persuade me to take their rites. I refused. One night she cuddled close and spoke into my ear.

'The blessings of Christos,' she whispered, 'will protect you against the demons of the underworld.'

For the first time in a long, long while I threw my head back and laughed uproariously. Demons! Fear of demons? Why should I be frightened of demons? I've lived with them all my life!

Suetonius, Tacitus and the other Roman authors give a detailed description of the bloody, violent politics of Imperial Rome during the first century AD. Naturally, they are biased. Such writers yearned for a mythical Golden Republican Age when the virtuous ruled and the common good was pursued. Nevertheless, the convoluted, violent politics of the imperial court require little exaggeration. Rivals fought to the death and, when they fell, always dragged others with them. Agrippina's task was doubly hard; being a woman she had to strike quickly and ruthlessly, relying more on her wits than on the power of the sword. Hemingway claimed the greatest virtue was courage: Agrippina, daughter of Germanicus, certainly possessed such a virtue. She truly was a '*Mulier fortis et audax*', a brave and audacious woman. She rose to the pinnacle of Roman imperial power and lost it because of her love for her son, Nero.

In the main I have kept faithfully to sources,

including the well-documented stories of Caligula's ghost and the eerie hauntings which took place after his death. I must point out, before readers write in, that Nero may have used an emerald or a monocle with a concave lens. Seneca certainly discovered how letters could be magnified through a water-filled ball of glass which would operate like a concave lens. The various descriptions of Nero's attempt to drown his mother are rather confused. I believe that the shipwreck described in this novel, is a probable and accurate account. Agrippina's grave can still be visited and, quite recently, the German city of Cologne paid her public recognition by erecting a statue to her. Agrippina would have been amused, but at the same time deeply appreciative of such a gesture.

Paul Doherty

The Anubis Slayings

Paul Doherty

Hatusu, the remarkable young widow of Pharaoh Tuthmosis II, has forced Egyptian society to acknowledge her as Pharaoh, and her success in battle is spreading Egypt's glory well beyond its frontiers. In the Temple of Anubis, negotiations are taking place between Hatusu and the defeated King Tushratta of Mitanni for a peace treaty that will seal her greatest victory. But in one night, two hideous murders in the temple and the theft of the Glory of Anubis threaten the tenative truce. The respected judge Amerotke must find the truth or Egypt's fragile peace could be destroyed.

'Paul Doherty's *The Mask of Ra* is the best of its kind since the death of Ellis Peters. As ever, Doherty dazzles with his knowledge and intimate feel for Ancient Egypt' *Time Out*

'Doherty excels at his historical detail, bringing Ancient Egypt to life in his descriptions of daily life and characters drawn from every caste' *Publishers Weekly*

'Paul Doherty has a lively sense of history' *New Statesman*

0 7472 6309 4

headline

Now you can buy any of these other bestselling
books by **Paul Doherty** from your bookshop
or *direct from his publisher*.

FREE P&P AND UK DELIVERY
(Overseas and Ireland £3.50 per book)

A Tapestry of Murders	£5.99
Corpse Candle	£6.99
The Anger of God	£6.99
The House of Crows	£6.99
The Nightingale Gallery	£6.99
The Field of Blood	£6.99
The Treason of the Ghosts	£5.99
The Anubis Slayings	£5.99
The Grail Murders	£6.99
The White Rose Murders	£6.99
A Brood of Vipers	£6.99
The Horus Killings	£6.99
The Mask of Ra	£6.99

TO ORDER SIMPLY CALL THIS NUMBER

01235 400 414

or e-mail <u>orders@bookpoint.co.uk</u>

Prices and availability subject to change without notice